500 **HISTORIC DAYS OUT**

Produced by AA Publishing

Editorial: lifestyleguides@theAA.com

Cover Photos: (top) AA/Van Greaves; (middle) AA/
Mike Hayward; (bottom) AA/Caroline Jones

All photographs in this guide: 1 AA/Stephen
Whitehorne; 3 AA/John Miller

Printed in China by Leo Paper Products

Directory compiled by AA Lifestyle Guides Department
and managed in the Librios Information Management
System and generated from the AA establishment
database system.

theAA.com/shop

Published by AA Publishing, a trading name of AA
Media Limited whose registered office is Fanum
House, Basing View, Basingstoke, Hampshire,
RG21 4EA
Registered number 06112600.

A CIP catalogue record for this book is available from
the British Library

ISBN 978-0-7495-6460-5

A04301

Welcome to the Guide

This mini guide features a wide range of attractions that can be described as 'historic' in some way. There are steam railways, museums, stately homes, megalithic sites and other attractions across Britain and Ireland. Entries include contact details, along with a short description and details of opening times, prices and special facilities. We hope this guide will help you and your family get the most out of your visit.

Contents

England	**7**
Channel Islands	**176**
Isle of Man	**179**
Scotland	**181**
Scottish Islands	**216**
Wales	**221**
Northern Ireland	**241**
Republic of Ireland	**246**

❶ CHALFONT ST GILES

Milton's Cottage

Dean Way HP8 4JH

❷ ☎ 01494 872313
e-mail: info@miltonscottage.org
web: www.miltonscottage.org

❸ dir: 0.5m W of A413. 3m N of M40 junct 2

A timber-framed, 16th-century cottage with a charming garden, the only surviving home in which John Milton lived and worked. He completed Paradise Lost and started Paradise Regained here. First editions of these works are among the many rare books and artefacts on display.

❹ **Times** Open Mar-Oct, Tue-Sun 10-1 & 2-6. Also
❺ open Spring & Summer BH.* **Fees** £4 (ch 15
❻ £2). Group rate 20+ £3 each.* **Facilities** ♿🅿🍴
❼ licensed ♿ (partly accessible) (ground floor only accessible) shop ⊗

❶ The directory is arranged in countries, counties, and in alphabetical location order within each county.

❷ Telephone Numbers have the STD code shown before the telephone number. (If dialling Northern Ireland from England use the STD code, but for the Republic you need to prefix the number with 00353, and drop the first zero from the Irish area code).

❸ Directions may be given after the address of each attraction and where shown have been provided by the attractions themselves.

❹ Opening Times quoted in the guide are inclusive - for instance, where you see Apr-Oct, that place will be open from the beginning of April to the end of October.

❺ Fees quoted for the majority of entries are current. If no price is quoted, you should check with the attraction concerned before you visit. Places which are open 'at all reasonable times' are usually free, and many places which do not charge admission at all may ask for a voluntary donation. Remember that prices can go up, and those provided to us by the attractions are provisional.

✳**Admission prices** followed by a star relate to 2009. It should be noted that in some entries the opening dates and times may also have been supplied as 2009. Please check with the establishment before making your journey.

Free Entry **FREE**

These attractions do not charge a fee for entry, although they may charge for use of audio equipment, for example. We have not included attractions that expect a donation in this category.

⑥ Facilities This section includes parking, dogs allowed, refreshments etc. See page 6 for a key to Symbols and Abbreviations used in this guide.

⑦ Visitors with Mobility Disabilities should look for the wheelchair symbol showing where all or most of the establishment is accessible to the wheelchair-bound visitor. We strongly recommend that you telephone in advance of your visit to check the exact details, particularly regarding access to toilets and refreshment facilities. Assistance dogs are usually accepted where the attractions show the 'No Dogs' symbol ⊗ unless stated otherwise. For the hard of hearing induction loops are indicated by a symbol at the attraction itself.

Credit & Charge cards are taken by a large number of attractions for admission charges. To indicate which do not accept credit cards we have used this symbol at the end of the entry. ⊜

Photography is restricted in some places and there are many where it is only allowed in specific areas. Visitors are advised to check with places of interest on the rules for taking photographs and the use of video cameras.

Special events are held at many of these attractions, and although we have listed a few in individual entries, we cannot hope to give details of them all, so please ring the attractions for details of exhibitions, themed days, talks, guided walks and more.

Attractions with *italic* headings. These are entries that were unable to provide the relevant information in time for publication.

...and finally Opening times and admission prices can be subject to change. Please check with the attraction before making your journey.

Symbols and Abbreviations

- ☎ Telephone number
- ♿ Suitable for visitors in wheelchairs
- 🅟 Parking at Establishment
- Ⓟ Parking nearby
- ☕ Refreshments
- ⛱ Picnic Area
- 🍽 Restaurant
- ⊗ No Dogs
- 🚌 No Coaches
- ✳ Admission prices relate to 2009
- ✤ Cadw (Welsh Monuments)
- ♯ English Heritage
- ❦ National Trust
- ❦ The National Trust for Scotland
- ▮ Historic Scotland

Abbreviations

BH Bank Hoildays
PH Public Holidays
Etr Easter
ex except
ch Children
Pen Senior Citizens
Concessions (Students, unemployed etc)

6

BEDFORD

Bedford Museum FREE

Castle Ln MK40 3XD
☎ 01234 353323   🖷 01234 273401
e-mail: bmuseum@bedford.gov.uk
web: www.bedfordmuseum.org
dir: close to town bridge and Embankment

Embark on a fascinating journey through the human and natural history of north Bedfordshire, pausing briefly to glimpse at wonders from more distant lands. Go back in time and visit the delightful rural room sets and the Old School Museum, where Blackbeard's Sword, 'Old Billy' - the record breaking longest-living horse, and numerous other treasures and curiosities can be found. Housed in the former Higgins and Sons Brewery, Bedford Museum is situated within the gardens of what was once Bedford Castle, beside the Great Ouse embankment. The courtyard and galleries provide an excellent setting for the varied collections.

Times Open all year, Tue-Sat 11-5, Sun 2-5. (Closed Mon ex BH Mon, Good Fri, Xmas & New Year).* **Facilities** ℗ ⬛ 🛱 (outdoor) ♿ toilets for disabled shop ⊗

OLD WARDEN

The Shuttleworth Collection

Old Warden Park SG18 9EP
☎ 01767 627927   🖷 01767 627949
web: www.shuttleworth.org
dir: 2m W from rdbt on A1, Biggleswade by-pass

Housed in eight hangars on a classic grass aerodrome, 40 working historic aeroplanes span the progress of aviation with exhibits ranging from a 1909 Bleriot to a 1941 Spitfire. A garage of roadworthy motor vehicles explores the eras of the 1898 Panhard Levassor to the Railton sports car of 1937. The 19th-century coach house displays horse-drawn vehicles from 1880 to 1914. Flying displays of historic aeroplanes are held on the first Sunday of the month between May and October.

Times Open Apr-Oct 10-5 (last admission 4), Nov-Feb 10-4 (last admission 3). Closed Xmas-New Year. **Fees** £10 (concessions £9). Flying displays £20.* **Facilities** ℗ ⬛ 🍽 licensed 🛱 (outdoor) ♿ toilets for disabled shop ⊗

WOBURN

Woburn Abbey

MK17 9WA

☎ 01525 290333 🖃 01525 290271
e-mail: admissions@woburnabbey.co.uk
web: www.woburn.co.uk
dir: Just off M1 junct 12/13

Set in a beautiful 3,000 acre deer park, Woburn Abbey has been home to the Dukes of Bedford for over 300 years and is currently occupied by the 15th Duke and his family. The Abbey houses one of the most important private art collections in the world including paintings by Canaletto, Gainsborough, Reynolds, Van Dyck and Cuyp and collections of silver, gold and porcelain. Various events throughout the year include Plays in the Park season between June and August.

Times Open 15 Mar-3 Apr & 5-25 Oct, wknds only. 4 Apr-4 Oct, daily, 11-5.30 (last entry 4).*
Fees £13 (ch 3-15 £6, pen £11). Passport ticket for Woburn Abbey and Woburn Safari Park allows one visit to each attraction on same or different days £22.50 (ch £15.50, pen £19). Please phone or check website for further details.* **Facilities** ℗ ⏤ ⏀ licensed ⏢ (outdoor) ⏦ (partly accessible) (limited access to house, only 3 rooms on ground floor. Other areas can only be accessed by means of stairs) toilets for disabled shop ⏣

LOWER BASILDON

Basildon Park

RG8 9NR

☎ 0118 984 3040 🖃 0118 976 7370
e-mail: basildonpark@nationaltrust.org.uk
web: www.nationaltrust.org.uk/basildonpark
dir: 7m NW of Reading on W side of A329 between Pangbourne & Streatley

This 18th-century house, built of Bath stone, fell into decay in the 20th century, but has been beautifully restored by Lord and Lady Iliffe. The classical front has a splendid central portico and pavilions, and inside there are delicate plasterwork decorations on the walls and ceilings. The Octagon drawing room has fine pictures and furniture, and there is a small formal garden. The house more recently featured in the 2005 film adaptation of Jane Austen's Pride and Prejudice. Please contact for details of special events.

Times House open mid Mar-Oct, Wed-Sun & BH Mon 12-5. Park & garden, shop & tea room mid Feb-mid Dec, Wed-Sun & BH Mon 11-3. **Fees** House & grounds £8.80 (ch £4.40). **Facilities** ℗ ⏀ licensed ⏢ (outdoor) ⏦ (partly accessible) (grd floor ramped access to exhibition rooms, tea rooms & shop) toilets for disabled shop ⏥

OLD WINDSOR

Runnymede

North Lodge, Windsor Rd SL4 2JL
☎ 01784 432891 📄 01784 479007
e-mail: runnymede@nationaltrust.org.uk
web: www.nationaltrust.org.uk/runnymede
dir: From M25 junct 13. 2m W of Runnymede
Bridge on S side of A308. 6m E of Windsor

Partly designated as a Site of Special Scientific
Interest, Runnymede is an area of meadows,
grassland, and woodland that sits alongside the
Thames. Best known as the site where King John
signed the Magna Carta in 1215, this momentous
event was commemorated by the American Bar
Association, who built a monument here in 1957.
There is also a memorial to American President,
John F Kennedy. Also there are the Fairhaven
Lodges, designed by Edward Lutyens, one which
is now an art gallery.

Times Car parks: Oct-Mar 9-5, Apr-Sep 9-7
Fees Car parking £1.50-£6, Coaches £6
Facilities 🅿 ℗ 🖵🍴 licensed 🎋 (outdoor) ♿
(partly accessible) (steps to front of tea rooms &
art gallery) toilets for disabled

READING

Museum of English Rural Life
FREE

University of Reading, Redlands Rd RG1 5EX
☎ 0118 378 8660 📄 0118 378 5632
e-mail: merl@reading.ac.uk
web: www.merl.org.uk
dir: close to Royal Berkshire Hospital, museum
100mtrs on right

Recently moved to larger premises, this museum
houses a national collection of agricultural,
domestic and crafts exhibits, including wagons,
tools and a wide range of other equipment used
in the English countryside over the last 150
years. Special facilities are available for school
parties. The museum also contains extensive
documentary and photographic archives, which
can be studied by appointment. There is a regular
programme of events and activities, please see
website for details.

Times Open all year, Tue-Fri, 9-5, Sat & Sun
2-4.30 (Closed BHs & Xmas-New Year).*
Facilities 🅿 🎋 (outdoor) ♿ toilets for disabled
shop 🚫

WINDSOR

Frogmore House

Home Park SL4 1NJ

☎ 020 7766 7305 📄 020 7930 9625
e-mail: bookinginfo@royalcollection.org.uk
web: www.royalcollection.org.uk
dir: entrance via The Long Walk, from B3021
between Datchet & Old Windsor

Frogmore House has been a royal retreat since
the 18th century, and is today used by the Royal
Family for private entertaining. It is especially
linked with Queen Charlotte, the wife of George
III, and her daughters, whose love of botany and
art is reflected throughout the house. Queen
Victoria loved Frogmore so much that she
broke with royal tradition and chose to build a
mausoleum for herself and Prince Albert there.
Please note the Royal Mausoleum is not open to
visitors.

Times Open Aug BH wknd, 10-5.30 (last
admission 4). Prebooked coach groups Aug-
Sep, Tue-Thu. **Fees** Contact Ticket Sales and
Information Office (020 7766 7305) for details of
admission prices. **Facilities** 🅿 Ⓟ ⊼ (outdoor)
♿ (partly accessible) shop ⊗

WINDSOR

Windsor Castle

SL4 1NJ

☎ 020 7766 7304 📄 020 7930 9625
e-mail: bookinginfo@royalcollection.org.uk
web: www.royalcollection.org.uk
dir: M4 junct 6 & M3 junct 3

Covering 13 acres, Windsor Castle is the official
residence of HM The Queen, and the largest
occupied castle in the world. Begun as a wooden
fort by William the Conqueror, it has been added
to by almost every monarch since. A visit takes
in the magnificent State Apartments, St George's
Chapel, Queen Mary's doll's house, the Drawings
Gallery, and between October and March, the
semi-state rooms created by George IV.

Times Open daily except Good Fri & 25-26 Dec.
Nov-Feb, 9.45-4.15 (last admission 3); Mar-Oct,
9.45-5.15 (last admission 4). May be subject
to change at short notice (24hr info line: 01753
831118) **Fees** £16 (ch under 17 £9.50, under 5's
free, concessions £14.50) Family (2ad+3ch) £42
Facilities Ⓟ ♿ toilets for disabled shop ⊗

BRISTOL

Brunel's ss Great Britain

Great Western Dock, Gas Ferry Rd BS1 6TY
☎ 0117 926 0680 📄 0117 925 5788
e-mail: admin@ssgreatbritain.org
web: www.ssgreatbritain.org
dir: off Cumberland Rd

Built and launched in Bristol in 1843, Isambard
Kingdom Brunel's maritime masterpiece was
the first ocean-going, propeller-driven, iron ship.
Launched in 1843 to provide luxury travel to New
York, the world's first great ocean liner set new
standards in engineering, reliability and speed.
Find out about passengers and crew - from the
rich and famous to those leaving 1850s England
to begin a new life. Steer the ship on a westerly
course, prepare her for sail and climb to the
crow's nest. Descend beneath the glass 'sea'
for a close up view of the ship's giant hull and
propeller and the state-of-the-art equipment
which will save her for the next hundred years.
Another feature is the Dockyard Museum charting
the history of Brunel's Masterpiece. A replica
of the square rigger 'Matthew' is moored at the
same site when in Bristol.

Times Open all year daily 10-6, 4.30 in winter.
(Closed 17, 24-25 Dec).* **Facilities** 🅿️Ⓟ 🖵♿
toilets for disabled shop ⊗

BLETCHLEY

Bletchley Park

The Mansion, Bletchley Park MK3 6EB
☎ 01908 640404 📄 01908 274381
e-mail: info@bletchleypark.org.uk
web: www.bletchleypark.org.uk
dir: Approach Bletchley from V7 Saxon St. At rdbt,
southern end of Saxon St under railway bridge
towards Buckingham & follow signs to Bletchley
Park

Known as 'Station X' during World War II, this
was the home of the secret scientific team that
worked to decipher German military messages
sent using the Enigma code machine. Visitors
can find out more about the Enigma machine; the
'bombes', computers used to crack the code; Alan
Turing, one of the leading mathematicians of his
day, who worked on the project; as well as see
a number of other displays including the use of
pigeons during the war, wartime vehicles, and a
Churchill collection.

Times Open daily 9.30-5.30 (Tours at 11 & 2).
Wknds open 10.30-5. Closed 25 & 26 Dec.*
Facilities 🅿️Ⓟ 🖵🍴 licensed 🚻 toilets for
disabled shop

11

CHALFONT ST GILES

Chiltern Open Air Museum

Newland Park, Gorelands Ln HP8 4AB
☎ 01494 871117 📠 01494 872774
e-mail: coamuseum@netscape.net
web: www.coam.org.uk
dir: M25 junct 17, M40 junct 2. Follow brown signs

Chiltern Open Air Museum is an independent charity, established over 30 years ago, with the aim of preserving some of the historic buildings that are unique examples of the heritage of the Chilterns. The museum is now home to more than 30 historic buildings all rescued from demolition and re-erected on this 45-acre woodland and parkland site. Events take place weekends and school holidays throughout the season, please check website for details.

Times Open 27 Mar-29 Oct, daily 10-5 (last admission 3.30). **Fees** £7.50 (ch 5-16 £5, under 5's free), concessions £6.50) Family ticket (2ad+2 ch) £22.* **Facilities** 🅿 ⬛ 🎋 (indoor & outdoor) ♿ (partly accessible) (Some paths/areas and buildings not accessible for all on this 45 acre site - full details on website or phone) toilets for disabled shop ⊗

CHALFONT ST GILES

Milton's Cottage

Dean Way HP8 4JH
☎ 01494 872313
e-mail: info@miltonscottage.org
web: www.miltonscottage.org
dir: 0.5m W of A413. 3m N of M40 junct 2

A timber-framed, 16th-century cottage with a charming garden, the only surviving home in which John Milton lived and worked. He completed Paradise Lost and started Paradise Regained here. First editions of these works are among the many rare books and artefacts on display.

Times Open Mar-Oct, Tue-Sun 10-1 & 2-6. Also open Spring & Summer BH.* **Fees** £4 (ch 15 £2). Group rate 20+ £3 each.* **Facilities** 🅿 🍽 licensed ♿ (partly accessible) (ground floor only accessible) shop ⊗

CLIVEDEN

Cliveden

SL6 0JA

☎ 01628 605069   🖹 01628 669461
e-mail: cliveden@nationaltrust.org.uk
web: www.nationaltrust.org.uk
dir: 2m N of Taplow, follow brown signs on A4

Cliveden's 375 acres of garden and woodland overlook the River Thames, and include a magnificent parterre, topiary, lawns with box hedges, and water gardens. The palatial house, former home of the Astors, is now a hotel - The Great Hall and French Dining Room can be visited on certain afternoons.

Times Open Grounds Mar-Oct daily 11-6, Nov-23 Dec daily 11-4 House Apr-Oct, Thu & Sun 3-5.30 by timed ticket. **Fees** Grounds: £8 (ch £4). House: £1 extra (ch 50p extra). Family ticket £20. Group £7 each. Woodlands £3 (ch £1.50) Family £7.50. **Facilities** 🅿 🍽 licensed 🎪 (outdoor) ♿ (partly accessible) (most garden paths accessible) toilets for disabled shop ⊗ 👗

HIGH WYCOMBE

Hughenden Manor

HP14 4LA

☎ 01494 755573   🖹 01494 474284
e-mail: hughenden@nationaltrust.org.uk
web: www.nationaltrust.org.uk
dir: 1.5m N of High Wycombe, on W side of A4128

This fascinating Victorian manor was home to Prime Minister Benjamin Disraeli from 1848 to 1881. Many of his possessions are still on display, along with beautiful gardens designed by his wife Mary-Anne. Other facilities include circular woodland walks, family tracker packs, I-spy sheets in the Manor and an exhibition revealing Hughenden's role in WWII. See website for special event details.

Times House open 17 Feb-Oct, Wed-Sun & BH Mon 12-5 (last admission 4.30); 3 Nov-19 Dec 11-4. Gardens 17 Feb-Oct, 11-5. Park open all year. **Fees** £8 (ch £4.10). Family ticket £20. Garden only £3.20 (ch £2.20). Park free. **Facilities** 🅿 🍽 licensed 🎪 (outdoor) ♿ (partly accessible) (Ground floor only fully accessible) toilets for disabled shop ⊗ 👗

WADDESDON

Waddesdon Manor

HP18 0JH
☎ 01296 653211, 653226 & 653203
📄 01296 653212
e-mail: waddesdonmanor@nationaltrust.org.uk
web: www.waddesdon.org.uk
dir: entrance off A41, 6m NW of Aylesbury

Built in the 19th century by Baron Ferdinand de Rothschild, this French-style chateau was created as a showcase for his fine collection of French decorative arts. The Victorian gardens are known for seasonal displays, a parterre, walks, views, fountains and statues. The wine cellar contains Rothschild wines dating back to 1868.

Times Gardens: 3 Jan-29 Mar, wknds only; Apr-23 Dec, Wed-Sun & BHs; 27-31 Dec, Wed-Sun & 28-29 Dec, 10-5. House: Apr-1 Nov, Wed-Sun & BHs. Bachelors Wing Apr-1 Nov, Wed-Fri; 11 Nov-23 Dec, Wed-Fri 12-4; Sat-Sun, 21-22 Dec; 27-31 Dec Wed-Sun & 28-29 Dec, Sat-Sun 11-4 & Wed-Fri 12-4.* **Fees** Gardens, 6 Jan-18 Mar (wknds only) 21 Mar-23 Dec, 27-31 Dec (Wed-Fri) £5.50, (ch £2.75). Family £13.75. 19 Mar-23 Dec, 27-31 Dec (wknds & BHs) £7, (ch £3.50). Family £17.50. House & gardens, 21 Mar-28 Oct (Wed-Fri) £13.20, (ch £9.35), wknds & BHs £15, (ch £11).* **Facilities** ℗ 🍽 licensed ♿ toilets for disabled shop ⊗ 🐾

CAMBRIDGE

Fitzwilliam Museum **FREE**

Trumpington St CB2 1RB
☎ 01223 332900 📄 01223 332923
e-mail: fitzmuseum-enquiries@lists.cam.ac.uk
web: www.fitzmuseum.cam.ac.uk
dir: M11 junct 11, 12 or 13. Near city centre

The Fitzwilliam is the art museum of the University of Cambridge and one of the oldest public museums in Britain. It contains magnificent collections spanning centuries and civilisations, including antiquities from Ancient Egypt, Greece and Rome; sculpture, furniture, armour, ceramics, manuscripts, coins and medals, paintings, drawings and prints.

Times Open all year Tue-Sat 10-5, Sun 12-5. (Closed Mon ex BH, & 24-26, 31 Dec & 1 Jan).* **Facilities** ℗ ⊡ 🍴 (outdoor) ♿ toilets for disabled shop ⊗

CAMBRIDGE

Scott Polar Research Institute Museum

Lensfield Rd CB2 1ER
☎ 01223 336540 📄 01223 336549
e-mail: enquiries@spri.cam.ac.uk
web: www.spri.cam.ac.uk
dir: 1km S of city centre

An international centre for polar studies, including a museum featuring displays of Arctic and Antarctic expeditions, with special emphasis on those of Captain Scott and the exploration of the Northwest Passage. Other exhibits include Inuit work and other arts of the polar regions, as well as displays on current scientific exploration. Public lectures run from October to December and February to April. Departure of Captain Scott's Terra Nova from London on 1 June 1910 will be celebrated by the opening of a new Polar Museum on the centenary.

Times Closed for renovation until 1 Jun 2010, then open Tue-Fri 11-1 & 2-4. Sat 12-4. Closed BH wknds, public hols & University hols. Please call 01223 336540 or check the website for further details. **Fees** Free admission, donations welcome. **Facilities** Ⓟ ♿ toilets for disabled shop ⊗

CAMBRIDGE

University Museum of Archaeology & Anthropology **FREE**

Downing St CB2 3DZ
☎ 01223 333516 📄 01223 333517
e-mail: cumaa@hermes.cam.ac.uk
web: www.maa.cam.ac.uk
dir: opposite Crowne Plaza Hotel in city centre

The museum is part of the Faculty of Archaeology and Anthropology of the University of Cambridge. It was established in 1884 and is still housed in its 1916 building on the Downing Site in the city centre. Some of the highlights are Pacific material collected on Captain Cook's voyages of exploration and a 46-foot high totem pole from Canada. Find out about local, national and world archaeology in the Archaeology Galleries, including painted pottery from Peru, giled Anglo-Saxon brooches, and Roman altar stones.

Times Open Tue-Sat, 10.30-4.30.* **Facilities** Ⓟ toilets for disabled shop ⊗

DUXFORD

Imperial War Museum Duxford

CB22 4QR

☎ 01223 835000 📄 01223 837267
e-mail: duxford@iwm.org.uk
web: www.iwm.org.uk/duxford
dir: off M11 junct 10, on A505

Duxford is Europe's premier aviation museum with many original buildings such as the control tower and hangars which are still in use, alongside state-of-the-art, award-winning exhibition buildings including AirSpace and the American Air Museum. A collection of nearly 200 aircraft includes over 50 historic aircraft that regularly take to the sky. Duxford also has one of the finest collections of tanks, military vehicles and artillery in the UK. The Museum holds four air shows throughout the summer plus other special events such as American Air Day, Military Vehicle Show and car shows and more.

Times Open all year, 15 Mar-26 Oct, daily 10-6 (last admission 5); 28 Oct-14 Mar, daily 10-4 (last admission 3). Closed 24-26 Dec.* Fees £16 (ch under 16 free, concessions £12.80). Events & airshow prices vary.* Facilities ℗ 🖵 🍽 licensed 🎋 (indoor & outdoor) ♿ toilets for disabled shop ⊗

ELY

Oliver Cromwell's House

29 St Mary's St CB7 4HF

☎ 01353 662062 📄 01353 668518
e-mail: tic@eastcambs.gov.uk
web: www.visitely.org.uk
dir: follow brown tourist signs from main roads. Adjacent to Saint Mary's Church

Cromwell inherited the house and local estates from a maternal uncle and moved here in 1636, along with his mother, sisters, wife and eight children. There are displays and period rooms dealing with Cromwell's life, the Civil War and domestic life in the 17th century, as well as the history of The Fens and the house itself, from its medieval origins to its role as an inn in the 19th century. Various special events are held during the year including Living History days.

Times Open all year: Apr-Oct, daily 10-5; Nov-Mar, Mon-Fri 11-4, Sat 10-5. Sun, 11.15-4.* Fees £4.30 (ch £3, concessions £3.85). Family ticket £12.50* Facilities ℗ ♿ (partly accessible) (wheelchair access to two rooms) shop ⊗

ELY

The Stained Glass Museum

The South Triforium, Ely Cathedral CB7 4DL
☎ 01353 660347   🖷 01353 665025
e-mail: curator@stainedglassmuseum.com
web: www.stainedglassmuseum.com
dir: Museum inside Ely Cathedral on corner of
Market St & Lynn Rd

800 years of stained-glass history are illustrated
in this unique museum inside Ely Cathedral. Over
100 panels of original stained-glass windows
rescued from the UK and abroad are on display.
The medieval section includes important loans
from the Victoria and Albert Museum in London.
There are also exhibits from Buckingham Palace
and Windsor Castle, work by William Morris
and John Piper, and changing exhibitions of
contemporary work.

Times Open all year (ex Good Fri & 25-26 Dec)
Etr-Oct, Mon-Fri 10.30-5, Sat 10.30-5, Sun
12-6. Nov-Etr, Mon-Sat 10.30-5, Sun 12-4.30
Fees £3.50 (ch under 16 & concessions £2.50).
Family ticket (up to 4 with 1 under 16) £7.
Facilities ℗ 🖵 🍽 licensed 🎪 (outdoor) ♿
(partly accessible) toilets for disabled shop ⊗

PETERBOROUGH

Flag Fen Archaeology Park

The Droveway, Northey Rd PE6 7QJ
☎ 01733 313414   🖷 01733 349957
e-mail: info@flagfen.org
web: www.flagfen.org
dir: From A1139 exit at Boongate junct. At rdbt
3rd exit, through lights, turn right. At T-junct turn
right, Flag Fen signed

Although visitors enter this site through a 21st-
century roundhouse, the rest of their day will be
spent in the Bronze Age, some 3,000 years ago.
Flag Fen's Museum contains artefacts found
over the last 20 years of excavating on site, and
includes among them the oldest wheel in Britain.
In the Park there is a reconstructed Bronze Age
settlement and Iron Age roundhouse, while in the
Preservation Hall visitors can see the excavated
Bronze Age processional way that spanned over
one mile. The Hall also contains a 60-ft mural
depicting the fens in ancient times.

Times Open daily Mar-Oct 10-5 (last admission
4). **Fees** £5.50 (ch £4.15, concessions £4.95).
Family £15.15. Prices include gift aid.* **Facilities**
℗ 🖵 🎪 (outdoor) ♿ toilets for disabled shop ⊗

WATERBEACH

The Farmland Museum and Denny Abbey

Ely Rd CB25 9PQ
☎ 01223 860988 ≣ 01223 860988
e-mail: info@farmlandmuseum.org.uk
web: www.dennyfarmlandmuseum.org.uk
dir: on A10 between Cambridge & Ely

Explore two areas of rural life at this fascinating museum. The Abbey tells the story of those who have lived there, including Benedictine monks, Franciscan nuns, and the mysterious Knights Templar. The farm museum features the craft workshops of a wheelwright, a basketmaker, and a blacksmith. There is also a 1940s farmworker's cottage and a village shop. Special events on Easter, May and August Bank Holidays.

Times Open daily, Apr-Oct, 12-5.* **Facilities** 𝐏 ☐ ☐ (outdoor) ♿ (partly accessible) toilets for disabled shop

CHESTER

The Cheshire Military Museum

The Castle CH1 2DN
☎ 01244 327617 ≣ 01244 401700
e-mail: museum@chester.ac.uk
web: www.chester.ac.uk/militarymuseum
dir: follow signs to Military Museum from town centre

This military museum boasts exhibits from the history of the Cheshire Regiment, Cheshire Yeomanry, 5th Royal Inniskilling Dragoon Guards, and 3rd Carabiniers. There is a display of the work of George Jones, Victorian battle artist, and an exhibition of life in barracks in the 1950s. Research resources are available by written appointment and donation. There are special events throughout the year, please phone for details.

Times Open all year, daily 10-5 (last entry 4). (Closed 22 Dec-3 Jan).* **Fees** £3 (ch & concessions £2).* **Facilities** 𝐏 ♿ toilets for disabled shop ⊗

CHESTER

Dewa Roman Experience

Pierpoint Ln, (off Bridge St) CH1 1NL
☎ 01244 343407 📄 01244 347737
e-mail: info@dewaromanexperience.co.uk
web: www.dewaromanexperience.co.uk
dir: city centre

Stroll along reconstructed streets experiencing the sights, sounds and smells of Roman Chester. From the streets of Dewa (the Roman name for Chester) you return to the present day on an extensive archaeological 'dig', where you can discover the substantial Roman, Saxon and medieval remains beneath modern Chester. Try on Roman armour, solve puzzles and make brass rubbings and make mosaics in the hands-on/activity room. Roman soldier patrols available.

Times Open all year, daily Feb-Nov 9-5, Dec-Jan 10-4 . (Closed 25-26 & 31 Dec & 1 Jan).*
Facilities ℗ shop ⊗

ELLESMERE PORT

The National Waterways Museum

South Pier Rd CH65 4FW
☎ 0151 355 5017 📄 0151 355 4079
e-mail: bookings@thewaterwaystrust.org
web: www.nwm.org.uk
dir: M53 junct 9

The National Waterways Museum aims to bring Britain's canal history to life. The fascinating museum is set within a 200-year-old seven acre dock complex and includes the world's largest floating collection of canal craft. With the dock workers cottages, blacksmiths forge, boat trips and events throughout the year there is something for everyone to enjoy. Check website or telephone for details of future events.

Times Open Summer daily 10-5. Winter Thu-Sun 10-4. Closed 1 Jan.* **Facilities** ℗ ⊑ ⊓ (indoor & outdoor) ♿ (partly accessible) (85% of the site is accessible to wheelchairs) toilets for disabled shop

JODRELL BANK VISITOR CENTRE & ARBORETUM

Jodrell Bank Visitor Centre & Arboretum

SK11 9DL

☎ 01477 571339 🖷 01477 571695

web: www.manchester.ac.uk/jodrellbank

dir: M6 junct 18, A535 Holmes Chapel to Chelford road

At Jodrell Bank, a scientific and engineering wonder awaits you - the magnificent Lovell telescope, one of the largest radio telescopes in the world. A pathway leads you 180 degrees around the telescope as it towers above you surveying and exploring the universe. Then, the visitor can wander along pathways amongst the trees of the extensive arboretum. The Centre is currently under a redevelopment, which will take 2-3 years to complete.

Times Open daily Nov-mid Mar 10.30-3, wknds 11-4; mid Mar-end Oct 10.30-5.30* **Facilities** Ⓟ ☕ ⛩ (outdoor) ♿ toilets for disabled shop ⊗

KNUTSFORD

Tatton Park

WA16 6QN

☎ 01625 374400 & 374435

🖷 01625 374403

e-mail: tatton@cheshireeast.gov.uk

web: www.tattonpark.org.uk

dir: Signed on A556, 4m S of Altrincham. Entrance to Tatton Park on Ashley Rd, 1.5m NE of junct A5034 with A50

Tatton Park is one of England's most complete historic estates, with gardens and a 1,000-acre country park. The centrepiece is the Georgian mansion, with gardens laid out by Humphry Repton and Sir Joseph Paxton. More recently, a Japanese garden with a Shinto temple was created. The Tudor Old Hall is the original manor house, where a guided tour is available. There is also a working 1930s farm and a children's adventure playground. Special events most weekends include the RHS flower show and open air concerts.

Times 28 Mar-4 Oct, 10-7; 5 Oct-26 Mar 11-5* **Fees** Car entry £4.50. Each attraction £4.50 (ch £2.50). Family ticket £11.50. Totally Tatton Ticket (up to 3 attractions) £7 (ch £3.50). Family £17.* **Facilities** Ⓟ 🍽 licensed ⛩ (outdoor) ♿ (partly accessible) (old hall & areas of farm not accessible) toilets for disabled shop ✻

MACCLESFIELD

Paradise Mill & Silk Industry Museum

Park Ln SK11 6TJ
☎ 01625 612045 🖹 01625 612048
e-mail: info@macclesfield.silk.museum
web: www.macclesfield.silk.museum
dir: turn off A523 'The Silk Rd' & follow brown signs

A working silk mill until 1981, with restored jacquard hand looms in their original location. Knowledgeable guides, many of them former silk mill workers, illustrate the silk production process with the help of demonstrations from weavers. Exhibitions and room settings give an impression of working conditions at the mill during the 1930s. The adjacent Silk Industry Museum opened in 2002 and focuses on design and manufacturing processes.

Times Open all year, BH Mon & Mon-Sat 11-5 (Closed Sun, 25-26 Dec & 1 Jan, Good Fri). Please ring for winter opening times.* **Fees** £5 (concessions £4.50) includes Park Lane Galleries & Paradise Mill, all inclusive ticket £8.75 (concessions £7.75)* **Facilities** Ⓟ toilets for disabled shop ⊗

NANTWICH

Hack Green Secret Nuclear Bunker

French Ln, Hack Green CW5 8AP
☎ 01270 629219 🖹 01270 629218
e-mail: coldwar@hackgreen.co.uk
web: www.hackgreen.co.uk
dir: from Nantwich take A530 towards Whitchurch, follow brown signs

One of the nation's most secret defence sites. Declassified in 1993, this underground bunker would have been the centre of regional government had nuclear war broken out. Observe the preparations the government made for nuclear war and step into the lives of people who worked here. View the Minister of State's office, life support, communication centre, decontamination facilities, telephone exchange and much more.

Times Open 20 Apr-30 Oct, daily 10.30-5.30; Nov, Jan, Feb wknds, 11-4. Closed Dec.* **Fees** £6.30 (ch £4.50, concessions £5.90). Family £19* **Facilities** Ⓟ Ⓟ ⊑ ⍩ licensed ⊼ (outdoor) ৬ (partly accessible) (1st floor & bistro partly accessible) toilets for disabled shop ⊗

NORTHWICH

Salt Museum

162 London Rd CW9 8AB
☎ 01606 271640 🖷 01606 350420
e-mail: cheshiremuseums@cheshire.gov.uk
web: www.saltmuseum.org.uk
dir: on A533, 0.5m S of town centre & 0.5m N of
A556. Well signed from A556

Britain's only Salt Museum tells the fascinating
story of Cheshire's oldest industry. Models,
reconstructions, original artefacts and audio-
visual programmes throw new light on something
we all take for granted. Various temporary
exhibitions are held here, please contact for
details.

Times Open Tue-Fri 10-5, wknds 2-5 (Sat & Sun,
12-5 in Aug). Open BH & Mons in Aug 10-5.*
Facilities ℗ ⊑ 🆙 (outdoor) ♿ toilets for
disabled shop ⊗

STYAL

Quarry Bank Mill & Styal Estate

SK9 4LA
☎ 01625 527468 & 445896
🖷 01625 539267
e-mail: quarrybankmill@nationaltrust.org.uk
web: www.quarrybankmill.org.uk
dir: 1.5m N of Wilmslow off B5166, 2.5m from
M56 junct 5. Follow signs from A34 & M56

Founded in 1784, Quarry Bank Mill is one of
the finest surviving cotton mills of the period.
Hands-on exhibits and demonstrations show
how traditional spinning and weaving was
transformed through the ingenuity of early textile
engineers. Using the most powerful working
waterwheel in Europe, two mill engines bring
the past to life. At the Apprentice House you can
discover what home life was like for the pauper
children who worked in the mill in the 1830s.

Times Open Mar-Oct, daily 11-5; Nov-Feb, Wed-
Sun 11-4 (last admission 1hr before closing).
Apprentice House timed tours. Garden open Mar-
Oct.* Fees Mill & Apprentice House or Garden
£10 (ch £5). Family ticket £24. Mill only £7 (ch
£3.70). Family ticket £17.70. Facilities ℗ ⊑
⦿ licensed 🆙 ♿ (partly accessible) (Apprentice
House level access to ground floor only) toilets for
disabled shop ⊗ 🦋

CALSTOCK

Cotehele

St Dominick PL12 6TA
☎ 01579 351346 & 352739 (info)
🖷 01579 351222
e-mail: cotehele@nationaltrust.org.uk
web: www.nationaltrust.org.uk
dir: between Tavistock & Callington. Turn off
A390 at St. Ann's Chapel, signed 2.5m S of junct

A 15th-century house that contains tapestries,
embroideries, furniture and armour; and outside,
a beautiful garden on different levels, including a
formal Italian-style garden, medieval stewpond,
dovecote, and an 18th-century tower with lovely
views. There is a restored water mill in the valley
below, and at the Victorian riverside quay is a
Maritime Museum.

Times Open 13 Mar-Oct. Garden open all year
daily 10-dusk. Limited opening Nov-24 Dec.
Fees House, Garden & Mill £9.20. Garden & Mill
£5.20 (ch 1/2 price, under 5's & NT members
free). Family tickets available. Garden & mill only
£5.50 (ch 1/2 price, under 5's & NT members
free).* **Facilities** 🅿 ♿🍽 licensed 🎪 (outdoor)
♿ (partly accessible) (garden & house limited
access) toilets for disabled shop 🚫 🌱

FALMOUTH

National Maritime Museum Cornwall

Discovery Quay TR11 3QY
☎ 01326 313388 🖷 01326 317878
e-mail: enquiries@nmmc.co.uk
web: www.nmmc.co.uk
dir: follow signs from A39 for park/float ride and
museum

Recently voted the south west's Visitor Attraction
of the Year, this award winning museum offers
something for everyone from ever changing
exhibitions, hands-on family activities, talks,
lectures, displays, events, crabbing and the
opportunity to sail and see marine and bird
life. Admire the views from the 29 metre tower,
descend the depths in one of only three natural
underwater viewing galleries in the world and
discover Cornwall, journey through time, explore
the seas and go mad about boats. The purchase
of a full price individual ticket gives you free
entry to the Museum for a year.

Times Open daily 10-5. Closed 25-26 Dec.*
Fees £8.75 (ch under 5 free, ch 6-15 & students
£6, pen £7). Family ticket £24.* **Facilities** 🅿 Ⓟ
♿🍽 licensed ♿ toilets for disabled shop 🚫

FALMOUTH

Pendennis Castle

Pendennis Headland TR11 4LP
☎ 01326 316594 🗎 01326 212044
web: www.english-heritage.org.uk
dir: 1m SE

Together with St Mawes Castle, Pendennis forms the end of a chain of castles built by Henry VIII along the south coast as protection from attack from France. Journey through 450 years of history and discover the castle's wartime secrets.

Times Open all year, Apr-Jun & Sep, daily 10-5 (Sat 10-4); Jul-Aug, daily 10-6 (Sat 10-4); Oct-Mar, daily 10-4. Closed 24-26 Dec & 1 Jan. Fees £5.70 (ch £2.90, concessions £4.80). Family £14.30. Prices and opening times are subject to change in March 2010. Please call 0870 333 1181 for the most up to date prices and opening times when planning your visit. Facilities ❷ ▢ ㅈ �& (partly accessible) (two steep steps ticket point, spiral staircase, difficult steps to upper floor) toilets for disabled shop ⊗ ♯

HELSTON

Goonhilly Satellite Earth Station Experience

Goonhilly Downs TR12 6LQ
☎ 0800 679593 🗎 01326 221438
e-mail: goonhilly.visitorscentre@bt.com
web: www.goonhilly.bt.com
dir: From Helston follow the brown direction signs

Future World is on the site of what was the largest satellite earth station in the world, with over 60 dishes, which makes a dramatic impression on the Lizard Peninsula landscape. Enter a world of historic predictions, past inventions and ideas and see artefacts from jet packs and space helmets to the Sinclair C5 and the first mobile phones, complete with 'brick' size batteries. Journey into a zone of interactive displays where you can record your own visions of the future. Discover the history and heritage of Goonhilly itself in the main visitors' centre, and learn how international communications have developed over the past 200 years. You an also book a tour into the heart of 'Arthur', the Grade II listed iconic satellite dish.

Times Open 15 Mar-27 Jun & 6 Sep-Oct 10-5; 28 Jun-5 Sep 10-6; Nov-27 Mar 11-4.* Facilities ❷ ▢ ￼ licensed ㅈ (outdoor) �& toilets for disabled shop ⊗

LANHYDROCK

Lanhydrock

PL30 5AD

☎ 01208 265950 🖷 01208 265959

e-mail: lanhydrock@nationaltrust.org.uk

web: www.nationaltrust.org.uk

dir: 2.5m SE of Bodmin, signed from A30, A38 & B3268

Part-Jacobean, part-Victorian building that gives a vivid picture of life in Victorian times. The 'below stairs' sections have a huge kitchen, larders, dairy, bakehouse, cellars, and servants' quarters. The long gallery has a moulded ceiling showing Old Testament scenes, and overlooks the formal gardens with their clipped yews and bronze urns. The higher garden, famed for its magnolias and rhododendrons, climbs the hillside behind the house.

Times House open 13 Mar-Oct daily (ex Mon) 11-5 (Apr-Sep 5.30), open BH Mon & Mon during school hols. Gardens open all year, daily 10-6. **Fees** House & Grounds £10.90 (ch £5.40). Family tickets available. Garden & Grounds £6.40 (ch £5.80). Reduced rate when arriving by cycle or public transport. **Facilities** 🅿 🅿 ⌨ ⋔◎ licensed 🅰 (outdoor) ♿ toilets for disabled shop ⊗ ✦

MARAZION

St Michael's Mount

TR17 0HT

☎ 01736 710507 & 710265

🖷 01736 719930

e-mail: mail@stmichaelsmount.co.uk

web: www.stmichaelsmount.co.uk

dir: 0.5m S of A394 at Marazion, access is by foot at low tide, or by motorboat in summer

After the Norman Conquest, the abbey on St Michael's Mount was granted to the Benedictine order and miracles were said to have occurred here in the 1260s. In 1588 the Mount was where the first beacon was lit to warn of the arrival of the Spanish Armada, and in the Civil War it was a Royalist stronghold attacked by Cromwell's forces. Today it is the home of the St Aubyn family who have lived here since the 17th century. The island is separated from the mainland by a causeway which is covered by the sea at high tide.

Times Open: Castle 29 Mar-1 Nov 10.30-5. (last entry 45mins before closing). Winter Tue & Fri by guided tour only. Garden May-June, Mon-Fri, Jul-Oct Thu & Fri 10.30-5.* **Fees** £6.60 (ch £3.30) Family ticket £16.50 (1ad family £9.90). Groups 15+ £5.60. Garden £3 (ch £1). Castle & gardens free to NT members.* **Facilities** 🅿 ⌨ ⋔◎ licensed 🅰 (outdoor) shop ⊗ ✦

PENDEEN

Geevor Tin Mine

TR19 7EW

☎ 01736 788662   🖹 01736 786059
e-mail: bookings@geevor.com
web: www.geevor.com
dir: From Penzance take A3071 towards St Just, then B3318 towards Pendeen. From St Ives follow B3306 to Pendeen

A preserved tin mine and museum provide an insight into the methods and equipment used in the industry that was once so important in the area. The Geevor Tin Mine only actually stopped operation in 1990. Guided tours let visitors see the tin treatment plant, and a video illustrates the techniques employed. A museum of hard rock mining has recently opened, and the underground tour is well worth the trip.

Times Open daily (ex Sat) 9-5 (9-4 Nov-Mar). Closed 21-26 Dec & 1 Jan **Fees** £8.50 (ch & students £4.50, concessions £7.50) Family ticket £25. **Facilities** 🅿 Ⓟ ⬚ 🍽 licensed ᴁ (outdoor) ♿ (partly accessible) (access to new museum, shop & cafe) toilets for disabled shop ⊗

PENTEWAN

The Lost Gardens of Heligan

PL26 6EN

☎ 01726 845100   🖹 01726 845101
e-mail: info@heligan.com
web: www.heligan.com
dir: signed from A390 & B3273

Heligan, seat of the Tremayne family for more than 400 years, is one of the most mysterious estates in England. At the end of the 19th-century its thousand acres were at their zenith, but only a few years after the Great War, bramble and ivy were already drawing a green veil over this sleeping beauty. Today the garden offers 200 acres for exploration, which include productive gardens, pleasure grounds, a sub-tropical jungle, sustainably-managed farmland, wetlands, ancient woodlands and a pioneering wildlife project. Please telephone for details of spring-time and harvest-time events and for summer evening theatre.

Times Open Apr-Sep, daily 10-6 (last tickets 4.30); Oct-Mar, daily 10-5 (last tickets 3.30)* **Fees** £8.50 (ch £5, pen £7.50). Family £23.50 (2ad+3ch)* **Facilities** 🅿 Ⓟ ⬚ ᴁ (indoor & outdoor) ♿ (partly accessible) (northern gardens, wildlife project, shop, plant sales & tearooms all accessible) toilets for disabled shop ⊗

ST AUSTELL

Charlestown Shipwreck & Heritage Centre

Quay Rd, Charlestown PL25 3NJ
☎ 01726 69897 📄 01726 69897
e-mail: admin@shipwreckcharlestown.com
web: www.shipwreckcharlestown.com
dir: signed off A390 from St. Austell close to Eden Project

Charlestown is a small and unspoilt village with a unique sea-lock, china-clay port, purpose built in the 18th century. The Shipwreck and Heritage Centre was originally a dry house for china clay built on underground tunnels. Now it houses the largest display of shipwreck artefacts in the UK, along with local heritage, diving exhibits, and an RMS Titanic display. A recent addition is a Nelson display which commemorates the 200th anniversary of the Battle of Trafalgar.

Times Open Mar-Oct, daily 10-5. (Last admission 1 hour before closing) **Fees** £5.95 (ch under 10 free if accompanied by paying adult, ch under 16 £2.50, concessions £3.95) group prices on request. **Facilities** 🅿 🅟 ⊑ 🍴 licensed ♿ toilets for disabled shop

ST AUSTELL

The China Clay Country Park

Carthew PL26 8XG
☎ 01726 850362 📄 01726 850362
e-mail: info@chinaclaycountry.co.uk
web: www.chinaclaycountry.co.uk
dir: 2m N on B3274, follow brown signs 'China Clay Museum'

This museum tells the story of Cornwall's most important present-day industry: china clay production. The open-air site includes a complete 19th-century clayworks, with huge granite-walled settling tanks, working water-wheels and a wooden slurry pump. There is a fully interactive gallery, nature trails and a children's adventure trail. Exhibition halls and interactive displays depict the life of claypit workers from 1800 to the present.

Times Open all year 10-6, last admission summer 4, winter 3* **Facilities** 🅿 🅟 ⊑ 🍴 licensed 🎋 (outdoor) ♿ toilets for disabled shop

TINTAGEL

Tintagel Castle

PL34 0HE

☎ 01840 770328 📄 01841 772105
web: www.english-heritage.org.uk
dir: on Tintagel Head, 0.5m along uneven track
from Tintagel, no vehicles

Overlooking the wild Cornish coast, Tintagel
is one of the most spectacular spots in the
country and associated with King Arthur and
Merlin. Recent excavations revealed Dark Age
connections between Spain and Cornwall,
alongside the discovery of the 'Arthnou' stone
suggesting that this was a royal place for the
Dark Age rulers of Cornwall.

Times Open all year, Apr-Sep, daily 10-6; Oct-1
Nov, daily 10-5; 2 Nov-Mar, daily 10-4. Closed
24-26 Dec & 1 Jan. Beach cafe open daily, Apr-
Oct (closes 1/2hr before castle) Nov-Mar 11-3.30.
Fees £4.90 (concessions £4.20, ch £2.50).
Family ticket £12.30. Prices and opening times
are subject to change in March 2010. Please call
0870 333 1181 for the most up to date prices
and opening times when planning your visit.
Facilities ℗ shop ⊗ ♯

WENDRON

Poldark Mine and Heritage Complex

TR13 0ER

☎ 01326 573173 📄 01326 563166
e-mail: info@poldark-mine.com
web: www.poldark-mine.com
dir: 3m from Helston on B3297 Redruth road,
follow brown signs

The centre of this attraction is the 18th-century
tin mine where visitors can join a guided tour
of workings which retain much of their original
character. The site's Museum explains the history
of tin production in Cornwall from 1800BC
through to the 19th century and the fascinating
story of the Cornish overseas. In addition to the
Museum, the audio-visual presentation gives
more insight into Cornwall's mining heritage.
Ghost tours through July and August, please
phone for details.

Times Open Etr-end Oct, 10-5.30 (last tour
4).* **Facilities** ℗ ⊡ ⌗⍥ licensed ⊼ (indoor &
outdoor) ⅙ (partly accessible) (surface area only)
toilets for disabled shop

ALSTON

Nenthead Mines

Nenthead CA9 3PD
☎ 01434 382726 📠 01434 382043
e-mail: mines@npht.com
web: www.npht.com/nentheadmines
dir: 5m E of Alston, on A689

Set in 200 acres in the North Pennines, this hands-on heritage centre contains exhibitions and displays on geology, local wildlife, and social history. Visitors can operate three enormous water wheels, gaze down a 328ft deep brewery shaft, and take an underground trip through the Nenthead mines, last worked for lead in 1915. Special events take place throughout the year.

Times Open Etr-Oct, daily 11-5 (last entry to mine 3.30).* **Facilities** 🅿 🅿 ⊡ 🍴 (indoor & outdoor) ♿ (partly accessible) (ltd disabled access underground) toilets for disabled shop

AMBLESIDE

The Armitt Collection

Rydal Rd LA22 9BL
☎ 015394 31212 📠 015394 31313
e-mail: info@armitt.com
web: www.armitt.com
dir: On A591 opposite Rydal Rd car park in Ambleside. Next to St Martins College

A fascinating and entertaining place that celebrates over 2000 years of Lake District history, from the time of Ambleside's Roman occupation to the 20th century. Facts, artefacts, historic photographs and renowned works of art by not only the area's better known former inhabitants such as Beatrix Potter, Kurt Schwitters and John Ruskin, but also displays about the daily lives of its hard-working townspeople in past times. Over 11,000 books are contained within a reference library and there is a changing programme of exhibitions. The Collection is pre-eminently a research source, using the gallery to demonstrate the range of material within the collection.

Times Open all year, daily 10-5 (last entrance 4.30). Closed 24-26 Dec. **Fees** £2.50 (ch £1 under 5 free, concessions £2) Family ticket (2 ad +up to 3 ch) £6. **Facilities** 🅿 ♿ toilets for disabled shop ⊗

BIRDOSWALD

Birdoswald Roman Fort

CA8 7DD

☎ 016977 47602   ▤ 016977 47605

e-mail:
birdoswald.romanfort@english-heritage.org.uk
web: www.english-heritage.org.uk
dir: signed off A69 between Brampton & Hexham

A visitor centre introduces you to Hadrian's Wall and the Roman Fort. This unique section of Hadrian's Wall overlooks the Irthing Gorge, and is the only point along the Wall where all the components of the Roman frontier system can be found together. Birdoswald isn't just about the Romans, though, it's also about border raids in the Middle Ages, and recent archaeological discoveries. Please telephone for details of re-enactments and family activities.

Times Open Apr-Sep, daily 10-5.30 (last admission 5). Oct-1 Nov daily, 10-4 **Fees** £4.50 (ch £2.30, concessions £3.80). **Facilities** ❷ ℗ ⌷ ⇴ (outdoor) & (partly accessible) toilets for disabled shop ⌗

BORROWDALE

Honister Slate Mine

Honister Pass CA12 5XN

☎ 01768 777230   ▤ 01768 777958

e-mail: info@honister.com
web: www.honister.com
dir: from Keswick take B5289 through Borrowdale & Rosthwaite, follow road to top of pass. From Cockermouth take B5292 towards Keswick for 4m, turn right onto B5289 to Low Larton & Buttermere. Follow road to top of pass

The last working slate mine in England. Fully guided tours allow you to explore the caverns hacked out by Victorian miners. Learn the history of the famous Honister green slate, how to rive slates, and see local skills in action.

Times Open Mon-Fri 9-5, wknds 10-5. Closed 19 Dec-12 Jan.* **Facilities** ❷ ℗ ⌷ ⋈ licensed ⇴& (partly accessible) toilets for disabled shop

COCKERMOUTH

Wordsworth House

Main St CA13 9RX
☎ 01900 820882 📠 01900 820883
e-mail: wordsworthhouse@nationaltrust.org.uk
web: www.wordsworthhouse.org.uk
dir: W end of Main Street

William Wordsworth was born here on 7th April 1770, and happy memories of the house had a great effect on his work. The house is imaginatively presented for the first time as the home of the Wordsworth family in the 1770s. It offers a lively and interactive visit with hands-on activities and costumed living history.

Times Open 27 Mar-28 Oct, 11-4.30. Jul, Aug & BHs Mon-Sat, other times Tue-Sat.* **Fees** £6.20 (ch £3.10). Family ticket £15.50. **Facilities** Ⓟ toilets for disabled shop ⊗ ♨

CONISTON

Brantwood

LA21 8AD
☎ 015394 41396 📠 015394 41263
e-mail: enquiries@brantwood.org.uk
web: www.brantwood.org.uk
dir: 2.5m SE off B5285, unclass road. Regular ferry services from Coniston Pier

Brantwood, home of John Ruskin, is a beautifully situated house with fine views across Coniston Water. Inside, there is a large collection of Ruskin paintings and memorabilia, and visitors can enjoy delightful nature walks through the Brantwood Estate.

Times Open mid Mar-mid Nov, daily 11-5.30. Winter, Wed-Sun 11-4.30. (Closed 25-26 Dec).* **Facilities** Ⓟ Ⓟ ⫐🍴 licensed ⓓ (partly accessible) toilets for disabled shop ⊗

31

CONISTON

The Ruskin Museum

Yewdale Rd LA21 8DU

☎ 015394 41164 ◻ 01539 441132

web: www.ruskinmuseum.com

dir: In village centre opposite fire station, accessed from Mines Rd between Black Bull and Co-op

John Ruskin (1819-1900) was one of Britain's most versatile and important political thinkers and artists. The museum contains many of his watercolours, drawings, letters, sketchbooks and other relics. The geology, mines and quarries of the area and Arthur Ransome's Swallows and Amazons country are also explored in the Museum. The conservation rebuild of Donald Campbell's iconic hydroplane is underway, and should be completed by autumn 2010. Permission has been granted for future low-speed engineering proving trials on Coniston Water. The housing of Bluebird A7 in a new museum wing is also planned.

Times Open 2-4 Jan, 6 Jan-5 Mar, Wed-Sun 10.30-3.30; from 6 Mar, daily 10-5.30. Contact or see website for details of winter opening hours.
Fees £4.50 (ch £2). Family ticket £12. Ticket gives 50p discount for cruise on S.Y. Gondola/Coniston Launch and/or visit to Brantwood.
Facilities 🅿 🅟 ♿ toilets for disabled shop ⊗

CONISTON

Steam Yacht Gondola

Coniston Pier LA21 8AJ

☎ 015394 41288 ◻ 015394 41962

e-mail: gondola@nationaltrust.org.uk

web: www.nationaltrust.org.uk/gondola

dir: A593 to Coniston, follow signs near garage 'to boats' & S Y Gondola. Coniston Pier at end of Lake Road

Originally launched in 1859, the graceful Gondola plied the waters of Coniston Water until 1936. Beautifully rebuilt, she came back into service in 1980, and visitors can once again enjoy her silent progress and old-fashioned comfort.

Times Open Apr-Oct to scheduled daily timetable.
Fees Round trip £7 (ch £3.50). Family ticket (2ad+3ch) £17.50, including NT members.
Facilities 🅿 🅟 ♿ (partly accessible) (Gondola not accessible to wheelchair bound visitors) shop ⊗ 🐾

GRASMERE

Dove Cottage, The Wordsworth Museum and Art Gallery

LA22 9SH
☎ 015394 35544 🖹 015394 35748
e-mail: enquiries@wordsworth.org.uk
web: www.wordsworth.org.uk
dir: A591S of rdbt for Grasmere village

Dove Cottage was the inspirational home of William Wordsworth between 1799-1808, and it was here that he wrote some of his best-known poetry. The cottage has been open to the public since 1891, and is kept in its original condition. The museum displays manuscripts, works of art and items that belonged to the poet. There is a changing programme of special events, both historical and modern. Please visit website for details.

Times Open daily 9.30-5.30 (last admission 5). Closed 24 Dec & Jan. **Fees** £7.50 (ch £4.50). Family ticket £17.20. Discounts for pre-bkd groups. **Facilities** 🅿 🅟 ⎁ ⎮⎔⎮ licensed ⏇ (partly accessible) (Museum, galleries & ground floor of cottage accessible) toilets for disabled shop ⊗

KENDAL

Museum of Lakeland Life

Abbot Hall LA9 5AL
☎ 01539 722464 🖹 01539 722494
e-mail: info@lakelandmuseum.org.uk
web: www.lakelandmuseum.org.uk
dir: M6 junct 36, follow signs to Kendal. Located at south end of Kendal beside Abbot Hall Art Gallery

The life and history of the Lake District is captured by the displays in this museum, housed in Abbot Hall's stable block. The working and social life of the area are well illustrated by a variety of exhibits including period rooms, a Victorian Cumbrian street scene, a farming display, Arts and Crafts movement textiles and furniture and a recreation of Arthur Ransome's study, furnished with many of his personal possessions.

Times Open 13 Jan-12 Dec, Mon-Sat 10.30-5. (Closing at 4 Jan-Mar & Nov-Dec)* **Fees** £4.75 (ch £3.40). Family ticket £13.60.* **Facilities** 🅿 🅟 ⎁⏇ (partly accessible) toilets for disabled shop ⊗

NEAR SAWREY

Hill Top

LA22 0LF

☎ 015394 36269 📄 015394 36811
e-mail: hilltop@nationaltrust.org.uk
web: www.nationaltrust.org.uk
dir: 2m S of Hawkshead or 2m from Bowness
Car Ferry

This small 17th-century house is where Beatrix
Potter wrote many of her famous children's
stories. It remains as she left it, and in each
room can be found something that appears in
one of her books.

Times House open 13 Feb-25 Mar, Sat-Thu
11-3.30; 27 Mar-Oct, Sat-Thu 10.30-4.30. Garden
open 13 Feb-25 Mar, daily 11-4; 26 Mar-Oct,
daily 10-5; Nov-24 Dec, daily 10-4 **Fees** £6.20
(ch £3.10). Family ticket £15.50 (2ad+3ch).
Entry to garden free on Fri when house is closed.
Facilities 🅿 ♿ (partly accessible) (access by
arrangement) shop ⊗ ♨

RYDAL

Rydal Mount and Gardens

LA22 9LU

☎ 015394 33002 📄 015394 31738
e-mail: info@rydalmount.com
web: www.rydalmount.co.uk
dir: 1.5m from Ambleside on A591 to Grasmere

The family home of William Wordsworth from
1813 until his death in 1850. The house contains
important family portraits, furniture, and many
of the poet's personal possessions, together
with first editions of his work. In a lovely setting
overlooking Windermere and Rydal Water, the
gardens were designed by Wordsworth himself.
Evening visits for groups can be organised.

Times Open Mar-Oct, daily 9.30-5; Nov, Dec &
Feb, daily (ex Tue) 10-4. Closed 24-25 Dec &
Jan* **Facilities** 🅿 🅿 ⋈ (outdoor) ♿ (partly
accessible) shop ⊗

BUXTON

Poole's Cavern (Buxton Country Park)

Green Ln SK17 9DH
☎ 01298 26978   ▤ 01298 73563
e-mail: info@poolescavern.co.uk
web: www.poolescavern.co.uk
dir: 1m from Buxton town centre, off A6 and A515

Limestone rock, water, and millions of years created this natural cavern containing thousands of crystal formations. A 45-minute guided tour leads the visitor through chambers used as a shelter by Bronze Age cave dwellers, Roman metal workers and as a hideout by the infamous robber Poole. Attractions include the underground source of the River Wye, the 'Poached Egg Chamber', Mary, Queen of Scots' Pillar, the Grand Cascade and underground sculpture formations.

Times Open Mar-Oct, daily 9.30-5; Nov-Feb wknds 10-4.* **Fees** £7.50 (ch £4.50, concessions £6). Family ticket £22. Please check website or telephone for current details* **Facilities** ❷ ☷ ⦿ licensed ⩑ (outdoor) ♿ (partly accessible) (access to visitor centre & 1st 100mtrs of cave tour to main chamber, no access to woods) toilets for disabled shop ⊗

CASTLETON

Blue-John Cavern & Mine

Buxton Rd S33 8WP
☎ 01433 620638 & 620642
▤ 01433 621586
e-mail: lesley@bluejohn.gemsoft.co.uk
web: www.bluejohn.gemsoft.co.uk
dir: follow brown 'Blue-John Cavern' signs from Castleton

A remarkable example of a water-worn cave, over a third of a mile long, with chambers 200ft high. It contains 8 of the world's 14 veins of Blue John stone, and has been the major source of this unique form of fluorspar for nearly 300 years.

Times Open all year, daily, 9.30-5 (or dusk). Guided tours of approx 1hr every 10 mins tour. Closed 25-26 Dec & 1 Jan. **Fees** £8 (ch £4, pen & students £6) Family ticket £22. Party rates on request.* **Facilities** ❷ ℗ ☷ shop

CASTLETON

Peak Cavern

S33 8WS

☎ 01433 620285
e-mail: info@peakcavern.co.uk
web: www.devilsarse.com
dir: on A6187, in centre of Castleton

One of the most spectacular natural limestone caves in the Peak District, with an electrically-lit underground walk of about half a mile. Ropes have been made for over 500 years in the 'Grand Entrance Hall', and traces of a row of cottages can be seen. Rope-making demonstrations are included on every tour.

Times Open all year, daily 10-5. Nov-Mar limited tours, please call in advance for times. Closed 25 Dec.* **Fees** £7.25 (ch £5.25, other concessions £6.25). Family ticket (2ad+2ch) £22.* **Facilities** ❷ ❷ ♒ (indoor & outdoor) ♿ (partly accessible) (number of stairs throughout the cave) shop

CASTLETON

Speedwell Cavern

Winnats Pass S33 8WA

☎ 01433 620512 📠 01433 621888
e-mail: info@speedwellcavern.co.uk
web: www.speedwellcavern.co.uk
dir: A625 becomes A6187 at Hathersage. 0.5m W of Castleton

Descend 105 steps to a boat that takes you on a one-mile underground exploration of floodlit caverns part of which was once a lead mine. The hand-carved tunnels open out into a network of natural caverns and underground rivers. See the Bottomless Pit, a huge subterranean lake in a huge, cathedral-like cavern.

Times Open all year, daily 10-5 (Closed 25 Dec). Phone to check winter opening times due to weather. Last boat 4 **Fees** £7.75 (ch £5.75).* **Facilities** ❷ ❷ ♿ (partly accessible) (105 steps in one flight down to boat & back up again to surface) shop ⊗

CASTLETON

Treak Cliff Cavern

S33 8WP

☎ 01433 620571   📠 01433 620519
e-mail: treakcliff@bluejohnstone.com
web: www.bluejohnstone.com
dir: 0.75m W of Castleton on A6187

An underground world of stalactites, stalagmites, flowstone, rock and cave formations, minerals and fossils. There are rich deposits of the rare and beautiful Blue John stone, including 'The Pillar', the largest piece ever found. These caves contain some of the most impressive stalactites in the Peak District. Visitors can also polish their own Blue John stone in school holidays, and purchase Blue John stone jewellery and ornaments in the Castleton Gift Shop.

Times Open all year, Mar-Oct, daily 10-last tour 4.20; Nov-Feb daily - call for special tour times. All tours are guided & last about 40 mins. Enquire for last tour of day & possible closures. Closed 24-26 & 31 Dec & 1 Jan. All dates & times are subject to change without notice.* **Fees** £7.95 (ch 5-15 £4). Family ticket (2ad+2ch) £22.* **Facilities** 🅿 Ⓟ ♿ 🏖 (indoor & outdoor) ♿ (partly accessible) (no wheelchair access, walking disabled only) shop

CHATSWORTH

Chatsworth

DE45 1PP

☎ 01246 565300   📠 01246 583536
e-mail: visit@chatsworth.org
web: www.chatsworth.org
dir: 8m N of Matlock off B6012. 16m from M1 junct 29, signposted via Chesterfield, follow brown signs

Home of the Duke and Duchess of Devonshire, Chatsworth contains a massive private collection of fine and decorative arts. There is a splendid painted hall, and a great staircase leads to the chapel, decorated with statues and paintings. There are pictures, furniture and porcelain, and a trompe l'oeil painting of a violin on the music room door. The park was laid out by 'Capability' Brown, but is most famous as the work of Joseph Paxton, head gardener in the 19th century. The park is also home to the Duke and Duchess' personal collection of contemporary sculpture.

Times Open mid Mar-23 Dec, House & Garden 11-5.30, Farmyard 10.30-5.30.* **Facilities** 🅿 Ⓟ ♿ 🍽 licensed ♿ (partly accessible) toilets for disabled shop ⊗

CRESWELL

Creswell Crags Museum and Education Centre

Crags Rd, Welbeck S80 3LH
☎ 01909 720378 🗎 01909 724726
e-mail: info@creswell-crags.org.uk
web: www.creswell-crags.org.uk
dir: off B6042, Crags Road, between A616 & A60, 1m E of Creswell village

Creswell Crags, a picturesque limestone gorge with lakes and caves, is one of Britain's most important archaeological sites. The many caves on the site have yielded Ice Age remains, including bones of woolly mammoth, reindeer, hyena and bison, stone tools of Ice Age hunters from over 10,000 years ago and new research has revealed the only Ice Age rock art in Britain (about 13,000 years old). Visit the Museum and Education Centre to learn more about your Ice Age ancestors through an exhibition, touch-screen computers and video.

Times Open all year, Feb-Oct, daily, 10.30-4.30; Nov-Jan, Sun only 10.30-4.30.* **Facilities** 🅿 🎪 ♿ (partly accessible) (accessible round Gorge. Tour may be unsuitable for mobility scooters, due to steps) toilets for disabled shop ⊗

CRICH

Crich Tramway Village

DE4 5DP
☎ 01773 854321 🗎 01773 854320
e-mail: enquiry@tramway.co.uk
web: www.tramway.co.uk
dir: off B5035, 8m from M1 junct 28

A mile-long scenic journey through a period street to open countryside with panoramic views. You can enjoy unlimited vintage tram rides, and the exhibition hall houses the largest collection of vintage electric trams in Britain. The village street contains a bar and restaurant, tearooms, a sweet shop, ice cream shop, and police sentry box, among others. There is also a Workshop Viewing Gallery where you can see the trams being restored. Ring for details of special events.

Times Open Apr-Oct, daily 10-5.30 (6.30 wknds Jun-Aug & BH wknds). 10.30-4 until Nov.* **Fees** £10.50 (ch 4-15 £5.50, pen £9.50). Family ticket (2ad+3ch)* **Facilities** 🅿 🅿 🖵 🍴 licensed 🎪 (outdoor) ♿ toilets for disabled shop

HADDON HALL

Haddon Hall

DE45 1LA
☎ 01629 812855 📠 01629 814379
e-mail: info@haddonhall.co.uk
web: www.haddonhall.co.uk
dir: 1.5m S of Bakewell off A6

Originally held by the illegitimate son of William the Conqueror, Haddon has been owned by the Manners family since the 16th century. Little has been added since the reign of Henry VIII, and, despite its time-worn steps, few medieval houses have so successfully withstood the ravages of time.

Times Open Apr-Oct, Sat-Mon; Etr Good Fri-Tue; May-Sep, daily 12-5 (closed 27-28 Jul); 5-13 Dec 10.30-4.* **Fees** £8.75 (ch £4.75 & pen £7.75). Family ticket £22.50. Party 15+.* **Facilities** 🅿 🍴 licensed ♿ (partly accessible) (steps & uneven floors, not accessible for w/chairs due to distance from carpark) toilets for disabled shop ⊗

HARDWICK HALL

Hardwick Hall

Doe Lea S44 5QJ
☎ 01246 850430 📠 01246 858424
e-mail: hardwickhall@nationaltrust.org.uk
web: www.nationaltrust.org.uk
dir: 2m S M1 junct 29 via A6175. Access by Stainsby Mill entrance only

One of the most splendid houses in England. Built by Bess of Hardwick in the 1590s and unaltered since, its huge windows and high ceilings make it feel strikingly modern. Climbing up through the house, from one floor to the next, is a thrilling architectural experience. Rich tapestries, plaster friezes and alabaster fireplaces colour the rooms, culminating in the hauntingly atmospheric Long Gallery. Note: The Old Hall is owned by the NT and administered by English Heritage.

Times Opening details not confirmed for 2010. Please telephone or see website for details. **Fees** Admission price details not confirmed for 2010. Please telephone or see website for details. **Facilities** 🅿 🍴 licensed 🏕 (outdoor) ♿ (partly accessible) (Ramped entrance. Ground floor accessible, stairs with handrail to other floors, Grounds partly accessible with slopes, grass paths & some cobbles) toilets for disabled shop ⊗ 🐾

KEDLESTON HALL

Kedleston Hall

DE22 5JH

☎ 01332 842191 📠 01332 841972
e-mail: kedlestonhall@nationaltrust.org.uk
web: www.nationaltrust.org.uk
dir: 5m NW of Derby, signed from rdbt where A38
crosses A52, close to Markeaton Park

A spectacular neo-classical mansion framed
by historic parkland. Designed for lavish
entertaining and displaying an extensive
collection of paintings, sculpture and original
furnishings, Kedleston is a stunning example of
the work of architect Robert Adam. The Curzon
family have lived here since the 12th century and
continue to live at the Hall. Lord Curzon's Eastern
Museum is full of fascinating objects acquired
on his travels in Asia and while Viceroy of India
(1899-1905).

Times Open all year: House; Mar-2 Nov, Sat-Wed
12-5 (last admission 4.15). Garden; same as
house but open daily 10-6. Park open daily,
Mar-2 Nov 10-6 & 3 Nov-27 Feb10-4. (Closed
25-26 Dec & some restrictions may apply in Dec
& Jan).* **Fees** With Gift Aid donation: House &
Garden £8.50 (ch £4.20). Family ticket £21.50.
Park and Garden only: £3.80 (ch £1.90). Family
ticket £9.60. Park (winter) £4.* **Facilities** 🅿 🍴
licensed toilets for disabled shop 🚫 🐾

MATLOCK BATH

Peak District Mining Museum

The Pavilion DE4 3NR
☎ 01629 583834
e-mail: mail@peakmines.co.uk
web: www.peakmines.co.uk
dir: On A6 alongside River Derwent

A large display explains the history of the
Derbyshire lead industry from Roman times to the
present day. The geology of the area, mining and
smelting processes, the quarrying and the people
who worked in the industry, are illustrated by a
series of static and moving exhibits. The museum
also features an early 19th-century water
pressure pumping engine. There is a recycling
display in the Pump Room.

Times Open all year, daily Apr-end Sep 10-5, Oct-
end Mar 11-3. Closed 25 Dec.* **Facilities** 🅿 🅿
🚻 ♿ shop 🚫

MATLOCK BATH

Temple Mine

Temple Rd DE4 3NR
☎ 01629 583834
e-mail: mail@peakmines.co.uk
web: www.peakmines.co.uk
dir: off A6. Please telephone for directions

A typical Derbyshire mine which was worked from the early 1920s until the mid 1950s for fluorspar and associated minerals. See examples of mining methods which give an insight into working conditions underground.

Times Open Apr-end Sep timed visits noon & 2pm daily, Oct-end Mar timed visits noon & 2pm wknds only* **Facilities** Ⓟ ⊗

BUCKFASTLEIGH

Buckfast Abbey **FREE**

TQ11 0EE
☎ 01364 645500   📄 01364 643891
e-mail: enquiries@buckfast.org.uk
web: www.buckfast.org.uk
dir: 0.5m from A38, midway between Exeter and Plymouth. Turn off at 'Dart Bridge' junct and follow brown tourist signs

The Abbey, founded in 1018, was dissolved by Henry VIII in the 16th century. Restoration began in 1907, when four monks with little building experience began the work. The church was built on the old foundations, using local blue limestone and Ham Hill stone. The precinct contains several medieval monastic buildings, including the 14th-century guest hall which contains an exhibition of the history of the Abbey.

Times Open all year daily. Closed Good Fri & 24-26 Dec.* **Facilities** Ⓟ ⊑ ⅅⓄⅼ licensed ⍭ (outdoor) ♿ toilets for disabled shop ⊗

CHITTLEHAMPTON

Cobbaton Combat Collection

Cobbaton EX37 9RZ
☎ 01769 540740
e-mail: info@cobbatoncombat.co.uk
web: www.cobbatoncombat.co.uk
dir: signed from A361 & A377

World War II British and Canadian military vehicles, war documents and military equipment can be seen in this private collection. There are over 50 vehicles including tanks, one a Gulf War Centurian, and a recently added Warsaw Pact section. There is also a section on `Mum's War' and the Home Front. The Home Front section is now in a new purpose-built building.

Times Open Apr-Oct, daily (ex Sat) 10-5; Jul-Aug, daily. Winter most wkdays, phone for details.
Fees £6.25 (ch £4, concessions £5.25).*
Facilities ❷ ⌷ ⛱ (outdoor) ♿ toilets for disabled shop ⊗

DREWSTEIGNTON

Castle Drogo

EX6 6PB
☎ 01647 433306 🖨 01647 433186
e-mail: castledrogo@nationaltrust.org.uk
web: www.nationaltrust.org.uk
dir: 5m S of A30 Exeter-Okehampton. Coaches turn off A382 at Sandy Park

India tea baron Julius Drewe's dream house, this granite castle, built between 1910 and 1930, is one of the most remarkable works of Sir Edward Lutyens, and combines the grandeur of a medieval castle with the comfort of the 20th century. A great country house with terraced formal garden, woodland spring garden, huge circular croquet lawn and colourful herbaceous borders. Standing at more than 900 feet overlooking the wooded gorge of the River Teign with stunning views of Dartmoor, and delightful walks. Lots of events in school holidays, ring for details.

Times Castle open 14 Mar-1 Nov, daily 11-5; Garden, tearooms & shop open 14 Mar-1 Nov 10.30-5.30* Facilities ❷ ⌷ ⛱ (outdoor) ♿ (partly accessible) (Gardens, Hall & Library fully accessible, other areas only accessible via stairs) toilets for disabled shop ⊗ 🐾

KINGSBRIDGE

Cookworthy Museum of Rural Life

The Old Grammar School, 108 Fore St TQ7 1AW
☎ 01548 853235
e-mail: wcookworthy@talk21.com
web: www.kingsbridgemuseum.net
dir: A38 onto A384, then A381 to Kingsbridge,
museum at top of town

The 17th-century schoolrooms of this former
grammar school are now the setting for another
kind of education. Reconstructed room-sets of a
Victorian kitchen, a costume room and extensive
collection of local historical items are gathered to
illustrate South Devon life. A walled garden and
farm gallery are also features of this museum,
founded to commemorate William Cookworthy,
'father' of the English china clay industry. The
Local Heritage Resource Centre with public
access databases, microfilm of local newspapers
since 1855 and Devon record service point are
available to visitors.

Times Open 31 Mar-Sep, Mon-Sat 10.30-5;
Oct 10.30-4. Nov-Mar groups by arrangement.
Local Heritage Resource Centre open all year,
Mon-Thu 10-12 & Wed also 2-4, other times by
appointment. **Fees** £2.50 (ch £1, concessions
£2). Family £6 (2ad+ up to 4ch).* **Facilities** ℗
🎋 (outdoor) ♿ (partly accessible) toilets for
disabled shop ⊗

MORWELLHAM

Morwellham Quay

PL19 8JL
☎ 01822 832766 & 833808
📄 01822 833808
e-mail: enquiries@morwellham-quay.co.uk
web: www.morwellham-quay.co.uk
dir: 4m W of Tavistock, off A390. Midway between
Gunnislake & Tavistock. Signed

A unique, open-air museum based around the
ancient port and copper mine workings in the
heart of the Tamar Valley. Journey back into
another time as costumed interpreters help you
re-live the daily life of a 19th-century mining
village and shipping quay. A tramway takes
you deep into the workings of the George and
Charlotte mine. Special events include music
festivals, classic car shows, and a Victorian food
festival.

Times Open all year (ex Xmas wk) 10-6 (4.30
Nov-Etr). Last admission 3.30 (2.30 Nov-Etr).*
Facilities ℗ 💻 🍴 licensed 🎋 (indoor &
outdoor) toilets for disabled shop

TORQUAY

Kents Cavern

Cavern House, 91 Ilsham Rd, Wellswood
TQ1 2JF
☎ 01803 215136
e-mail: caves@kents-cavern.co.uk
web: www.kents-cavern.co.uk
dir: 1.25m NE off B3199, follow brown tourist
signs. 1m from Torquay harbour

Probably the most important Palaeolithic site in
Britain and recognised as one of the country's
most significant archaeological areas. This is
not only a world of spectacular natural beauty,
but also a priceless record of past times, where
a multitude of secrets of mankind, animals and
nature have become trapped and preserved
over the last 500,000 years. 170 years after the
first excavations and with over 80,000 remains
already unearthed, modern research is still
discovering new clues to our past. Please visit
website for details of special events.

Times Open all year daily from 10, last tour 3.30
Nov-Feb, 4 Mar-Jun & Sep-Oct, 4.30 Jul-Aug.*
Facilities ❷ ⓟ ⏛ ⏍ licensed ⏢ (outdoor) ♿
(partly accessible) toilets for disabled shop ⊗

UFFCULME

Coldharbour Mill Working Wool Museum

Coldharbour Mill EX15 3EE
☎ 01884 840960
e-mail: info@coldharbourmill.org.uk
web: www.coldharbourmill.org.uk
dir: 2m from M5 junct 27, off B3181. Follow signs
to Willand, then brown signs to museum

The picturesque Coldharbour Mill is set in idyllic
Devon countryside. It has been producing textiles
since 1799 and is now a working museum, still
making knitting wools and fabrics on period
machinery. With machine demonstrations, a
water wheel and steam engines, Coldharbour
Mill is a wonderful and very different family day
out. The Power Trail Tour is available Tue, Wed
and Thu at 11.30 and 2.30. There are engines
in steam regularly throughout the year plus
special events, please see the website for details.
The new self-guided tour of the Woollen Mill is
available every day.

Times Open all year, daily 11-4.* **Fees** General
visit £4 (ch £2 concessions £3.50: Power Trail
Tour £5.50 (ch £2.75 concessions £5): Steam Up
Event £7 (ch £4, concessions £6.50)* **Facilities**
❷ ⏛ ⏍ licensed ⏢ (outdoor) ♿ (partly
accessible) (indoor restaurant not accessible but
assistance given) toilets for disabled shop ⊗

BLANDFORD FORUM

Royal Signals Museum

Blandford Camp DT11 8RH
☎ 01258 482248   📠 01258 482084
e-mail: info@royalsignalsmuseum.com
web: www.royalsignalsmuseum.com
dir: signed off B3082 (Blandford/Wimborne road)
& A354 (Salisbury road). Follow brown signs for
Royal Signals Museum

The Royal Signals Museum depicts the history of
military communications, science and technology
from the Crimea to current day. As well as
displays on all major conflicts involving British
forces, there are the stories of the ATS, the Long
Range Desert Group, Air Support, Airborne, Para
and SAS Signals. D-Day and Dorset explores the
Royal Signals involvement in Operation Overlord.
For children there are trails and interactive
exhibits.

Times Open Mar-Oct, Mon-Fri 10-5, Sat-Sun
10-4. Closed 10 days over Xmas & New Year*
Facilities 🅿 ℗ ⬜ 🍴 ♿ toilets for disabled
shop ⊗

BOVINGTON CAMP

Clouds Hill

BH20 7NQ
☎ 01929 405616
e-mail: cloudshill@nationaltrust.org.uk
web: www.nationaltrust.org.uk
dir: 1m N of Bovington Camp & Tank Museum,
1.5m E of Waddock x-rds B3390, 4m S of A35

T E Lawrence ('Lawrence of Arabia') bought this
cottage in 1925 when he was a private in the
Tank Corps at Bovington. He would escape here
to play records and entertain friends to feasts of
baked beans and China tea. The furniture and
contents were Lawrence's own and a new display
tells the story of Lawrence's life.

Times Open 20 Mar-26 Oct, Thu-Sun. 12-5*
Facilities 🅿 ♿ (partly accessible) shop ⊗
🍽 ♨

45

BOVINGTON CAMP

The Tank Museum

BH20 6JG

☎ 01929 405096 ▤ 01929 405360
e-mail: info@tankmuseum.org
web: www.tankmuseum.org
dir: off A352 or A35, follow brown tank signs from
Bere Regis & Wool

The Tank Museum houses the world's best
collection of tanks. From the first tank ever built
to the modern Challenger II, the Museum houses
examples from all over the world. This definitive
collection comprises of over 250 vehicles dating
back to 1909. The Tank Museum is the only place
where many of these rare and historic vehicles
can be seen. You will come face to face with
tanks that have seen action in all the major wars
of the 20th century. There are plenty of live action
displays all year, please see website for details.

Times Open all year, daily 10-5 (limited opening
over Xmas).* **Facilities** 🅿 🅟 ⊑ 🍽 licensed
🗮 (outdoor) ♿ toilets for disabled shop ⊗

BROWNSEA ISLAND

Brownsea Island

BH13 7EE

☎ 01202 707744 ▤ 01202 701635
e-mail: brownseaisland@nationaltrust.org.uk
web: www.nationaltrust.org.uk
dir: located in Poole Harbour

Peaceful island of woodland, wetland and heath
with a rich diversity of wildlife. The island is
most famous for its rare red squirrels and as the
site of the first experimental Scout camp held by
Lord Baden-Powell in 1907. 2010 is the Guiding
centenary.

Times Open 13 Mar-Oct, daily, 10-5 (13-26
Mar boats from Sandbanks only, 27-31 Mar full
boat service from Poole Quay & Sandbanks).
Fees £4.90 (ch £2.40). Family ticket £12.20.
Group £4.20 (ch £2.10)* **Facilities** ⊑ 🍽
licensed 🗮 (outdoor) ♿ (partly accessible)
(countryside property with rough terrain in
places. Contact ferry operators to discuss
carrying of wheelchairs on boats) toilets for
disabled shop ⊗ 🌺

CORFE CASTLE

Corfe Castle

BH20 5EZ

☎ 01929 481294　📠 01929 477067

e-mail: corfecastle@nationaltrust.org.uk

web: www.nationaltrust.org.uk

dir: follow A351 from Wareham to Swanage. Corfe Castle approx 5m

Built in Norman times, the castle was added to by King John. It was defended during the Civil War by Lady Bankes, who surrendered after a stout resistance. Parliament ordered the demolition of the castle, and today it is one of the most impressive ruins in England. Please ring for details of special events.

Times Open all year, daily Mar 10-5; Apr-Sep 10-6; Oct 10-5; Nov-Feb 10-4. (Last admission 30 mins before closing). Closed 25-26 Dec. **Fees** £6.20 (ch £3.10). Family ticket (2ad+3ch) £15.50 or (1ad+3ch) £9.30. Groups £5 (ch £2.50). **Facilities** 🅿 🅿 ⬜ 🍴 licensed ♿ (partly accessible) (steep, uneven cobbled paths & steps, wheelchair access restricted to Outer Bailey only) toilets for disabled shop ♨

DORCHESTER

Hardy's Cottage

Higher Bockhampton DT2 8QJ

☎ 01305 262366

e-mail: hardyscottage@nationaltrust.org.uk

web: www.nationaltrust.org.uk

dir: 3m NE of Dorchester, 0.5m S of A35. Turn off A35 at Kingston Maurward rdbt towards Stinsford and Bockhampton. Left onto Bockhampton Ln, signed to Hardy's Cottage

The small cob and thatch cottage where novelist and poet Thomas Hardy was born in 1840 and from where he would walk 6 miles to school in Dorchester every day. It was built by his great-grandfather and is little altered since. The interior has been furnished by the Trust. It was here that he wrote his early novels Under the Greenwood Tree and Far from the Madding Crowds. It has a charming cottage garden.

Times Open Apr-Oct, Sun-Thu, 11-5* **Facilities** 🅿 shop ⊗ ♨

DORCHESTER

Maiden Castle FREE

DT1 9PR
web: www.english-heritage.org.uk
dir: 2m S of Dorchester, access off A354, N of
bypass

The Iron Age fort ranks among the finest in
Britain. It covers 47 acres, and has daunting
earthworks, with a complicated defensive
system around the entrances. One of its main
purposes may well have been to protect grain
from marauding bands. The first single-rampart
fort dates from around 700BC, and by 100BC
the earthworks covered the whole plateau. It was
finally overrun by Roman troops in AD43.

Times Open at any reasonable time.* **Facilities**
P ♯

PORTLAND

Portland Castle

Castleton DT5 1AZ
☎ 01305 820539 📄 01305 860853
web: www.english-heritage.org.uk
dir: overlooking Portland harbour

Visit one of Henry VIII's finest coastal forts, in
use right up to World War II. Home to the Wrens
and scene of the US troops' embarkation for the
D-Day invasion in 1944. Explore the Captain's
House and Gardens.

Times Open Apr-Jun & Sep, daily 10-5; Jul-Aug,
daily 10-6; Oct-1 Nov, daily 10-4. Closed 2 Nov-
Mar. **Fees** £4 (concessions £3.40, ch £2). Family
ticket £10. Prices and opening times are subject
to change in March 2010. Please call 0870 333
1181 for the most up to date prices and opening
times when planning your visit. **Facilities** **P** ⊑
toilets for disabled shop ⊗ ♯

TOLPUDDLE

Tolpuddle Martyrs Museum **FREE**

DT2 7EH

☎ 01305 848237   🖹 01305 848237

e-mail: jpickering@tuc.org.uk

web: www.tolpuddlemartyrs.org.uk

dir: off A35 from Dorchester Tolpuddle signed at Troytown turn off. Continue on old A35. If coming from the East, the museum has Brown Heritage sign.

One dawn, in the bitter February of 1834, six Tolpuddle farm labourers were arrested after forming a trade union. A frightened squire's trumped up charge triggered one of the most celebrated stories in the history of human rights. That dawn arrest created the Tolpuddle Martyrs, who were punished with transportation as convicts to Australia. Packed with illustrative displays, this interactive exhibition tells the Tolpuddle Martyrs' story. Every summer on the weekend of the third Sunday in July, the museum holds the Tolpuddle Martyrs Festival. The weekend combines celebration with tradition offering traditional and contemporary music as well as many other attractions.

Times Open all year, Apr-Oct, Tue-Sat 10-5, Sun 11-5; Nov-Mar, Thu-Sat 10-4, Sun 11-4. Also open BHs. Closed 21 Dec-6 Jan.* **Facilities** ℗ ⋔ (outdoor) ♿ toilets for disabled shop ⊗

WEST LULWORTH

Lulworth Castle & Park

BH20 5QS

☎ 0845 450 1054   🖹 01929 400563

e-mail: estate.office@lulworth.com

web: www.lulworth.com

dir: from Wareham, W on A352 for 1m, left onto B3070 to E Lulworth, follow tourist signs

Glimpse life below stairs in the restored kitchen, and enjoy glorious views from the top of the tower of this historic castle set in beautiful parkland. The 18th-century chapel is the first Catholic chapel built in England after the Reformation. Children will enjoy the animal farm, play area, indoor activity room and pitch and putt. Visit website for details of future events.

Times Open Jan-22 Mar, Sun-Fri 10.30-4; 23 Mar-26 Sep, Sun-Fri, 10.30-6; 28 Sep-Dec, Sun-Fri, 10.30-4. Closed Sat (ex Etr Sat), 24-25 Dec & 6-19 Jan.* **Fees** £8 (ch £4, concessions £5) Family ticket (1ad+3ch) £16 non-jousting season. £9.50 (ch £4.50, concessions £8) Family ticket (1ad+3ch) £18.50 jousting season (24 Jul-25 Aug)* **Facilities** ℗ ⋤⋔ (outdoor) ♿ (partly accessible) (access limited in castle due to grade one listing) toilets for disabled shop ⊗

BEAMISH

Beamish Museum

DH9 0RG
☎ 0191 370 4000 ▯ 0191 370 4001
e-mail: museum@beamish.org.uk
web: www.beamish.org.uk
dir: off A693 & A6076. Signed from A1M junct 63.

Set in 300 acres of countryside, award-winning Beamish recreates life in the early 1800s and 1900s. Costumed staff welcome visitors to a 1913 town street, colliery village, farm and railway station; a re-creation of how people lived and worked. Ride on early electric tramcars, take a ride on a replica of an 1825 steam railway and visit Pockerley Manor where a yeoman farmer and his family would have lived.

Times Open Apr-Oct, daily 10-5; Oct-Mar 10-4 (last admission 3). Closed Mon, Fri & part of Dec.* **Fees** Summer £16 (ch £10, pen £12.50). Winter £6 (ch & pen £6). Winter visit is centered on town, colliery village & tramway only, other areas are closed.* **Facilities** Ⓟ ☕ ⛩ (outdoor) ♿ (partly accessible) (some 1st floor areas inaccessible, some ground floor areas have steeped access & narrow doorways) toilets for disabled shop ⊗

BOWES

Bowes Castle **FREE**

DL12 9LD
web: www.english-heritage.org.uk
dir: in Bowes village, just off A66

Massive ruins of Henry II's tower keep, three storeys high, set within the earthworks of a Roman fort and overlooking the valley of the River Greta.

Times Open at any reasonable time.* **Facilities** ⛩ 🚌 #

COWSHILL

Killhope The North of England Lead Mining Museum

DL13 1AR
☎ 01388 537505　📠 01388 537617
e-mail: info@killhope.org.uk
web: www.killhope.org.uk
dir: beside A689 midway between Stanhope & Alston

Equipped with hard hats and lamps, you can explore the working conditions of Victorian lead miners. The lead mine and 19th-century crushing mill have been restored to look as they would have done in the 1870s, and the 34ft water wheel has been restored to working order. There is also a visitor centre and mineral exhibition, a woodland walk, children's play area and red squirrel and bird hides. Please ring for information on workshops and events.

Times Open Apr-Oct, daily 10.30-5. **Fees** Mine & Site: £6.50 (ch £3.50, concessions £6). Family £17. Site: £4.50 (ch £1.50, concessions £4). Family £11.50* **Facilities** 🅿 ⛾🍴 (indoor & outdoor) ♿ (partly accessible) (accessible hide for wildlife viewing) toilets for disabled shop

DURHAM

Durham Light Infantry Museum & Durham Art Gallery

Aykley Heads DH1 5TU
☎ 0191 384 2214　📠 0191 386 1770
e-mail: dli@durham.gov.uk
web: www.durham.gov.uk/dli
dir: 0.5m NW, turn right off A691

The history of the Regiment is told in displays of artefacts, medals, uniforms and vehicles. The Art Gallery has a continuous programme of temporary exhibitions, and holds regular lectures and concerts.

Times Open all year, Apr-Oct, daily 10-5; Nov-Mar, daily 10-4. Closed 24-25 Dec.* **Fees** £3.25 (ch £1.35, concessions £2.15). Family ticket £7.50. Seaon ticket £13 (concessions £7.50).* **Facilities** 🅿 🅿 ⛾🍴 (outdoor) ♿ toilets for disabled shop 🚫

51

DURHAM

Old Fulling Mill Museum of Archaeology

The Banks DH1 3EB
☎ 0191 334 1823 📄 0191 334 5694
e-mail: archaeology.museum@durham.ac.uk
web: www.dur.ac.uk/fulling.mill
dir: On river bank directly below Cathedral

Once a key part of Durham's cloth making industry, the Old Fulling Mill is now home to Durham University's Museum of Archaeology. The collections on display provide a fascinating insight into the rich heritage of the north east of England, as well as showcasing items from across Europe. Highlights include outstanding Roman collections together with Anglo-Saxon, Medieval and Tudor finds from Durham City and the local area. Up to date details of exhibitions and the lively programme of family activities at weekends and during school holidays can be found on the museum's website.

Times Open Apr-Oct, daily 10-4; Nov-Mar, Fri-Mon 11.30-3.30* **Fees** £1 (ch & concessions 50p, students free). Family ticket £2.50.* **Facilities** ℗ ♿ (partly accessible) (ground floor only accessible) shop ⊗

HARTLEPOOL

Hartlepool's Maritime Experience

Maritime Av TS24 0XZ
☎ 01429 860077 📄 01429 867332
e-mail: info@hartlepoolsmaritimeexperience.com
web: www.hartlepoolsmaritimeexperience.com
dir: from N A19 take A179 and follow signs for marina then historic quay. From S A19 take A689 and follow signs for marina then historic quay

Britain's maritime heritage is brought to life, with the sights, sounds and smells of an 1800s quayside. Learn about the birth of the Royal Navy, and visit the Quayside shops, the admiral's house, Europe's oldest warship afloat HMS Trincomalee and the children's Maritime Adventure Centre. Other features include regular demonstrations of sword fighting, and cannon firing. The new HMS Trincomalee exhibition is now open.

Times Open all year daily summer 10-5, winter 11-3. Closed 25-26 Dec & 1 Jan.* **Fees** £7.75 (ch £4.75, concessions £4.75-£5.75). Family ticket (2ad+3ch) £20. Museum is free.* **Facilities** ℗ 🍽 licensed ⊟ (outdoor) ♿ (partly accessible) toilets for disabled shop ⊗

SHILDON

Locomotion: The National Railway Museum at Shildon

DL4 1PQ

☎ 01388 777999 📄 01388 777999
e-mail: info@locomotion.uk.com
web: www.locomotion.uk.com
dir: A1(M) junct 68, take A68 & A6072 to Shildon, attraction is 0.25m SE of town centre

Timothy Hackwood (1786-1850) was an important figure in the development of steam travel. He constructed Puffing Billy for William Hedley, ran Stephenson's Newcastle Works, and also became the first superintendent of the Stockton & Darlington Railway. The museum and house detail Hackwood's life and the steam transport revolution, as well as displaying working models and locomotives from various periods. Steam train rides are available throughout the year, on event days. The Collections building contains 60 vehicles from the National Collection.

Times Open Apr-5 Oct, daily 10-5; 6 Oct-1 Apr, daily, 10-4. Buildings at western end of site are closed Mon & Tue in winter. **Fees** Free, small charge for train rides.* **Facilities** 🅿 ℗ ⏛ 🍴 (indoor & outdoor) ♿ toilets for disabled shop ⊗

AUDLEY END

Audley End House & Gardens

CB11 4JF

☎ 01799 522842 📄 01799 521276
web: www.english-heritage.org.uk
dir: 1m W of Saffron Walden on B1383

One of the most significant Jacobean houses in England with 31 opulent rooms on view. Set in a 'Capability' Brown landscaped park, with walled Victorian kitchen garden.

Times Open Apr-Sep, Wed-Sun & BH 11-5 (Sat last admission 2.30); Oct-1 Nov, Wed-Sun 11-4. (Sat last admission 2.30). Closed Nov-Mar except for Festive Fun wknds (21-22, 28-29 Nov & 5-6, 12-13, 19-20 Dec). **Fees** House & Gardens: £10.70 (concessions £9.10, ch £5.40). Family £26.80. Service Wing & Gardens: £7.70 (concessions £6.50, ch £3.90). Family £19.30. Prices & opening times are subject to change in March 2010. Please call 0870 333 1181 for the most up to date prices and opening times.
Facilities 🅿 ⏛ 🍴 ♿ (partly accessible) (bridges either have a step or steep slope) toilets for disabled shop ⌗

53

COLCHESTER

Colchester Castle Museum

Castle Park, High St CO1 1TJ
☎ 01206 282939 📠 01206 282925
e-mail: museums@colchester.gov.uk
web: www.colchestermuseums.org.uk
dir: at E end of High St

The largest Norman castle keep in Europe - built over the remains of the magnificent Roman Temple of Claudius which was destroyed by Boudicca in AD60. Colchester was the first capital of Roman Britain, and the archaeological collections are among the finest in the country. Please telephone or visit website for details of a range of events held throughout the year.

Times Open all year, Mon-Sat 10-5, Sun 11-5. Closed Xmas/New Year* **Fees** £5.50 (ch & concessions £3.50).* **Facilities** ℗ ㅠ (indoor & outdoor) ᕼ (partly accessible) (Roman vaults not accessible) toilets for disabled shop ⊗

STANSTED

Mountfitchet Castle Experience

CM24 8SP
☎ 01279 813237 📠 01279 816391
e-mail: office@mountfitchetcastle.com
web: www.mountfitchetcastle.com
dir: off B1383, in village. 2m from M11 junct 8

Come and see a Norman motte and bailey castle and village reconstructed as it was in Norman England of 1066, on its original historic site. A vivid illustration of village life in Domesday England, complete with houses, church, seige tower, seige weapons, and many types of animals roaming freely. Animated wax figures in all the buildings give historical information to visitors. Adjacent to the castle is the House on the Hill Toy Museum, a nostalgic trip through memories of childhood days. The whole experience is a unique all-weather, all-in-one heritage entertainment complex.

Times Open daily, mid Mar-mid Nov, 10-5. **Fees** £8.50 (ch £6.50, concessions £8).* **Facilities** ℗ ℗ ⊡ ㅠ (outdoor) ᕼ (partly accessible) (partly accessible due to grassy slopes, cobbled areas & steps) toilets for disabled shop ⊗

WALTHAM ABBEY

Royal Gunpowder Mills

Beaulieu Dr EN9 1JY
☎ 01992 707370 📄 01992 707372
e-mail: info@royalgunpowdermills.com
web: www.royalgunpowdermills.com
dir: M25 junct 26. Follow signs for A121 to Waltham Abbey at rdbt, entrance in Beaulieu Drive

Set in 170 acres of natural parkland with 20 buildings of major historic importance, the site mixes fascinating history, exciting science and beautiful surroundings to produce a magical day out for all ages. Over 20 special weekend events with may living history and re-enactments, VE Day celebrations, Steam & Country Show, Rocket & Space event and a Classic Vehicle Show. Easy access, children's activities, exhibitions, guided land train tours, a woodland walk and so much more!

Times Open end Apr-end Sep, 11-5, last entry 3.30. (Wknds, BHs & Wed in summer school hols) **Fees** £7.20 (ch 5-15 £4.40, concessions £6.20, under 5's free) Family ticket (2ad & 3ch) £23.20* **Facilities** 🅿 ⓟ 🖵 🎪 (outdoor) ♿ (partly accessible) (stairs provide access to top of Wildlife Tower. Some paths on nature walk are uneven. Lift available in main exhibition, number of ramps on site) toilets for disabled shop ⊗

BERKELEY

Edward Jenner Museum

Church Ln, High St GL13 9BN
☎ 01453 810631 📄 01453 811690
e-mail: info@edwardjenner.co.uk
web: www.jennermuseum.com
dir: follow tourist signs from A38 to town centre, left into High St & left again into Church Lane

This beautiful Georgian house was the home of Edward Jenner, the discoverer of vaccination against smallpox. The house and the garden, with its Temple of Vaccinia, are much as they were in Jenner's day. The displays record Jenner's life as an 18th-century country doctor, his work on vaccination and his interest in natural history.

Times Open Apr-Sep, Tue-Sat 12.30-5.30, Sun 12-5.30. Oct, Sun 1-5.30, (26-30 Oct 12.30-5.30); daily in Jul & Aug (Closed Mon, ex BH Mon 12.30-5.30).* **Fees** £4.80 (ch £2.50, concessions £4). Family ticket £12. Party 15+.* **Facilities** 🅿 ⓟ 🎪 (indoor & outdoor) ♿ (partly accessible) (ground floor accessible) toilets for disabled shop ⊗

CHELTENHAM

Holst Birthplace Museum

4 Clarence Rd GL52 2AY
☎ 01242 524846 ▤ 01242 580182
e-mail: holstmuseum@btconnect.com
web: www.holstmuseum.org.uk
dir: opposite gateway of Pittville Park. 10 min walk from town centre

Gustav Holst, composer of The Planets was born at this Regency house in 1874. The museum contains unique displays on Holst's life, including his original piano. The rooms of the house have been carefully restored, each area evoking a different period in the history of the house from Regency to Edwardian times.

Times Open Tue-Sat 10-4 (Closed Mon ex BH & mid Dec-mid Jan, ex pre-booked groups).
Fees £3.50 (ch & concessions £3). Family ticket (2ad+3ch) £8.* **Facilities** Ⓟ ♿ (partly accessible) (ground floor accessible but steps to front door) shop ⊗

CIRENCESTER

Corinium Museum

Park St GL7 2BX
☎ 01285 655611
e-mail: museums@cotswold.gov.uk
web: www.cotswold.gov.uk/go/museum
dir: in town centre

Discover the treasures of the Cotswolds at the new Corinium Museum. Two years and over £5 million in the making, it has been transformed into a must-see attraction. Featuring archaeological and historical material from Cirencester and the Cotswolds, from prehistoric times to the 19th century. The museum is known for its Roman mosaic sculpture and other material from one of Britain's largest Roman towns. New on display are Anglo-Saxon treasures from Lechlade bringing to life this little-known period. The museum also houses Medieval, Tudor, Civil War and 18th-19th century displays.

Times Open Mon-Sat 10-5, Sun 2-5 (closes 4pm Nov-Mar). Closed Xmas & New Year. **Fees** £4.25 (ch £2.25, students £2.75, concessions £3.50). Family ticket £11.50 **Facilities** Ⓟ ⊑ꚏ꘡ licensed ♿ toilets for disabled shop ⊗

CLEARWELL

Clearwell Caves Ancient Iron Mines

GL16 8JR

☎ 01594 832535   📄 01594 833362

e-mail: jw@clearwellcaves.com

web: www.clearwellcaves.com

dir: 1.5m S of Coleford town centre, off B4228 follow brown tourist signs

These impressive natural caves have also been mined since the earliest times for paint pigment and iron ore. Today visitors explore nine large caverns with displays of local mining and geology. There is a colour room where ochre pigments are still produced and a blacksmith shop. Deep level excursions available for more adventurous visitors, must be pre-booked. Christmas fantasy event when the caverns are transformed into a world of light and sound.

Times Open Mar-Oct, daily 10-5; Jan-Feb, Sat-Sun 10-5; Xmas Fantasy 1-24 Dec, daily 10-5. **Fees** £5.80 (ch £3.80, concessions £5.30) Family ticket £17.30. **Facilities** 🅿 ⓟ ⬛🍴 (outdoor) ♿ (partly accessible) (w/chair need 2 helpers on steep pathway) toilets for disabled shop 🚫

CRANHAM

Prinknash Abbey

GL4 8EX

☎ 01452 812066   📄 01452 812066

web: www.prinknashabbey.org.uk

dir: on A46 between Cheltenham & Stroud

Set in a large park, the old priory building is a 12th to 16th-century house, used by Benedictine monks and guests of Gloucester Abbey until 1539. It became an abbey for Benedictine monks from Caldey in 1928. Home to the reconstruction of the Great Orpheus Pavement, the largest mosaic in Britain, as mentioned in the Guinness Book of Records. Also visit the bird and deer park.

Times Open all year Wed-Sun 10-4. Closed Good Fri, 25-26 Dec & 1 Jan. **Fees** Admission free to grounds. Orpheus Pavement closes Jan 2010. **Facilities** 🅿 ⬛🍴 (outdoor) ♿ toilets for disabled

GLOUCESTER

Gloucester Folk Museum FREE

99-103 Westgate St GL1 2PG
☎ 01452 396868 & 396869
📠 01452 330495
e-mail: folk.museum@gloucester.gov.uk
web: www.gloucester.gov.uk/folkmuseum
dir: from W - A40 & A48; from N - A38 & M5, from E - A40 & B4073; from S - A4173 & A38

Three floors of splendid Tudor and Jacobean timber-framed buildings dating from the 16th and 17th centuries along with new buildings housing the dairy, ironmonger's shop and wheelwright and carpenter workshops. Local history, domestic life, crafts, trades and industries from 1500 to the present, including Toys and Childhood gallery with hands-on toys and a puppet theatre, the Siege of Gloucester, a Victorian class room, Victorian kitchen and laundry equipment. A wide range of exhibitions, hands-on activities, events, demonstrations and role play sessions are held throughout the year. There is an attractive cottage garden and courtyard for events, often with live animals, and outside games.

Times Open all year, Tue-Sat, 10-5* **Facilities** ℗ ⧩ (outdoor) ♿ (partly accessible) shop ⊗

GLOUCESTER

The National Waterways Museum

Llanthony Warehouse, The Docks GL1 2EH
☎ 01452 318200 📠 01452 318202
e-mail: gloucester@thewaterwaystrust.org.uk
web: www.nwm.org.uk
dir: From M5, A40. In city follow brown signs for historic docks

Based in Gloucester Docks, this museum takes up three floors of a seven-storey Victorian warehouse, and documents the 200-year history of Britain's water-based transport. The emphasis is on hands-on experience, including working models and engines, interactive displays, actual craft, computer interactions and the national collection of inland waterways. Boat trips are also available between Easter and October.

Times Open all year, daily 10-5. (Last admission 4). Closed 25 Dec.* **Facilities** ℗ ℗ ⧩ ⊧◎⧩ licensed ⧩ (outdoor) ♿ toilets for disabled shop ⊗

ASHTON-UNDER-LYNE

Portland Basin Museum FREE

Portland Place OL7 0QA
☎ 0161 343 2878 ▤ 0161 343 2869
e-mail: portland.basin@tameside.gov.uk
web: www.tameside.gov.uk
dir: M60 junct 23 into town centre. Museum near Cross Hill Street & car park. Follow brown signs with canal boat image

Exploring the social and industrial history of Tameside, this museum is part of the recently rebuilt Ashton Canal Warehouse, constructed in 1834. Visitors can walk around a 1920s street, dress up in old hats and gloves, steer a virtual canal boat, and see the original canal powered waterwheel that once drove the warehouse machinery. Portland Basin Museum also features changing exhibitions and event programme- so there's always something new to see!

Times Open all year, Tue-Sun 10-5. (Closed Mon, ex BHs)* **Facilities** ❷ ⓟ 🍽 licensed ㋔ (outdoor) ♿ toilets for disabled shop ⊗

MANCHESTER

Gallery of Costume FREE

Platt Hall, Rusholme M14 5LL
☎ 0161 224 5217
e-mail: m.lambert@manchester.gov.uk
web: www.manchestergalleries.org.uk
dir: in Platt Fields Park, Rusholme, access from Wilmslow Rd. 2m S of city centre

With one of the most comprehensive costume collections in Great Britain, this gallery makes captivating viewing. Housed in a fine Georgian mansion, the displays focus on the changing styles of everyday fashion and accessories over the last 400 years. Contemporary fashion is also illustrated. Because of the vast amount of material in the collection, no one period is permanently illustrated.

Times Open from Apr, Wed-Sat 1.30-4.30. **Facilities** ❷ ㋔ (outdoor) ♿ (partly accessible) (stairs with handrails to first floor) toilets for disabled shop ⊗

MANCHESTER

Imperial War Museum North FREE

The Quays, Trafford Wharf Rd, Trafford Park
M17 1TZ
☎ 0161 836 4000 📄 0161 836 4012
e-mail: iwmnorth@iwm.org.uk
web: www.iwm.org.uk
dir: M60 junct 9, join Parkway (A5081) towards
Trafford Park. At 1st island take 3rd exit onto
Village Way. At next island take 2nd exit onto
Warren Bruce Rd. Right at T-junct onto Trafford
Wharf Rd. Alternatively, leave M602 junct 3 and
follow signs

Imperial War Museum North features a wide
range of permanent and temporary exhibitions
exploring all the ways people's lives have been
and still are affected by war and conflict. The
award-winning building (designed by architect
Daniel Libeskind) symbolises the world torn apart
by conflict.

Times Open all year, Mar-Oct, daily 10-6; Nov-Feb
10-5. Closed 24-26 Dec. **Facilities** 🅿 🅟 ⊑ 🛱
(indoor) ♿ toilets for disabled shop ⊗

MANCHESTER

Manchester Museum FREE

The University of Manchester, Oxford Rd
M13 9PL
☎ 0161 275 2634 & 2643
📄 0161 275 2676
e-mail: museum@manchester.ac.uk
web: www.manchester.ac.uk/museum
dir: S of city centre on B5117

Discover the natural wonders of the world and
the many cultures it is home to. The objects in
the Museum's 15 galleries tell the story of the
past, present and future of our planet. Come
face to face with live poison dart frogs, fossils
of prehistoric creatures and much more besides.
Handle objects from the collection, take part in
hands-on activities or enjoy a glass of wine or
cup of coffee whilst exploring the latest ideas
in science, culture and the arts. See website for
details of family and adult events.

Times Open all year, Tue-Sat 10-5, Sun-Mon &
BHs 11-4. Closed Good Fri.* **Facilities** 🅿 🅟
⊑ 🍴 licensed 🛱 (indoor) toilets for disabled
shop ⊗

MANCHESTER

Museum of Science and Industry

Liverpool Rd, Castlefield M3 4FP
☎ 0161 832 2244　🖷 0161 833 1471
e-mail: marketing@mosi.org.uk
web: www.mosi.org.uk
dir: follow brown tourist signs from city centre

Uncover Manchester's industrial past and learn the fascinating stories of the people who contributed to the history and science of a city which helped shape the modern world. Located on the site of the world's oldest passenger railway station, MoSI's action-packed galleries, working exhibits and costumed characters tell the amazing story of revolutionary discoveries and remarkable inventions both past and present. There is a programme of changing exhibitions, please see the website for details.

Times Open all year, daily 10-5. Last admission 4.30. Closed 24-26 Dec & 1 Jan.* **Facilities** 🅿
🄿 ⏁🍽 licensed 🎍 (indoor & outdoor) ♿ toilets for disabled shop ⊗

MANCHESTER

Museum of Transport

Boyle St, Cheetham M8 8UW
☎ 0161 205 2122　🖷 0161 205 1110
e-mail: e-mail@gmts.co.uk
web: www.gmts.co.uk
dir: museum adjacent to Queens Rd bus depot. 1.25m N of city centre on Boyle St

This museum is a must-see for fans of public transport. Among the many interesting exhibits are more than 80 beautifully restored buses and coaches from the region - the biggest collection in the UK. Displays of old photographs, tickets and other memorabilia complement the vehicles, some of which date back to 1890. Please telephone for details of special events, most of which, unsurprisingly, relate to transport in some way.

Times Open all year Mar-Oct, 10-5; Nov-Feb, 10-4; Wed, Sat, Sun & BH ex Xmas* **Facilities** 🅿
🄿 ⏁♿ toilets for disabled shop ⊗

MANCHESTER

People's History Museum **FREE**

Left Bank, Spinningfields M3 3ER
☎ 0161 228 7212
e-mail: info@phm.org.uk
web: www.phm.org.uk
dir: City centre, corner of Left Bank and Bridge St

The People's History Museum re-opens in late 2009 after a two-year closure and multi-million pound redevelopment. The Pump House, a former hydraulic power pumping station is being renovated to its former glory, and a new four-storey extension is being built next to it. The old and new buildings will be joined by a spectacular walkway. The Museum details the history of the British labour movement, trades unions, and other workers' organisations.

Times Open all year, Tue-Sun 10-5. **Facilities** Ⓟ
🖵🎔 (indoor) ♿ toilets for disabled shop ⊗

STOCKPORT

Hat Works Museum

Wellington Mill, Wellington Road South
SK3 0EU
☎ 0161 355 7770 📄 0161 480 8735
e-mail: bookings.hatworks@stockport.gov.uk
web: www.hatworks.org.uk
dir: M60 junct 1, on A6, Stockport town centre, follow signs for town centre. Museum opp bus station

Hat Works is the UK's only museum of the hatting industry, hats and headwear, offering an insight into a once flourishing industry. See how hats are made with a unique working collection of Victorian millinery machinery and take a tour with expert guides who will give visitors an insight into the Hatter's World. Exhibitions and events throughout the year, contact for details.

Times Open all year, Tue-Fri 10-5, Sat, Sun & BHs 11-5. (Telephone for Xmas opening times)*
Fees Free. (Guided tours £2.60 per person)*
Facilities Ⓟ 🖵♿ toilets for disabled shop ⊗

ALDERSHOT

Aldershot Military Museum

Evelyn Woods Rd, Queens Av GU11 2LG
☎ 0845 6035635 📠 01252 342942
e-mail: sally.1.day@hants.gov.uk
web: www.hants.gov.uk/museum/aldershot-museum
dir: A331 exit for 'Aldershot Military Town (North)', museum near to North Camp

Follow the development of the 'Home of the British army' and the 'Birthplace of British aviation' through brand new displays. Also discover the fascinating local history of Aldershot and Farnborough including the first British powered flight, which took place in October 1908.

Times Open all year, daily 10-5 (last admission 4.30)* **Fees** £2 (ch under 5 free, ch & concessions £1, pen £1.50)* **Facilities** 🅿 🅟 ⊓ (outdoor) ♿ toilets for disabled shop ⊗

BASINGSTOKE

Milestones - Hampshire's Living History Museum

Basingstoke Leisure Park, Churchill Way West RG22 6PG
☎ 01256 477766 📠 01256 477784
e-mail: louise.mackay@hants.gov.uk
web: www.milestones-museum.com
dir: M3 junct 6, take ringway road (West). Follow brown Leisure Park signs

Milestones brings Hampshire's recent past to life through stunning period street scenes and exciting interactive areas, all under one roof. Nationally important collections of transport, technology and everyday life are presented in an entertaining way. Staff in period costumes, mannequins and sounds all bring the streets to life. Various events through the year.

Times Open all year, Tue-Fri & BHs 10-5, Sat-Sun 11-5. Closed Mon, 25-26 Dec & 1 Jan.* **Fees** £7.50 (ch 5-15 £4.50, concessions £6.75). Family ticket (2ad+2ch) £22. **Facilities** 🅿 🅟 ⊔ ⊓ (indoor & outdoor) ♿ (partly accessible) toilets for disabled shop ⊗

BEAULIEU

Beaulieu : National Motor Museum

SO42 7ZN

☎ 01590 612345 📄 01590 612624
e-mail: info@beaulieu.co.uk
web: www.beaulieu.co.uk
dir: M27 junct 2, A326, B3054, then follow tourist signs

Set in the heart of William the Conqueror's New Forest, on the banks of the Beaulieu River, stands this 16th-century house. It has become most famous as the home of the National Motor Museum. The site also contains the picturesque abbey building ruins, which have an exhibition on life in the middle ages, and various family treasures and memorabilia. The Secret Army Exhibition tells the story of the secret agents trained at the Beaulieu 'Finishing School' during WWII.

Times Open all year - Palace House & Gardens, National Motor Museum, Beaulieu Abbey & Exhibition of Monastic Life, May-Sep 10-6; Oct-Apr 10-5. Closed 25 Dec.* **Fees** Please contact for current prices.* **Facilities** 🅿 Ⓟ 🖵 🍴 licensed 🌲 (outdoor) toilets for disabled shop

BUCKLERS HARD

Buckler's Hard Village & Maritime Museum

SO42 7XB

☎ 01590 616203 📄 01590 612624
e-mail: info@bucklershard.co.uk
web: www.bucklershard.co.uk
dir: M27 junct 2, A326, B3054 then follow tourist signs to Beaulieu & Buckler's Hard

An enticing port of call, the historic and picturesque shipbuilding village of Buckler's Hard is where ships from Nelson's fleet were built. Enjoy the Buckler's Hard Story, SS Persia Exhibition and the authentically reconstructed 18th-century historic cottages. Savour the sights and sounds of the countryside on a ramble along the Riverside Walk or enjoy a cruise on the Beaulieu River during the summer months.

Times Open all year daily from 10. Closed 25 Dec.* **Fees** Please contact for current prices.* **Facilities** 🅿 🖵 🍴 licensed 🌲 (outdoor) toilets for disabled shop

CHAWTON

Jane Austen's House

GU34 1SD

☎ 01420 83262

e-mail: enquiries@jane-austens-house-museum.org.uk

web: www.jane-austens-house-museum.org.uk

dir: 1m SW of Alton, in centre of village

Jane Austen lived and wrote here from 1809 to 1817. Restored to look as it would have done in the early 1800s, with items such as the author's donkey cart and writing table to be seen.

Times Open daily Mar-Dec; Jan-Feb wknds only. Also open 27 Dec-1 Jan & Feb half term.* **Facilities** ℗ ♯ (outdoor) toilets for disabled shop ⊗

FAREHAM

Royal Armouries Fort Nelson

Portsdown Hill Rd PO17 6AN

☎ 01329 233734   📄 01329 822092

e-mail: fnenquiries@armouries.org.uk

web: www.royalarmouries.org

dir: from M27 junct 11, follow brown tourist signs for Royal Armouries

Home to the Royal Armouries' collection of over 350 big guns and cannon, this superbly restored Victorian fort overlooks Portsmouth Harbour. Built in the 1860s to deter a threatened French invasion, there are secret tunnels, underground chambers and grass ramparts to explore with daily guided tours and explosive gun firings. There are free children's activity days on Tuesday and Thursday during school holidays.

Times Open all year, Apr-Oct, daily 10-5 (Wed 11-5); Nov-Mar, daily 10.30-4 (Wed 11.30-4). Closed 24-26 Dec. **Fees** Free. There may be a charge for special events/workshops. **Facilities** ℗ ⬚ ♯ (outdoor) ♿ toilets for disabled shop ⊗

Explosion! Museum of Naval Firepower

Priddy's Hard PO12 4LE
☎ 023 9250 5600 📄 023 9250 5605
e-mail: info@explosion.org.uk
web: www.explosion.org.uk
dir: M27 junct 11, A32 and follow signs

Explosion! The Museum of Naval Firepower is set in the green Heritage Area of Priddy's Hard in Gosport on the shores of Portsmouth Harbour, telling the story of naval firepower from the days of gunpowder to modern missiles. Come face to face with the atom bomb, the Exocet missile and the Gatling Gun and take a trip into the fascinating story of the men and women who supplied the Royal Navy. Walk around the buildings that were a state secret for 200 years and discover the Grand Magazine, an amazing vault once packed full with gunpowder, now a stunning multimedia film show.

Times Open all year, Sat-Sun only, 10-4.*
Fees £4 (ch £2, concessions £3). Family ticket £10* **Facilities** 🅿 ⬚ 🍽 licensed ⏢ (outdoor) toilets for disabled shop ⊗

Royal Navy Submarine Museum

Haslar Rd PO12 2AS
☎ 023 9251 0354 📄 023 9251 1349
e-mail: rnsubs@rnsubmus.co.uk
web: www.rnsubmus.co.uk
dir: M27 junct 11, follow brown tourist signs

Step inside at the Royal Navy Submarine Museum, which overlooks Portsmouth Harbour. Former submariners guide you through where they would work, eat and sleep on board HMS Alliance. Peer into the only surviving X-craft to have seen action during WWII and walk onto the Royal Navy's first submarine Holland 1.

Times Open all year, Apr-Oct 10-5.30; Nov-Mar 10-4.30. (Last tour 1 hour before closing). Closed 24 Dec & 25 Jan.* **Fees** £9 (ch & concessions £6). Family (2ad+4ch) £20.* **Facilities** 🅿 🅿 ⬚ ⏢ (outdoor) ♿ (partly accessible) (no wheelchair access to the Alliance WWII submarine - film version of tour available) toilets for disabled shop ⊗

HIGHCLERE

Highclere Castle & Gardens

RG20 9RN

☎ 01635 253210   📠 01635 255315
e-mail: theoffice@highclerecastle.co.uk
web: www.highclerecastle.co.uk
dir: 4.5m S of Newbury, off A34

This splendid early Victorian mansion stands in beautiful parkland on the site of a previous house, which in turn was built on the site of an even earlier house owned by the Bishops of Winchester. It has sumptuous interiors and numerous Old Master pictures. Also shown are early finds by the 5th Earl of Carnarvon, one of the discoverers of Tutankhamun's tomb. During WWI it was a hospital, and during WWII it was a home for evacuee children.

Times Open Jul-Aug, Sun-Thu (last entry 3.30). Telephone 01635 253210 before travelling as Highclere Castle reserves the right to close at other times.* **Facilities** 🅿 ⬚ 🏬 (outdoor) ♿ (partly accessible) (first floor landing/bedrooms not accessible) toilets for disabled shop ⊗

HURST CASTLE

Hurst Castle

SO4 0FF

☎ 01590 642344
web: www.english-heritage.org.uk
dir: on Pebble Spit S of Keyhaven

Built by Henry VIII, Hurst Castle was the pride of Tudor England's coastal defences. Crouched menacingly on a shingle spit, the castle has a fascinating history, including involvement in the smuggling trade in the 17th and 18th centuries.

Times Open 21 Mar-Oct, daily 10.30-5.30.*
Facilities ⬚ ⊗ ⚏

MIDDLE WALLOP

Museum of Army Flying

SO20 8DY

☎ 01264 784421 🗎 01264 781694
e-mail: administration@flying-museum.org.uk
web: www.flying-museum.org.uk
dir: on A343, between Andover & Salisbury

One of the country's finest historical collections of military kites, gliders, aeroplanes and helicopters. Imaginative dioramas and displays trace the development of Army flying from before the First World War to more recent conflicts in Ireland, the Falklands and the Gulf. Sit at the controls of a real Scout or Apache attack helicopters and test your skills on the flight simulator, plus children's education centre and 1940s house.

Times Open all year, daily 10-4.30. Closed week prior to Xmas. Evening visits by special arrangement. Private functions welcome.*
Fees £7 (ch £4.50, concessions £5) Family £21.*
Facilities 🅿 🖵 🍽 licensed 🎪 (outdoor) ♿ toilets for disabled shop ⊗

PORTSMOUTH

Charles Dickens' Birthplace Museum

393 Old Commercial Rd PO1 4QL
☎ 023 9282 7261 🗎 023 9287 5276
e-mail: mvs@portsmouthcc.gov.uk
web: www.charlesdickensbirthplace.co.uk
dir: M27/M275 into Portsmouth, from M275 turn left at 'The News' rdbt. Signed

A small terraced house built in 1805 which became the birthplace and early home of the famous novelist, born in 1812. On display are items pertaining to Dickens' work, portraits of the Dickens' family, and the couch on which he died. Dickens readings are given in the exhibition room on the first Sunday of each month at 3pm.

Times Open Apr-Sep, daily 10-5.30 (Last admission 5).* **Facilities** 🅿 shop ⊗

PORTSMOUTH

D-Day Museum & Overlord Embroidery

Clarence Esplanade PO5 3NT
☎ 023 9282 7261 ▤ 023 9287 5276
e-mail: mvs@portsmouthcc.gov.uk
web: www.ddaymuseum.co.uk
dir: M27/M275 or M27/A2030 into Portsmouth, follow signs for seafront then D-Day museum name signs

Portsmouth's D-Day Museum tells the dramatic story of the Allied landings in Normandy in 1944. The centrepiece is the magnificent 'Overlord Embroidery', 34 individual panels and 83 metres in length. Experience the world's largest ever seaborne invasion, and step back in time to scenes of wartime Britain. Military equipment, vehicles, landing craft and personal memories complete this special story.

Times Open all year, Apr-Sep, daily 10-5.30; Oct-Mar, 10-5. Closed 24-26 Dec* **Facilities** ❷ ⓟ ⊡ 쿠 (outdoor) ♿ toilets for disabled shop ⊗

PORTSMOUTH

Portsmouth Historic Dockyard

HM Naval Base PO1 3LJ
☎ 023 9283 9766 ▤ 023 9283 8228
e-mail: enquiries@historicdockyard.co.uk
web: www.historicdockyard.co.uk
dir: M27/M275 & follow brown historic waterfront and dockyard signs

Portsmouth Historic Dockyard is home to the world's greatest historic ships: Mary Rose - King Henry VIII's favourite ship, HMS Victory - Lord Nelson's flagship at the Battle of Trafalgar and HMS Warrior - the first iron-hulled warship. In addition, the Royal Naval Museum has the most significant, permanent collections relating to Nelson and the Battle of Trafalgar, and Action Stations gives an interactive insight into the modern day Royal Navy.

Times Open Apr-Oct, daily 10-6 (last entry 4.30); Nov-Mar, daily 10-5.30 (last entry 4).* **Fees** All inclusive ticket: £18 (ch & students £13.50 under 5 free, concessions £16) Family £50.50.* **Facilities** ❷ ⓟ ⊡ †⊚l licensed 쿠 (outdoor) ♿ (partly accessible) toilets for disabled shop ⊗

PORTSMOUTH

The Royal Marines Museum

Southsea PO4 9PX
☎ 023 9281 9385 ▤ 023 9283 8420
e-mail: info@royalmarinesmuseum.co.uk
web: www.royalmarinesmuseum.co.uk
dir: signed from seafront

The Royal Marines Museum celebrates the famous fighting spirit and long history of the Royal Marines. Based in the lavishly decorated former Officers' Mess of Eastney Barracks, built in the 1860s for the Royal Marine Artillery, the Museum is situated in the very heart of the Corps history. With displays and exhibits highlighting the history of the Royal Marines from their beginnings in 1664 through to the present day, and the new 'The Making of the Royal Marines Commando' exhibition, the Museum brings to life the history, character and humour of the Royal Marines.

Times Open all year, daily 10-5. Closed 24-26 Dec.* **Fees** £5.95 (ch 5-16 £3.75, concessions £3.75-£4.75). Family ticket (2ad+4ch) £14.50. Registered disabled £3 (free admission for one assistant).* **Facilities** ❷ ℗ ⬚ ⋢ (outdoor) ♿ toilets for disabled shop ⊗

SELBORNE

Gilbert White's House & The Oates Museum

High St GU34 3JH
☎ 01420 511275 ▤ 01420 511040
e-mail: info@gilbertwhiteshouse.org.uk
web: www.gilbertwhiteshouse.org.uk
dir: on village High St

Charming 18th-century house, home of famous naturalist, the Rev Gilbert White, author of The Natural History and Antiquities of Selborne. Over 20 acres of garden and parkland, shop and tea parlour serving some 18th-century fare. There is also an exhibition on Captain Lawrence Oates and his ill-fated expedition to the South Pole in 1911. Events, courses, exhibitions and lectures throughout the year.

Times Open Jan-24 Dec, Tue-Sun & BH 11-5; Jun-Aug, Mon 11-5. Last admissions 4.30*
Facilities ℗ ⬚ ♿ (partly accessible) (garden fully accessible, upstairs of house not acessible) toilets for disabled shop ⊗

WEYHILL

The Hawk Conservancy and Country Park

SP11 8DY

☎ 01264 773850　📄 01264 773772

e-mail: info@hawkconservancy.org

web: www.hawkconservancy.org

dir: 3m W of Andover, signed from A303

The Hawk Conservancy Trust is a registered charity and award winning visitor attraction that has for many years been working in the fields of conservation, education, rehabilitation and the research of birds of prey. The Trust is set in 22 acres of woodland and wild flower meadow, where there are over 150 birds of prey on view from the tiny Pygmy Owl to the impressive European Black Vulture. A day at the Trust has a packed itinerary including three flying demonstrations that see owls, kites, hawks, falcons and eagles showing off their skills. The birds come really close and there is even an opportunity for visitors to hold a British bird of prey!

Times Open all year, mid Feb-Oct daily 10-5.30. Nov-mid Feb wknds only 10-4.30. **Fees** £10 (ch £6, pen £9.25, students £9). Family ticket (2ad+2ch) £32.* **Facilities** 🅿 ⏛ 🍴 licensed ☕ (indoor & outdoor) ♿ toilets for disabled shop ⊗

WINCHESTER

Gurkha Museum

Peninsula Barracks, Romsey Rd SO23 8TS

☎ 01962 842832　📄 01962 877597

e-mail: curator@thegurkhamuseum.co.uk

web: www.thegurkhamuseum.co.uk

dir: M3 junct 9 to Winchester, follow one-way system into High St, 1st left after Westgate

This museum tells the fascinating story of the Gurkhas' involvement with the British Army. Travel from Nepal to the North-West Frontier and beyond, with the help of life-sized dioramas, interactive exhibits and sound displays.

Times Open all year, Mon-Sat 10-5, Sun 12-4. Closed 25-26 Dec & 1 Jan* **Fees** £2 (pen £1, ch under 16 free).* **Facilities** 🅿 🅟 ♿ toilets for disabled shop ⊗

WINCHESTER

Winchester City Mill

Bridge St SO23 8EJ

☎ 01962 870057   📠 01962 870057

e-mail: winchestercitymill@nationaltrust.org.uk

web: www.nationaltrust.org.uk

dir: by city bridge between King Alfred's statue & Chesil St

Built over the fastflowing River Itchen in 1744, the mill has a delightful small island garden and an impressive millrace. There are regular milling demonstrations and guided wildlife walks, as well as other special events and hands-on activities throughout the year.

Times Open: Mill & Shop, 5-27 Mar, Sat-Sun 11-5, 28 Mar-10 Apr & 4 Jul-23 Dec, daily 11-5, 13 Apr-3 Jul, Wed-Sun 11-5. Last admission to Mill 4.30* **Facilities** ℗ ♿ (partly accessible) shop ⊗ 🌿

WINCHESTER

Winchester College

College St SO23 9NA

☎ 01962 621209   📠 01962 621166

e-mail: enterprises@wincoll.ac.uk

web: www.winchestercollege.org

dir: S of Cathedral Close, beyond Kingsgate arch. Limited vehicle access along College St

Founded in 1382, Winchester College is believed to be the oldest continuously running school in England. The College has greatly expanded over the years but the original buildings remain intact. Visitors can follow in the footsteps of John Keats, and see the College's many historic buildings, including the 14th-century gothic chapel with one of the earliest examples of a fan-vaulted roof constructed from wood rather than stone, the original scholars' dining room and the cloister containing memorials to former members of the college including one to Mallory the Mountaineer.

Times Open all year. Guided tours available Mon, Wed, Fri & Sat; 10.45, 12, 2.15 & 3.30. Tue & Thu 10.45 & 12. Sun 2.15 & 3.30. Groups of 10+ at times to suit by arrangement only. Closed 24 Dec-1 Jan.* **Fees** £4 (concessions £3.50).* **Facilities** ℗ ♿ (partly accessible) (one building in the tour has access via staircase) toilets for disabled shop ⊗

HEREFORD

Hereford Cathedral

HR1 2NG

☎ 01432 374200 📠 01432 374220
e-mail: office@herefordcathedral.org
web: www.herefordcathedral.org
dir: A49 signed from city inner ring roads

Built on the site of a place of worship that dates back to Saxon times, Hereford Cathedral contains some of the finest examples of architecture from the Norman era to the present day, including the 13th-century Shrine of St Thomas of Hereford, the recently restored 14th-century Lady Chapel, and the award-winning new library building. The Mappa Mundi and Chained Library exhibition tells the stories of these famous national treasures through models, artefacts and changing exhibitions.

Times Cathedral open daily 7.30-Evensong; Mappa Mundi & Chained Library Exhibition Summer: Mon-Sat 10-4.30, Sun 11-3.30. Winter: Mon-Sat 11-3.30 (closed Sun).* **Facilities** Ⓟ 🖵 🛒 toilets for disabled shop ⊗

AYOT ST LAWRENCE

Shaw's Corner

AL6 9BX

☎ 01438 820307 📠 01438 820307
e-mail: shawscorner@nationaltrust.org.uk
web: www.nationaltrust.org.uk/shawscorner
dir: A1(M) junct 4 or M1 junct 10. Follow B653 signed Wheathampstead & follow National Trust signs to Shaw's Corner

An Edwardian 'Arts and Crafts'influenced house, this was the home of George Bernard Shaw from 1906 until his death in 1950. The rooms remain much as he left them, with many literary and personal effects evoking the individuality and genius of this great dramatist. The kitchen and outbuildings are evocative of early 20th-century domestic life. Shaw's writing hut is hidden at the bottom of the garden, which has richly planted borders and views over the Hertfordshire countryside. A selection of plants in addition to a small collection of George Bernard Shaw plays are available to buy.

Times House:14 Mar-1 Nov, Wed-Sun 1-5. Garden: 14 Mar-1 Nov, Wed-Sun 12-5.30 & all BHs* **Fees** £5.20 (ch £2.95). Family ticket £14.95.* **Facilities** Ⓟ 🛒 ♿ (partly accessible) (Grd floor limited access, stairs to other floors, grounds partly accessible for wheelchairs). ⊗ 🐾

73

HATFIELD

Hatfield House, Park and Gardens

AL9 5NQ

☎ 01707 287010   🖷 01707 287033
e-mail: visitors@hatfield-house.co.uk
web: www.hatfield-house.co.uk
dir: 2m from junct 4 A1(M) on A1000, 7m from
M25 junct 23. House opposite Hatfield railway
station

The house, built by Robert Cecil in 1611, is the
home of the 7th Marquess of Salisbury and is
full of exquisite tapestries, furniture and famous
paintings. The 42 acres of gardens include
formal, knot, scented and wilderness areas,
and reflect their Jacobean history. Includes
the national collection of model soldiers and
children's play area. The Tudor Palace of Hatfield,
close by the house, was the childhood home of
Elizabeth I and where she held her first Council
of State when she became Queen in 1558. Events
take place throughout the year - see website for
details.

Times Open Etr Sat-Sep, Wed-Sun & BH Mon,
House 12-4; Park & West Garden 11-5.30.*
Fees House, Park & Garden: £10.50 (ch £5,
concessions £9.50). Park only £3 (ch £2), Park
& West Garden £6 (ch £4.50).* Facilities 🅿 ⊡
⊚ licensed ⊓ (outdoor) & (partly accessible)
(lift to 1st floor) toilets for disabled shop ⊗

LONDON COLNEY

de Havilland Aircraft Heritage Centre

Salisbury Hall AL2 1BU

☎ 01727 826400 & 822051 (info)
🖷 01727 826400
e-mail: w4050.dhamt@fsmail.net
web: www.dehavillandmuseum.co.uk
dir: M25 junct 22. Follow signs for 'Mosquito
Aircraft Museum' onto B556

The site of the hall and museum is a very old one.
The aircraft museum opened in 1959 to preserve
and display the de Havilland Mosquito prototype
on the site of its conception. A working museum
with displays of 20 de Havilland aircraft and
sections together with a comprehensive collection
of de Havilland engines and memorabilia.
Selective cockpits are open to enter. Education
storyboard 'maze style' gives an outline history of
de Havilland Enterprise.

Times Open first Sun Mar-last Sun Oct, Sun &
BHs 10.30-5.30, Tue, Thu & Sat 2-5.30.* Fees £5
(ch under 5 free, ch 5-16 £3, pen £4) Family
ticket £13 (2ad+2ch)* Facilities 🅿 🅟 ⊡ ⊓
(indoor & outdoor) & toilets for disabled shop ⊗

ST ALBANS

Verulamium Museum

St Michaels AL3 4SW
☎ 01727 751810   📄 01727 859919
e-mail: museum@stalbans.gov.uk
web: www.stalbansmuseums.org.uk
dir: follow signs for St Albans, museum signed

Verulamium was one of the largest and most important Roman towns in Britain - by the lst century AD it was declared a `municipium', giving its inhabitants the rights of Roman citizenship, the only British city granted this honour. A mosaic and underfloor heating system can be seen in a separate building, and the museum has wall paintings, jewellery, pottery and other domestic items. On the second weekend of every month legionaries occupy the galleries and describe the tactics and equipment of the Roman Imperial Army and the life of a legionary.

Times Open all year Mon-Fri 10-5.30, Sun 2-5.30. Closed 25-26 Dec.* **Facilities** ℗ ⊓ (outdoor) ᕆ toilets for disabled shop ⊗

BROADSTAIRS

Dickens House Museum

2 Victoria Pde CT10 1QS
☎ 01843 863453   📄 01843 863453
e-mail: l.ault@btinternet.com
web: www.dickenshouse.co.uk
dir: on seafront

The house was immortalised by Charles Dickens in David Copperfield as the home of the hero's aunt, Betsy Trotwood, whom Dickens based on owner Miss Mary Pearson Strong. Dickens' letters and possessions are shown, with local and Dickensian prints, costumes and general Victoriana.

Times Open Etr-Oct, daily 2-5, also Sat-Sun mid Jun-Aug 10.30-5. **Fees** £3 (ch £1.75). Family ticket (2ad+2ch) £7.90. **Facilities** ℗ ᕆ (partly accessible) shop ⊗

CHARTWELL

Chartwell

TN16 1PS

☎ 01732 866368 (info line) & 868381

🖷 01732 868193

e-mail: chartwell@nationaltrust.org.uk
web: www.nationaltrust.org.uk/chartwell
dir: off A25 onto B2026 at Westerham, Chartwell 2m S of village

The former home of Sir Winston Churchill is filled with reminders of the great statesman, from his hats and uniforms to gifts presented by Stalin, Roosevelt, de Gaulle and many other State leaders. There are portraits by notable artists, and also many paintings by Churchill himself.

Times Open House, 13 Mar-Oct, Wed-Sun 11-5. Open BH Mon & Tue in Jul & Aug. (Last admission 4.15). Garden, shop & restaurant open all year, Wed-Sun; Jul-Aug, Tue-Sun. **Fees** Gift Aid admission House, Garden & Studio £11.80 (ch £5.90). Garden & Studio £5.90 (ch £2.95). Family ticket £29.50. Including a voluntary donation of 10% or more. Visitors can, however, choose to pay the standard admission prices which are displayed at the property & on NT website*
Facilities ❷ ⑪ licensed 🎮 (outdoor) ♿ (partly accessible) (house stairs to 1st, lower floors & steps, steep slopes in garden) toilets for disabled shop ⊗ 🐾

CHATHAM

The Historic Dockyard Chatham

ME4 4TZ

☎ 01634 823807 & 823800

🖷 01634 823801

e-mail: info@chdt.org.uk
web: www.thedockyard.co.uk
dir: M29 junct 6, M2 junct 3 onto A229 towards Chatham. Then A230 and A231, following brown tourist signs. Brown anchor signs lead to visitors entrance

Costumed guides bring this spectacular maritime heritage site alive. Discover over 400 years of maritime history as you explore the most complete dockyard of the Age of Sail, set in a stunning 80-acre estate. Various special events take place throughout the year, please see the website for details.

Times Open daily mid Feb-end Oct, Nov wknds only.* **Facilities** ❷ ⑫ ⌐ ⑪ licensed 🎮 (indoor & outdoor) ♿ (partly accessible) toilets for disabled shop

DOVER

Dover Castle & Secret Wartime Tunnels

CT16 1HU

☎ 01304 211067   📠 01304 214739
web: www.english-heritage.org.uk

Various exhibitions demonstrate how Dover Castle has served as a vital strategic centre for the Iron Age onwards. In May 1940 the tunnels under the castle became the nerve centre for 'Operation Dynamo' - the evacuation of Dunkirk. These wartime secrets are now revealed for all to see.

Times Open Apr-Jul & Sep, daily 10-6; Aug, daily 9.30-6; Oct-1 Nov, daily 10-5; 2 Nov-Jan, Thu-Mon 10-4; Feb-Mar, daily 10-4. Closed 24-26 Dec & 1 Jan. **Fees** £13.40 (concessions £11.40, ch £6.70). Family £33.50. (Additional charges may apply on event days). All prices and opening times are subject to change in March 2010. Please call 0870 333 1181 for the most up to date prices and opening times when planning your visit. **Facilities** 🅿 🅿 🍽 licensed ♿ (partly accessible) (steep slopes) toilets for disabled shop ⊗ ♯

DOVER

The White Cliffs of Dover

Visitor Centre, Langdon Cliffs, Upper Rd
CT16 1HJ

☎ 01304 202756   📠 01304 215484
e-mail: whitecliffs@nationaltrust.org.uk
web: www.nationaltrust.org.uk
dir: A2/A258 towards Dover town centre, in 1m turn left into Upper Rd, 0.75m turn right into entrance

The White Cliffs of Dover are one of England's most important national icon. Visitors enjoy their special appeal through the seasons by taking the cliff top paths offering views of the French coast, and savouring the rare flora and fauna that can be found across this chalk grassland. The visitor centre is full of useful information, as well as a coffee shop and National Trust shop.

Times Open all year. Visitor Centre: Nov-Feb, 11-4, Mar-Oct, 10-5. Car park Nov-Feb, 8-5, Mar-Oct, 8-6. **Fees** Free admission. Parking charges car £3, mobile home £4, coach £7. **Facilities** 🅿 ⊑ 🎋 (outdoor) ♿ (partly accessible) (some uneven and steep paths) toilets for disabled shop

GILLINGHAM

Royal Engineers Museum, Library & Archive

Prince Arthur Rd ME4 4UG
☎ 01634 822839 📄 01634 822371
e-mail: mail@re-museum.co.uk
web: www.remuseum.org.uk
dir: follow brown signs from Gillingham & Chatham town centres

The museum covers the diverse and sometimes surprising work of the Royal Engineers. Learn about the first military divers, photographers, aviators and surveyors; see memorabilia relating to General Gordon and Field Marshal Lord Kitchener, Wellington's battle map from Waterloo and a Harrier jump-jet. The superb medal displays include 25 Victoria Crosses, among 6,000 medals. Among the exhibits are locomotives, tanks, the first wire guided torpedo, bridges, and models.

Times Open all year, Tue-Fri 9-5, Sat-Sun & BH Mon 11.30-5. Closed Good Fri, Xmas week & 1 Jan. Library open by appointment (ex wknds).*
Fees £6.99 (concessions £4.66) Family £18.64. Gift aid ticket for 1yr entry.* **Facilities** 🅿 ℗ 🍴 (indoor & outdoor) ♿ (partly accessible) (one gallery not easily accessible) toilets for disabled shop ⊗

HAWKINGE

Kent Battle of Britain Museum

Aerodrome Rd CT18 7AG
☎ 01303 893140
e-mail:
kentbattleofbritainmuseum@btinternet.com
web: www.kbobm.org
dir: off A260, 1m along Aerodrome road

Once a Battle of Britain Station, today it houses the largest collection of relics and related memorabilia of British and German aircraft involved in the fighting. Also on display are full-size replicas of the Hurricane, Spitfire and Me109 used in Battle of Britain films. The year 2000 was the 60th anniversary of the Battle of Britain and a new memorial was dedicated. Artefacts on show, recovered from over 650 Battle of Britain aircraft, all form a lasting memorial to all those involved in the conflict.

Times Open Good Fri-May & Oct, 10-4; Jun-Sep, 10-5. (Last admission 1 hour before closing). Closed Mon ex BHs.* **Fees** £5 (ch £2.50, pen £4.50).* **Facilities** 🅿 ℗ 🍴 (outdoor) ♿ shop ⊗

HEVER

Hever Castle & Gardens

TN8 7NG

☎ 01732 865224   📄 01732 866796
e-mail: mail@hevercastle.co.uk
web: www.hevercastle.co.uk
dir: M25 junct 5 or 6, 3m SE of Edenbridge, off B2026

This enchanting, double-moated, 13th-century castle was the childhood home of Anne Boleyn. Restored by the American millionaire William Waldorf Astor at the beginning of the 20th century, it shows superb Edwardian craftsmanship. Astor also transformed the grounds, creating topiary, a yew maze, 35 acre lake and Italian gardens filled with antique sculptures. There is also a 100 metre herbaceous border, a 'splashing' water maze' on the Sixteen Acre Island, and a woodland walk known as Sunday Walk. Adventure play area with the Henry VIII Tower Maze.

Times Open Mar-Nov, daily. Castle 12-6, Gardens 11-6. (Last admission 5). (Closes 4pm Mar & Nov).* **Facilities** 🅿 🖵 🍴 licensed 🍽 (outdoor) toilets for disabled shop

MAIDSTONE

Leeds Castle

ME17 1PL

☎ 01622 765400   📄 01622 735616
e-mail: enquiries@leeds-castle.co.uk
web: www.leeds-castle.com
dir: 7m E of Maidstone at junct 8 of M20/A20

Set in 500 acres of beautiful parkland, a visit to Leeds Castle is full of discovery. With over 900 years of fascinating history, the castle has been a Norman stronghold, a royal residence for six medieval queens of England, a favourite palace of Henry VIII and a grand country house. Its blend of history and heritage, glorious gardens, aviary and birds of prey, maze and grotto, dog collar museum, craft centre and children's playground, make it the perfect choice for a day out.

Times Open all year, Grounds: Apr-Sep, daily 10-6 (Castle 10.30-5.30) Last admission 4.30. Grounds: Oct-Mar 10-4 (Castle 10.30-4) Last admission 3. Last entry to the castle is 30min after the last admission time. **Fees** £16.50 (ch £9.50, under 4 free, concessions £13.50). Every ticket purchased for entry to Leeds Castle is valid for unlimited use for an entire year (excluding special ticketed events). Prices are valid until 31 March 2010 **Facilities** 🅿 🍴 licensed 🍽 (outdoor) ♿ (partly accessible) (only ground floor of castle accessible) toilets for disabled shop ⊗

ROLVENDEN

C M Booth Collection of Historic Vehicles

Falstaff Antiques, 63 High St TN17 4LP

☎ 01580 241234

e-mail: info@morganmuseum.org.uk

web: www.morganmuseum.org.uk

dir: on A28, 3m from Tenterden

Not just vehicles, but various other items of interest connected with transport. There is a unique collection of three-wheel Morgan cars, dating from 1913, and the only known Humber tri-car of 1904, as well as a 1929 Morris van, a 1936 Bampton caravan, motorcycles and bicycles. There is also a toy and model car display.

Times Open all year, Mon-Sat 10-5.30. Closed 25-26 Dec.* Fees £2.50 (ch £1)* Facilities ℗ ⚒ (partly accessible) shop

LEIGHTON HALL

Leighton Hall

LA5 9ST

☎ 01524 734474 📄 01524 720357

e-mail: info@leightonhall.co.uk

web: www.leightonhall.co.uk

dir: M6 junct 35 onto A6 & follow signs

This is the historic family home of the Gillow furniture makers, and early Gillow furniture is displayed among other treasures in the fine interior of the neo-Gothic mansion. There are also fine gardens, a maze and a woodland walk. A varied programme of special events throughout the year, for full details please see website.

Times Open May-Sep, Tue-Fri & BH Sun & Mon; Aug, Tue-Fri, Sun & BH Mon 2-5. Groups all year by arrangement Fees £6.95 (ch 5-12 £4.75, pen £6). Family ticket £22. Facilities ℗ ⚒ ⋒ (outdoor) ⚒ (partly accessible) (upstairs not accessible) toilets for disabled shop ⊗

LEYLAND

British Commercial Vehicle Museum

King St PR25 2LE
☎ 01772 451011　📠 01772 451015
e-mail: enquiries@bcvm.co.uk
web: www.bcvm.co.uk
dir: 0.75m from M6 junct 28 in town centre

A unique line-up of historic commercial vehicles and buses spanning a century of truck and bus building. There are more than 50 exhibits on permanent display, and plenty of special events including transport model shows, transport shows, and the Ford Cortina Mk I gathering.

Times Open Apr-Sep, Sun, Tue-Thu & BH Mon (Oct open Tue & Sun only); 10-5.* **Facilities** ℗ ℗ 🖵 ♿ toilets for disabled shop ⊗

PRESTON

National Football Museum **FREE**

Sir Tom Finney Way, Deepdale PR1 6PA
☎ 01772 908442　📠 01772 908444
e-mail: enquiries@nationalfootballmuseum.com
web: www.nationalfootballmuseum.com
dir: 2m from M6 juncts 31, 31A or 32. Follow brown tourist signs

Take an amazing journey through football history. Discover the world's biggest football museum, packed full of great footballing moments, stories and objects -from the World Cup ball used in the first ever final in 1930, to the ball used in the 1966 World Cup final. There are fun interactive opportunities and the brilliant penalty shoot-out game Goalstriker. Plus events, activities and exhibitions all year round means there's always something new to see and do.

Times Open all year, Tue-Sat 10-5, Sun 11-5. Closed Mon ex BHs and school hols. (Museum closed 15 mins before 'kick off' on match days)* **Facilities** ℗ ℗ 🖵 ♿ toilets for disabled shop ⊗

81

MARKET BOSWORTH

Bosworth Battlefield Visitor Centre & Country Park

Ambion Hill, Sutton Cheney CV13 0AD
☎ 01455 290429 📄 01455 292841
e-mail: bosworth@leics.gov.uk
web: www.leics.gov.uk
dir: follow brown tourist signs from A447, A444 & A5

The Battle of Bosworth Field was fought in 1485 between the armies of Richard III and the future Henry VII. The visitor centre offers a comprehensive interpretation of the battle, with exhibitions, models and a film theatre. Special medieval attractions are held in the summer months.

Times Open: Country Park daily Apr-Sep, 8.30-5.30, Oct-Mar 8.30-4.40. Heritage Centre open daily Apr-Oct, 10-5, Nov-Mar, 10-4 (last admission 1hr before closing). Closed Jan & 24-27 Dec.* **Fees** £6 (ch 3-16 yrs £3, ch under 3 free, concessions £4). Family ticket (2ad+2ch) £15.* **Facilities** ℗ Ⓟ ☐ ◖ licensed ⊼ (outdoor) toilets for disabled shop

CONINGSBY

Battle of Britain Memorial Flight Visitor Centre

LN4 4SY
☎ 01522 782040 📄 01526 342330
e-mail: bbmf@lincolnshire.gov.uk
web: www.lincolnshire.gov.uk/bbmf
dir: on A153 in Coningsby village - follow heritage signs

View the aircraft of the Battle of Britain Memorial Flight, including the only flying Lancaster in Europe, five Spitfires, two Hurricanes, a Dakota and two Chipmunks. Because of operational commitments, specific aircraft may not be available. Please ring for information before planning a visit.

Times Open Mon-Fri, conducted tours 10.30-3.30; (winter 10.30-3). Closed 2 wks Xmas. Times may be reviewed, please check before visiting.* **Fees** £4.10 (children 5-16 & concessions £2.70). Family £10.90* **Facilities** ℗ Ⓟ ⊼ (outdoor) ♿ toilets for disabled shop ⊗

GRIMSBY

Fishing Heritage Centre

Alexandra Dock DN31 1UZ
☎ 01472 323345 📠 01472 323555
web: www.nelincs.gov.uk/leisure/museums
dir: follow signs off M180

Sign on as a crew member for a journey of discovery, and experience the harsh reality of life on board a deep sea trawler built inside the Centre. Through interactive games and displays, your challenge is to navigate the icy waters of the Arctic in search of the catch.

Times Open Nov-Apr, Mon-Fri 10-4, Wknds & BHs 11-9* **Facilities** 🅿 🅟 ⌴ toilets for disabled shop ⊗

LINCOLN

The Collection: Art & Archaeology in Lincolnshire

Danes Ter LN2 1LP
☎ 01522 550990 📠 01522 550991
e-mail: thecollection@lincolnshire.gov.uk
web: www.thecollection.lincoln.museum
dir: follow signs for Lincoln City Centre, then parking for cultural quarter then pedestrian signs to The Collection

Housed in an impressive new building, the Collection consists of the combined collections of the City and County Museum and the Usher Gallery. The art collection includes contemporary art and craft, paintings, sculpture, porcelain, clocks and watches. There are paintings by Turner, Stubbs and Lowry, major porcelain collections and clocks by Robert Sutton. The archaeological collection covers 300,000 years of history up to the 18th-century.

Times Open all year daily, 10-4. (Last entry 3.30). Closed 25-26 Dec & 1 Jan.* **Facilities** 🅟 ⌴ 🍽 licensed ╦ (outdoor) ♿ toilets for disabled shop ⊗

WOOLSTHORPE

Woolsthorpe Manor

23 Newton Way NG33 5PD

☎ 01476 862826 📠 01476 860338

e-mail: woolsthorpemanor@nationaltrust.org.uk

web: www.nationaltrust.org.uk

dir: 7m S of Grantham, 1m W of A1

Isaac Newton was born in this modest manor house in the mid 1600s and he made many of his most important discoveries about light and gravity here. A complex figure, Newton notched up careers as diverse as Cambridge Professor and Master of the Royal Mint; spent years studying alchemy and the Bible as well as science, and was President of the Royal Society, which celebrates its 350th anniversary in 2010.

Times Open 27 Feb-29 Mar & 4-26 Oct, Sat & Sun 1-5; Apr-28 Jun & 2-27 Sep, Wed-Sun (open BHs) 1-5; 2 Jul-Aug, Sat & Sun 11-5; Wed-Fri, 1-5; 2 Oct -1 Nov, Fri-Sun 1-5* **Fees** With Gift Aid donation: £5.80 (ch £2.90). Family ticket £14.50* **Facilities** ℗ & (partly accessible) (narrow doorways & small rooms, ramps available. Stairs to other floors. Grounds partly accessible, uneven & loose gravel paths, some steps) toilets for disabled shop ⊗ ❦

E2

Geffrye Museum

136 Kingsland Rd, Shoreditch E2 8EA

☎ 020 7739 9893 📠 020 7729 5647

e-mail: info@geffrye-museum.org.uk

web: www.geffrye-museum.org.uk

dir: S end of Kingsland Rd A10 in Shoreditch between Cremer St & Pearson St

The only museum in the UK to specialise in the domestic interiors and furniture of the urban middle classes. Displays span the 400 years from 1600 to the present day, forming a sequence of period rooms which capture the nature of English interior style. The museum is set in elegant, 18th-century buildings, surrounded by delightful gardens including an award-winning walled herb garden and a series of historical gardens which highlight changes in town gardens from the 17th to 20th centuries. Each December, the museum's period rooms are decorated in authentic, festive style to reflect 400 years of Christmas traditions in English homes.

Times Open all year, Tue-Sat 10-5, Sun & BH Mon 12-5. Closed Mon, Good Fri, 24-26 Dec & New Year.* **Facilities** ℗ ⑪ licensed ☶ (outdoor) & toilets for disabled shop ⊗

E14

Museum of London Docklands

No 1 Warehouse, West India Quay E14 4AL
☎ 020 7001 9844
e-mail: info@museumoflondon.org.uk
web: www.museumoflondon.org.uk/docklands
dir: Signposted from West India Quay DLR

From Roman settlement to Docklands' regeneration, unlock the history of London's river, port and people, in this historic warehouse. Discover a wealth of objects from whale bones to WWII gas masks in state-of-the-art galleries, including Mudlarks, an interactive area for kids; Sailortown, an atmospheric recreation of 19th century riverside Wapping; and London, Sugar & Slavery, which reveals the city's involvement in the transatlantic slave trade.

Times Open all year, daily 10-6. Closed 24-26 Dec. **Fees** £5 (ch16 free, concessions £3)* **Facilities** ℗ ⬜ 🍴 licensed ⦆ (indoor) ♿ toilets for disabled shop ⊗

EC2

Bank of England Museum **FREE**

Bartholomew Ln EC2R 8AH
☎ 020 7601 5545   📄 020 7601 5808
e-mail: museum@bankofengland.co.uk
web: www.bankofengland.co.uk/museum
dir: museum housed in Bank of London, entrance in Bartholomew Lane. Bank underground, exit 2

The museum tells the story of the Bank of England from its foundation in 1694 to its role in today's economy. Interactive programmes with graphics and video help explain its many and varied roles. Popular exhibits include a unique collection of banknotes and a genuine gold bar, which may be handled.

Times Open all year, Mon-Fri 10-5. Closed wknds & BHs. Open on day of Lord Mayor's Show & Open House London **Facilities** ℗ ♿ toilets for disabled shop ⊗

EC2

The Guildhall FREE

Gresham St EC2V 5AE

☎ 020 7606 3030 📠 020 7260 1119
e-mail: pro@corpoflondon.gov.uk
web: www.cityoflondon.gov.uk
dir: Underground - Bank, St Paul's

The Court of Common Council (presided over by the Lord Mayor) administers the City of London and meets in the Guildhall. Dating from 1411, the building was badly damaged in the Great Fire and again in the Blitz. The great hall, traditionally used for the Lord Mayor's Banquet and other important civic functions, is impressively decorated with the banners and shields of the livery companies, of which there are more than 90. The Clock Museum, which has a collection of 700 exhibits, charts the history of 500 years of time-keeping.

Times Open all year, May-Sep, daily 10-5; Oct-Apr, Mon-Sat 10-5. Closed Xmas, New Year, Good Fri, Etr Mon & infrequently for Civic occasions. Please contact 020 7606 3030 ext 1463 before visit to be certain of access.* **Facilities** Ⓟ toilets for disabled shop ⊗

EC2

Museum of London FREE

150 London Wall EC2Y 5HN

☎ 0870 444 3851 📠 0870 444 3853
e-mail: info@museumoflondon.org.uk
web: www.museumoflondon.org.uk
dir: Underground - St Paul's, Barbican. N of St Paul's Cathedral at the end of St Martins le Grand and S of the Barbican. S of Aldersgate St

Dedicated to the story of London and its people, the Museum of London exists to inspire a passion for London in all who visit it. As well as the permanent collection, the Museum has a varied exhibition programme with major temporary exhibitions and topical displays each year. There are also smaller exhibitions in the foyer gallery. A wide programme of lectures and events explore London's history and its evolution into the city of today.

Times Open all year, Mon-Sat 10-5.50, Sun 12-5.50. Last admission 5.30.* **Facilities** Ⓟ Ⓟ ⊉ ㄱ toilets for disabled shop ⊗

EC3

The Monument

Monument St EC3R 8AH

☎ 020 7626 2717 🖹 020 7403 4477

e-mail: enquiries@towerbridge.org.uk

web: www.towerbridge.org.uk

dir: Underground - Monument

Designed by Wren and Hooke and erected in 1671-7, the Monument commemorates the Great Fire of 1666 which is reputed to have started in nearby Pudding Lane. The fire destroyed nearly 90 churches and about 13,000 houses. This fluted Doric column stands 202ft high (Pudding Lane is exactly 202ft from its base) and you can climb the 311 steps to a platform at the summit, and receive a certificate as proof of your athletic abilities.

Times Open all year, daily, 9.30-5.* **Facilities** ⊗

EC3

Tower of London

Tower Hill EC3N 4AB

☎ 0870 756 6060

web: www.hrp.org.uk

dir: Underground - Tower Hill

Perhaps the most famous castle in the world, the Tower of London has played a central part in British history. Discover the stories of this awesome fortress; from gruesome tales of torture and escape to fascinating traditions that can still be seen today. Learn the legend of the ravens and be dazzled by the Crown Jewels. Join a Yeoman Warder tour and listen to their captivating tales of pain and passion, treachery and torture, all delivered with a smile and a swagger!

Times Open all year, Mar-Oct, Sun-Mon 10-5.30, Tue-Sat 9-5.30 (last admission 5); Nov-Feb, Tue-Sat 9-4.30, Sun-Mon 10-4.30 (last admission 4). Closed 24-26 Dec & 1 Jan.* **Fees** £17 (ch £9.50 under 5s free, children must be accompanied by an adult) concessions: full-time student, over 60 with ID £14.50). Family ticket (2ad+3ch) £47.* **Facilities** ℗ ⊊ ⍩◎⍩ licensed toilets for disabled shop ⊗

EC4

Dr Johnson's House

17 Gough Square EC4A 3DE
☎ 020 7353 3745 🖷 020 7353 3745
e-mail: curator@drjohnsonshouse.org
web: www.drjohnsonshouse.org
dir: Underground - Temple, Blackfriars, Chancery Lane

The celebrated literary figure, Dr Samuel Johnson, lived here between 1748 and 1759. He wrote his English Dictionary here, and a facsimile edition is on display at the house. The dictionary took nine and a half years to complete and contained over 40,000 words. The house is a handsome example of early 18th-century architecture, with many original features, and includes a collection of prints, letters and other Johnson memorabilia.

Times Open all year, May-Sep, Mon-Sat 11-5.30; Oct-Apr 11-5. Closed Sun, BHs, Good Fri. Please check website for Xmas opening times.*
Fees £4.50 (ch £1.50, concessions £3.50). Family £10.* **Facilities** ℗ ⑤ (partly accessible) (wheelchair access difficult, many steps) shop ⊗

EC4

Middle Temple Hall FREE

The Temple EC4Y 9AT
☎ 020 7427 4800 & 4820
🖷 020 7427 4801
e-mail: banqueting@middletemple.org.uk
web: www.middletemple.org.uk
dir: Underground - Temple, Blackfriars. Turn left at the embankment & left into Middle Temple Lane. Hall half way up on left

Between Fleet Street and the Thames are the Middle and Inner Temples, separate Inns of Court, so named after the Knights Templar who occupied the site from about 1160. Middle Temple Hall is a fine example of Tudor architecture, completed in about 1570, and has a double hammerbeam roof and beautiful stained glass. The 29ft-long high table was made from a single oak tree from Windsor Forest. Sir Francis Drake was a visitor to and friend of the Middle Temple, and a table made from timbers from his ship, the Golden Hind, survives to this day.

Times Open all year, Mon-Fri 10-12 & 3-4. Closed BH & legal vacations.* **Facilities** ℗ 🖵⑩ licensed ⑤ toilets for disabled shop

NW3

Freud Museum

20 Maresfield Gardens, Hampstead NW3 5SX
☎ 020 7435 2002 & 5167
🖶 020 7431 5452
e-mail: info@freud.org.uk
web: www.freud.org.uk
dir: Underground - Finchley Road, follow brown signs to museum

In 1938, Sigmund Freud left Vienna as a refugee from the Nazi occupation and chose exile in England, transferring his entire domestic and working environment to this house. He worked here until his death a year later. His extraordinary collection of Egyptian, Greek, Roman and Oriental antiquities, his working library and papers, and his fine furniture including the famous desk and couch are all here.

Times Open all year, Wed-Sun 12-5. Closed BHs, telephone for Xmas holiday times.* **Fees** £6 (pen £4.50, students £3).* **Facilities** Ⓟ ⅋ (partly accessible) (access to ground floor only) shop ⊗

NW3

2 Willow Road

2 Willow Rd, Hampstead NW3 1TH
☎ 020 7435 6166 🖶 020 7435 6166
e-mail: 2willowroad@nationaltrust.org.uk
web: www.nationaltrust.org.uk
dir: Hampstead tube (Northern Line), along High Street, left Flask Walk, right at end into Willow Rd

Discover the 1939 home built by the architect Ernö Goldfinger for himself and his family. On display is his modern art collection including works by Henry Moore, Bridget Riley, Max Ernst and Marcel Duchamp as well as an extensive collection of original furniture designed by the architect.

Times Open 13 Mar-Oct, Thu-Sun 12-5; 6-28 Nov, Sat & Sun only 12-5. Entry by timed tour only at 12, 1 & 2. Non-guided viewing 3-5. (Last admission 4.30). **Fees** £5.50 (ch £2.75). Joint admission with Fenton House £8. Family ticket £13.75. **Facilities** Ⓟ ⅋ (partly accessible) (wheelchair accessible on ground floor only) ⊗ ⅍

NW8

Lord's Tour & M.C.C. Museum

Lord's Ground NW8 8QN

☎ 020 7616 8595 & 8596

📄 020 7266 3825

e-mail: tours@mcc.org.uk

web: www.lords.org

dir: Underground - St John's Wood

Established in 1787, Lord's is the home of the MCC and cricket. Guided tours take you behind the scenes, and highlights include the Long Room and the MCC Museum, where the Ashes and a large collection of paintings and memorabilia are displayed. The Museum is open on match days for spectators.

Times Open all year, Nov-Mar tours at 12 & 2; Apr-Oct 10, 12 & 2 (restrictions on some match days). Telephone for details & bookings.* **Fees** Guided tour £14 (concessions £8). Family ticket (2ad+2ch) £37. Party 20. Museum only £3 (concessions £1) plus ground admission (match days only).* **Facilities** ℗ ⑩ licensed ⊟ ⑤ (partly accessible) (everything is accessible apart from 1st floor of museum) toilets for disabled shop ⊗

NW9

Royal Air Force Museum London
FREE

Grahame Park Way, Colindale NW9 5LL

☎ 020 8205 2266 📄 020 8358 4981

e-mail: groups@rafmuseum.org

web: www.rafmuseum.org

dir: within easy reach of the A5, A41, M1 and North Circular A406 roads. Tube on Northern Line to Colindale. Rail to Mill Hill Broadway station. Bus route 303 passes the door

Take off to the Royal Air Force Museum London and soar through the history of aviation from the earliest balloon flights to the latest Eurofighter. This is a world-class collection of over 100 aircraft, aviation/wartime memorabilia and artefacts together with an impressive sound and light show that takes you back to the Battle of Britain. The Aeronauts Interactive Centre offers hands-on entertainment and education for all ages and includes cockpit controls, co-ordination tests, engine lifting, air speed, drop zone, pilot testing and more.

Times Open all year, daily 10-6. (Last admission 5.30). Closed 24-26 Dec, 1 & 11-15 Jan. **Facilities** ℗ ⑫ 🖵 ⑩ licensed ⊟ (indoor & outdoor) ⑤ toilets for disabled shop ⊗

SE1

Florence Nightingale Museum

St Thomas' Hospital, Gassiot House, 2
Lambeth Palace Rd SE1 7EW
☎ 020 7620 0374   ▤ 020 7928 1760
e-mail: info@florence-nightingale.co.uk
web: www.florence-nightingale.co.uk
dir: Underground - Westminster, Waterloo. On the
site of St Thomas' Hospital

Florence Nightingale needs no introduction,
but this museum shows clearly that she was
more than `The Lady with the Lamp'. Beautifully
designed, the museum creates a setting in
which a large collection of Florence's personal
items including childhood souvenirs, her dress,
furniture from her houses, and honours awarded
to her in old age are displayed. There is a small
military history collection of souvenirs from the
Crimean War, including military medals and a
military nursing uniform. The museum will reopen
after efurbishment in May 2010.

Times Open all year, Mon-Fri 10-5; wknds &
BHs 10-5. (Last admission 1hr before closing).
Fees £5.80 (ch & concessions £4.80). Family
ticket £16 (2ad+ up to 5ch). Discounted rates
for pre-booked groups of 15+.* **Facilities** ℗ ♿
toilets for disabled shop ⊗

SE1

SE1

Golden Hinde Educational Trust

182 Pickfords Wharf, Clink St SE1 9DG
☎ 020 7403 0123   ▤ 020 7407 5908
e-mail: info@goldenhinde.org
web: www.goldenhinde.org
dir: On the Thames path between Southwark
Cathedral and the new Globe Theatre

An authentic replica of the galleon in which
Sir Francis Drake sailed around the world in
1577-1580. This ship has travelled over 140,000
miles, many more than the original. She is now
permanently berthed on London's South Bank.

Times Open all year, daily 10-5.30. Visitors are
advised to check opening times as they may vary
due to closures for functions.* **Facilities** ℗ ♿
(partly accessible) (stairs on main deck so no
access to wheelchairs) shop ⊗

SE1

HMS Belfast

Morgans Ln, Tooley St SE1 2JH
☎ 020 7940 6300 📠 020 7403 0719
e-mail: hmsbelfast@iwm.org.uk
web: www.iwm.org.uk/hmsbelfast
dir: Underground - London Bridge/Tower Hill/
Monument. Rail - London Bridge

Europe's last surviving big gun armoured
warship from the Second World War, HMS Belfast
was launched in 1938 and served in the North
Atlantic and Arctic with the Home Fleet. She
led the Allied naval bombardment of German
positions on D-Day, and was saved for the
nation in 1971. A tour of the ship will take you
from the Captain's Bridge through nine decks to
the massive Boiler and Engine Rooms. You can
visit the cramped Mess Decks, Officers' Cabins,
Galley, Sick Bay, Dentist and Laundry.

Times Open all year, daily. Mar-Oct 10-6 (last
admission 5); Nov-Feb 10-5 (last admission
4). Closed 24-26 Dec.* **Fees** £10.70 (ch under
15 free, concessions £8.60).* **Facilities** ⊑ 🍴
(indoor) ♿ (partly accessible) (wheelchair access
to main decks, but not all decks) toilets for
disabled shop ⊗

SE1

Imperial War Museum

Lambeth Rd SE1 6HZ
☎ 020 7416 5320 & 5321
📠 020 7416 5374
e-mail: mail@iwm.org.uk
web: www.iwm.org.uk
dir: Underground - Lambeth North, Elephant &
Castle or Waterloo

Founded in 1917, this museum illustrates
and records all aspects of the two World Wars
and other military operations involving Britain
and the Commonwealth since 1914. There are
always special exhibitions and the programme
of special and family events includes film shows
and lectures. The museum also has an extensive
film, photography, sound, document and art
archive as well as a library, although some
reference departments are open to the public
by appointment only. In 2010 it will be 70 years
since the Battle of Britain, and the introduction
of rationing.

Times Open all year, daily 10-6. Closed 24-26
Dec.* **Fees** Free admission (charges apply for
some temporary exhibitions)* **Facilities** ℗ ⊑
🍴 licensed 🍴 (indoor & outdoor) ♿ toilets for
disabled shop ⊗

SE1

Shakespeare's Globe Theatre Tours & Exhibition

21 New Globe Walk, Bankside SE1 9DT
☎ 020 7902 1500   📠 020 7902 1515
e-mail: info@shakespearesglobe.com
web: www.shakespeares-globe.org
dir: Underground - London Bridge, walk along Bankside. Mansion House, walk across Southwark Bridge. St Pauls, walk across Millennium Bridge

Guides help to bring England's theatrical heritage to life at the 'unparalleled and astonishing' recreation of this famous theatre. Discover what an Elizabethan audience would have been like, find out about the rivalry between the Bankside theatres, the bear baiting and the stews, hear about the penny stinkards and find out what a bodger is. Housed beneath the reconstructed theatre, the exhibition explores the remarkable story of the Globe, and brings Shakespeare's world to life using a range of interactive display and live demonstrations.

Times Open all year, May-early Oct, daily 9-12 (1-5 Rose Theatre tour); Oct-Apr 10-5.*
Fees £10.50 (ch 5-15 £6.50, pen & students £8.50). Family ticket (2ad+3ch) £28.* **Facilities** Ⓟ 🍽️ licensed ♿ toilets for disabled shop ⊗

SE1

The Tower Bridge Exhibition

Tower Bridge Rd SE1 2UP
☎ 020 7940 3985   📠 020 7357 7935
e-mail: enquiries@towerbridge.org.uk
web: www.towerbridge.co.uk
dir: Underground - Tower Hill or London Bridge

One of the capital's most famous landmarks, its glass-covered walkways stand 142ft above the Thames, affording panoramic views of the river. Much of the original machinery for working the bridge can be seen in the engine rooms. The Tower Bridge Exhibition uses state-of-the-art effects to present the story of the bridge in a dramatic and exciting fashion.

Times Open all year, Apr-Sep 10-6.30 (last ticket 5.30); Oct-Mar 9.30-5.30 (last ticket 5)*
Facilities Ⓟ ♿ toilets for disabled shop ⊗

SE1

Winston Churchill's Britain at War Experience

64/66 Tooley St SE1 2TF

☎ 020 7403 3171 📄 020 7403 5104

e-mail: info@britainatwar.org.uk

web: www.britainatwar.co.uk

dir: mid way down Tooley St, between London Bridge & Tower Bridge. 2min walk from London Bridge Stn

Step back in time to the 1940s and experience a realistic adventure of life in war-torn London. Take the lift to the underground where many spent sleepless nights. Explore evacuation, food and clothes rationing, the blackout and much more. Uniforms, gas masks and tin helmets are available to try on and photography is allowed. Voted top World War Two tourist attraction.

Times Open all year, Apr-Oct 10-5; Nov-Mar 10-4.30.* **Fees** £11.45 (ch under 5 free, ch 5-16 £5.50, concessions £6.50). Family £29 (2ad+2ch).* **Facilities** ℗ ♿ toilets for disabled shop ⊗

SE10

National Maritime Museum

Romney Rd SE10 9NF

☎ 020 8312 6565 📄 020 8312 6632

e-mail: RScates@nmm.ac.uk

web: www.nmm.ac.uk

dir: central Greenwich A206

Britain's seafaring history is displayed in this impressive modern museum. Themes include exploration and discovery, Nelson, trade and empire, passenger shipping and luxury liners, maritime London, costume, art and the sea, and the future of the sea. There are interactive displays for children.

Times Open all year, daily 10-5 Closed 24-26 Dec. (Partial closures 31 Dec, 1 Jan & Marathon day). **Fees** Free, except some special exhibtions. **Facilities** ℗ ☕ 🪑 (outdoor) ♿ toilets for disabled shop ⊗

SE10

Old Royal Naval College

Greenwich SE10 9LW
☎ 020 8269 4747　📠 020 8269 4757
e-mail: info@greenwichfoundation.org.uk
web: www.oldroyalnavalcollege.org
dir: In centre of Greenwich, off one way system,
(College Approach), on the Thames next to
Greenwich Pier

The Old Royal Naval College is one of London's
most famous riverside landmarks and a
masterpiece of Baroque architecture. The Grade
I listed group of buildings, designed by Sir
Christopher Wren as the Greenwich Hospital,
occupy the site of the Tudor palace where Henry
VIII and Elizabeth I were born. The buildings
incorporate the magnificent Painted Hall by
James Thornhill and the Chapel by James Stuart.

Times Open all year ex 24-26 Dec. (Painted Hall
& Chapel), daily 10-5 . Chapel open to visitors
from 12.30 on Sun, public worship from 11.*
Fees Admission free, guided tours £5 (ch under
16 free). Group tours of more than 10 people
booking necessary.* **Facilities** ⓟ 🍽 licensed
🎋 (outdoor) ♿ (partly accessible) (several
stairs make access difficult, stairmate carries
wheelchair users up and into Painted Hall &
Chapel) toilets for disabled ⊗

SE10

Royal Observatory Greenwich

Greenwich Park, Greenwich SE10 8XJ
☎ 020 8312 6565　📠 020 8312 6632
e-mail: bookings@nmm.ac.uk
web: www.nmm.ac.uk
dir: off A2, Greenwich Park, enter from
Blackheath Gate only

Charles II founded the Royal Observatory in
1675 'for perfecting navigation and astronomy'.
It stands at zero meridian longitude and is
the original home of Greenwich Mean Time.
Astronomy galleries and the Peter Harrison
Planetarium house an extensive collection
of historic timekeeping, astronomical and
navigational instruments.

Times Open all year, daily 10-5. (Partial closures
31 Dec, 1 Jan and Marathon day) **Fees** Free,
except for Planetarium shows from £6 (ch
£4). **Facilities** ❷ ⬚ 🎋 (outdoor) ♿ (partly
accessible) (narrow staircase to Octagon room)
toilets for disabled shop ⊗

95

SE18

Firepower Royal Artillery Museum

Royal Arsenal, Woolwich SE18 6ST
☎ 020 8855 7755 🖹 020 8855 7100
e-mail: info@firepower.org.uk
web: www.firepower.org.uk
dir: A205, right at Woolwich ferry onto A206, attraction signed

Firepower is the Royal Artillery Museum in the historic Royal Arsenal. It spans 2000 years of artillery and shows the development from Roman catapult to guided missile to self-propelled gun. Put science into action with touchscreen displays and be awed by the big guns.

Times Open all year, Wed-Sun & BHs 11-5.30. Phone for winter opening times.* **Facilities** Ⓟ Ⓟ ⛩ toilets for disabled shop ⊗

SW1

The Banqueting House, Whitehall

Whitehall SW1A 2ER
☎ 0870 751 5178 🖹 020 7930 8268
e-mail: banquetinghouse@hrp.org.uk
web: www.hrp.org.uk
dir: Underground - Westminster, Charing Cross or Embankment

Designed by Inigo Jones, this is the only surviving building of the vast Whitehall Palace, destroyed by fire 300 years ago. The Palace has seen many significant royal events, including the execution of Charles I in 1649. The Banqueting House's Rubens ceiling paintings are stunning examples of the larger works of the Flemish Master and its classical Palladian style set the fashion for much of London's later architecture.

Times Open all year, Mon-Sat 10-5. Closed Sun, BHs, 24 Dec-1 Jan. Subject to closure at short notice.* **Fees** £4.80 (ch under 16 free, concessions full-time student, over 60 with ID £4)* **Facilities** Ⓟ ♿ toilets for disabled shop ⊗

SW1

Buckingham Palace

Buckingham Palace Rd SW1A 1AA
☎ 020 7766 7300   📠 020 7930 9625
e-mail: bookinginfo@royalcollection.org.uk
web: www.royalcollection.org.uk
dir: Underground - Victoria, Green Park, St James'
Park, entrance in Buckingham Palace Road

Buckingham Palace has been the official London
residence of Britain's sovereigns since 1837.
Today it serves as both the home and office
of Her Majesty The Queen. Its nineteen State
Rooms, which open for eight weeks a year, form
the heart of the working palace and more than
50,000 people visit each year as guests at State,
ceremonial and official occasions and garden
parties. After visiting the State Rooms, visitors
can enjoy a walk along the south side of the
garden, which offers superb views of the west
front of the Palace and the 19th-century lake.

Times Open Aug-Sep 9.45-6 (last admission
3.45). Entry by timed-ticket. **Fees** £17 (ch under
17 £10, ch under 5 free, students & pen £15.50)
Family (2ad+3ch) £45. **Facilities** ℗ ♿ toilets
for disabled shop ⊗

SW1

Churchill Museum & Cabinet War Rooms

Clive Steps, King Charles St SW1A 2AQ
☎ 020 7930 6961   📠 020 7839 5897
e-mail: cwr@iwm.org.uk
web: www.iwm.org.uk/cabinet
dir: Underground - Westminster (exit 6) or St
James Park

Learn more about the man who inspired Britain's
finest hour at the interactive and innovative
Churchill Museum, the world's first major
museum dedicated to the life of the 'Greatest
Briton'. Step back in time and discover the secret
underground headquarters that were the nerve
centre of Britain's war effort. Located in the heart
of Westminster, visitors can view this complex of
historic rooms left as they were in 1945, while at
the same time taking in the Churchill Museum.

Times Open all year, daily 9.30-6. (last admission
5). Closed 24-26 Dec.* **Facilities** ℗ ⛉♿
(partly accessible) (2 wheelchairs available)
toilets for disabled shop ⊗

SW1

The Household Cavalry Museum

Horse Guards, Whitehall SW1A 2AX
☎ 020 7930 3070
e-mail: museum@householdcavalry.co.uk
web: www.householdcavalrymuseum.org.uk
dir: Underground - Charing Cross, Embankment
& Westminster

The Household Cavalry Museum is unlike any
other military museum because it offers a unique
'behind-the-scenes' look at the work that goes
into the ceremonial duties and operational role of
the Household Cavalry. Watch troopers working
with their horses in the original 18th-century
stables (via a glazed screen) and hear accounts
of their demanding training. Plus children's
trails, activity packs and dressing up areas.

Times Open all year daily, Mar-Sep 10-6, Oct-Feb
10-5.* **Fees** £6 (ch 5-16 & concessions £4).
Family ticket (2ad+3ch) £15. Group rate 10%
discount.* **Facilities** ℗ ♿ toilets for disabled
shop ⊗

SW1

Houses of Parliament

Westminster SW1A 0AA
☎ 020 7219 4272 📄 020 7219 5839
web: www.parliament.uk
dir: Underground - Westminster

The Houses of Parliament occupy the Palace
of Westminster, a royal palace for nearly 1000
years. Visitors will see the Queen's Robing
Room, the Royal Gallery, the Chambers of both
the House of Lords and House of Commons, the
voting lobbies, historic Westminster Hall (c.1097)
where Charles I and Guy Fawkes were put on
trial, plus other areas normally hidden from
public view.

Times Summer opening: Aug-Sep, open to all. At
other times by application to MP (UK constituents
only)* **Facilities** ℗ ⊑♿ (partly accessible)
(visitor route 95% accessible, one short detour
required for wheelchair users) toilets for disabled
shop ⊗

SW1

The Royal Mews

Buckingham Palace, Buckingham Palace Rd
SW1W 0QH
☎ 020 7766 7302 🖷 020 7930 9625
e-mail: bookinginfo@royalcollection.org.uk
web: www.royalcollection.org.uk
dir: Underground - Victoria, Green Park, St. James
Park. Entrance in Buckingham Palace Road

Designed by John Nash and completed in 1825,
the Royal Mews houses the State Coaches,
horse-drawn carriages and motor cars used for
Coronations, State Visits, Royal Weddings and
the State Opening of Parliament. These include
the Gold State Coach made in 1762, with panels
painted by the Florentine artist Cipriani. As one of
the finest working stables in existence, the Royal
Mews provides a unique opportunity for you to see
a working department of the Royal Household.

Times Open daily ex Fri. Mar-Oct 11-4; Aug-Sep
10-5. (Last admission 3.15, Aug-Sep 4.15).
Fees £8 (ch under 17 £5, ch under 5 free,
concessions £7) Family (2ad+3ch) £21.50.
Facilities Ⓟ ♿ toilets for disabled shop ⊗

SW3

National Army Museum FREE

Royal Hospital Rd, Chelsea SW3 4HT
☎ 020 7730 0717 🖷 020 7823 6573
e-mail: info@national-army-museum.ac.uk
web: www.national-army-museum.ac.uk
dir: Underground - Sloane Square

The museum will guide you through Britain's
Military History and its effect on Britain and
the world today. Permanent gallery displays,
exhibitions, celebrity speakers, lectures and
special events will both engage and entertain
you.

Times Open all year, daily 10-5.30. Closed Good
Fri, May Day, 24-26 Dec & 1 Jan.* **Facilities** Ⓟ
Ⓟ ⊿♿ toilets for disabled shop ⊗

SW3

Royal Hospital Chelsea **FREE**

Royal Hospital Rd SW3 4SR
☎ 020 7881 5200 📄 020 7881 5463
e-mail: info@chelsea-pensioners.org.uk
web: www.chelsea-pensioners.org.uk
dir: near Sloane Square, off A3216 & A3031

Founded in 1682 by Charles II as a retreat for army veterans who had become unfit for duty, through injury or long service, the Royal Hospital Chelsea was built on the site of a theological college founded by James I in 1610. The buildings were designed and built by Sir Christopher Wren, and then added to by Robert Adam and Sir John Soane. The hospital houses some 300 'In-Pensioners', some of whom do voluntary work as tour guides, clerical assistants and ground staff. Visitors can stroll around the grounds, gain admission to the Chapel, Great Hall and visit the Museum.

Times Open all year, daily Mon-Sat, 10-12 & 2-4, Sun 2-4. (Museum closed on Sun Oct-Mar). Closed 25-26 Dec & Good Friday.* **Facilities** Ⓟ 🍴 (outdoor) ♿ (partly accessible) toilets for disabled shop ⊗

SW7

The Natural History Museum

Cromwell Rd SW7 5BD
☎ 020 7942 5000 📄 020 7942 5075
e-mail: feedback@nhm.ac.uk
web: www.nhm.ac.uk
dir: Underground - South Kensington

This vast and elaborate Romanesque-style building, with its terracotta tiles showing relief mouldings of animals, birds and fishes, covers an area of four acres. Holding over 70 million specimens from all over the globe, from dinosaurs to diamonds and earthquakes to ants, the museum provides a journey into Earth's past, present and future. Discover more about the work of the museum through a daily programme of talks from museum scientists or go behind the scenes of the Darwin Centre, the museum's scientific research centre.

Times Open all year, daily 10-5.50 (last admission 5.30). Closed 24-26 Dec. **Fees** Free. Charge made for some special exhibitions.
Facilities Ⓟ 💻 🍴 licensed ⊓ (indoor) ♿ (partly accessible) (top floor/one gallery not accessible) toilets for disabled shop ⊗

SW7

Science Museum

Exhibition Rd, South Kensington SW7 2DD
☎ 0870 870 4868   📄 020 7942 4421
e-mail: sciencemuseum@sciencemuseum.org.uk
web: www.sciencemuseum.org.uk
dir: Underground - South Kensington, signed
from tube stn

See iconic objects from the history of science,
from Stephenson's Rocket to the Apollo 10
command module; be amazed by a 3D IMAX
movie; take a ride in a simulator; visit an
exhibition; and encounter the past, present
and future of technology in seven floors of free
galleries, including the famous hands-on section
where children can have fun investigating
science with the Museum's dedicated Explainers.
The Museum is free, but charges apply to the
IMAX cinema, special exhibitions and simulators.

Times Open all year, daily 10-6. Closed 24-26
Dec. **Fees** Admission free. Charges apply for
IMAX 3D cinema, simulators & some special
exhibitions. **Facilities** ℗ 🖵 🍴 licensed 🎃
(indoor) ♿ toilets for disabled shop ⊗

SW7

Victoria and Albert Museum

Cromwell Rd, South Kensington SW7 2RL
☎ 020 7942 2000
e-mail: vanda@vam.ac.uk
web: www.vam.ac.uk
dir: Underground - South Kensington, Museum
situated on A4, Buses C1, 14, 74, 414 stop
outside the Cromwell Road entrance

The V&A is the world's greatest museum of
art and design. It was established in 1852
to make important works of art available to
all, and also to inspire British designers and
manufacturers. The Museum's rich and diverse
collections span over three thousand years of
human creativity from many parts of the world,
and include ceramics, furniture, fashion, glass,
jewellery, metalwork, sculpture, textiles and
paintings. Highlights include the British Galleries
1500-1900, the Jameel Gallery of Islamic Art, and
the magnificent John Madejski Garden.

Times Open all year, daily 10-5.45. Fri 10am-
10pm* **Facilities** ℗ 🖵 🍴 licensed 🎃
(outdoor) toilets for disabled shop ⊗

W1

Apsley House, The Wellington Museum

148 Piccadilly, Hyde Park Corner W1J 7NT
☎ 020 7499 5676 📠 020 7493 6576
web: www.english-heritage.org.uk
dir: Underground - Hyde Park Corner, exit 1 overlooking rdbt

Number One, London, is the popular name for one of the Capital's finest private residences, 19th-century home of the first Duke of Wellington. Built in the 1770s, its rich interiors have been returned to their former glory, and house the Duke's magnificent collection of paintings, silver, porcelain, sculpture and furniture.

Times Open all year Apr-1 Nov, Wed-Sun & BHs 11-5; 2 Nov-Mar, Wed-Sun 11-4. Closed 24-26 Dec & 1 Jan. **Fees** £5.70 (ch £2.90, concessions £4.80). Prices & opening times are subject to change in March 2010. Please call 0870 333 1181 for the most up to date prices and opening times. **Facilities** ℗ shop ⊗ ♯

W1

The Wallace Collection FREE

Hertford House, Manchester Square W1U 3BN
☎ 020 7563 9500 📠 020 7224 2155
e-mail: visiting@wallacecollection.org
web: www.wallacecollection.org
dir: Underground - Bond St, Baker St, Oxford Circus, located minutes from Oxford St, in garden square behind Selfridges

Founded by the 1st Marquis of Hertford, the Wallace Collection was bequeathed to the nation in 1897 and came on public display three years later. This is one of the world's finest collections of art ever assembled by one family. The collection is shown in the family home, a tranquil oasis just a few minutes from Oxford Street. There are paintings by Titian, Canaletto, Rembrandt, Rubens, Hals, Fragonard, Velazquez, Gainsborough and many more. There is a very important collection of French porcelain and furniture, much of it of Royal providence, as well as amazing arms and armour, sculpture and Renaissance treasures. Many rooms have been recently restored creating wonderful intimate and opulent settings for the works of art.

Times Open all year, daily 10-5, closed 24-26 Dec & 1 Jan.* **Facilities** ℗ ⊑ ⑩ licensed & toilets for disabled shop ⊗

W8

Kensington Palace State Apartments & Royal Ceremonial Dress Collection

Kensington Gardens W8 4PX
☎ 0844 482 7777 📄 020 3166 6110
e-mail: kensingtonpalace@hrp.org.uk
web: www.hrp.org.uk
dir: Underground - High Street Kensington or Notting Hill Gate

Highlights of a visit to Kensington include the King's and Queen's Apartments with a fine collection of paintings from the Royal Collection. The rooms used by Princess Victoria are also shown, including her bedroom, where she was woken to be told she was Queen. The Royal Ceremonial Dress Collection includes representations of tailor's and dressmaker's workshops, and a display of dresses that belonged to Diana, Princess of Wales. Kensington Palace will undergo a major re-presentation with work commencing in 2010.

Times Open all year, Mar-Oct 10-6, Nov-Feb 10-5 (last admission 1hr before closing). Closed 24-26 Dec. **Fees** £12.50 (ch 5-16 £6.25, concessions £11). Family ticket (2ad+3ch) £34.* **Facilities** ℗ ⬜♿ (partly accessible) (ground floor & lower ground floor accessible) toilets for disabled shop ⊗

WC1

British Museum

Great Russell St WC1B 3DG
☎ 020 7323 8000 📄 020 7323 8616
e-mail: information@britishmuseum.org
web: www.thebritishmuseum.ac.uk
dir: Underground - Russell Sq, Tottenham Court Rd, Holborn

Of the world and for the world, the British Museum brings together astounding examples of universal heritage, for free. Enter through the largest covered square in Europe. Pick up your audio guide, children's pack or What's On programme. Then discover the world through objects like the Aztec mosaics, the Rosetta Stone, El Anatsui's African textiles or the colossal Ramesses II. And if you want a more intimate look, a fantastic evening meal or some world cinema, come late - every Thursday and Friday.

Times Open all year, Gallery: 10-5.30 selected galleries open late Thu-Fri until 8.30. Great Court: Sun-Wed 9-6, Thu-Sat 9am-11pm. Closed Good Fri, 24-26 Dec & 1 Jan.* **Facilities** ℗ ⬜⑩ licensed Ⅎ (indoor) toilets for disabled shop ⊗

WC2

Benjamin Franklin House

36 Craven St WC2N 5NF

☎ 020 7839 2006
e-mail: info@benjaminfranklinhouse.org
web: www.benjaminfranklinhouse.org
dir: Between Charing Cross & Embankment

The house is not only a museum, but an educational facility as well. Between 1757 and 1775 Dr Benjamin Franklin - scientist, diplomat, philosopher and inventor lived here. The Historical Experience Show presents the excitement and uncertainty of Franklin's London years.

Times Open all year, Wed-Sun, shows at 12, 1, 2 & 3.15 & 6.15. Closed Xmas & BHs.* Facilities shop ⊗

WC2

London Transport Museum

The Piazza, Covent Garden WC2E 7BB

☎ 020 7379 6344 & 7565 7299
📄 020 7565 7250
e-mail: enquiry@ltmuseum.co.uk
web: www.ltmuseum.co.uk
dir: Underground - Covent Garden, Leicester Sq, Holborn or Charing Cross

Situated in the old Victorian flower market, the museum tells the story of the development of London, its transport system and how it shaped the lives of people living and working in the capital. One of the world's best collections of graphic art and design is showcased in the 'Design for Travel' gallery including Harry Beck's famous Underground map, iconic transport posters, architecture and the story of a pioneering corporate identity. The museum also features past and present public transport including the Routemaster bus and the world's first Underground steam train.

Times Open all year Sat-Thu 10-6, Fri 11-6 (last admission 5.15). See website for Xmas & New Year opening times.* Fees With voluntary Gift Aid donation: £10 (under 16 free, pen £8, concessions £6).* Facilities ⓟ ⊑⊓ (indoor) ♿ toilets for disabled shop ⊗

WC2

National Gallery

Trafalgar Square WC2N 5DN
☎ 020 7747 2885   📠 020 7747 2423
e-mail: information@ng-london.org.uk
web: www.nationalgallery.org.uk
dir: Underground - Charing Cross, Leicester Square, Embankment & Piccadilly Circus. Rail - Charing Cross. Located on N side of Trafalgar Sq

All the great periods of Western European painting from the Middle Ages to the early 20th century are represented here. Artists on display include Leonardo da Vinci, Rembrandt, Titian, Caravaggio, Turner, Monet and Van Gogh. Major exhibitions and events throughout the year.

Times Open all year, daily 10-6, (Fri until 9). Special major changing exhibitions open normal gallery times. Closed 24-26 Dec & 1 Jan. **Fees** Free. Admission charged for some major exhibitions. **Facilities** Ⓟ 🖵 🍽 licensed ♿ toilets for disabled shop ⊗

WC2

National Portrait Gallery

St Martin's Place WC2H 0HE
☎ 020 7306 0055   📠 020 7306 0056
web: www.npg.org.uk
dir: Underground - Charing Cross, Leicester Square. Buses to Trafalgar Square

The National Portrait Gallery is home to the largest collection of portraiture in the world featuring famous British men and woman who have created history from the Middle Ages until the present day. Over 1000 portraits are on display across three floors from Henry VIII and Florence Nightingale to The Beatles and HM The Queen. If you want to rest your weary feet, visit the fabulous Portrait Restaurant on the top floor with roof-top views across London. Special events take place throughout the year, see website for details.

Times Open all year, Mon-Wed & Sat-Sun 10-6, Thu-Fri 10-9. Closed Good Fri, 24-26 Dec & 1 Jan. (Gallery closure commences 10mins prior to stated time).* **Fees** Free ex special exhibitions **Facilities** Ⓟ 🖵 🍽 licensed ♿ toilets for disabled shop ⊗

BARNET

Museum of Domestic Design & Architecture

Middlesex University, Cat Hill EN4 8HT
☎ 020 8411 5244 📠 020 8411 6639
e-mail: moda@mdx.ac.uk
web: www.moda.mdx.ac.uk
dir: from M25, junct 24 signed A111 Cockfosters to Cat Hill rdbt, straight over onto Chase side. Entrance 1st right opposite Chicken Shed Theatre on Cat Hill Campus

MoDA is a museum of the history of the home. It holds one of the world's most comprehensive collections of decorative design for the period 1870 to 1960, and is a rich source of information on how people decorated and lived in their homes. MoDA has two galleries, a lecture theatre for study days, a seminar room with practical workshops for both adults and children, and a study room which gives visitors access to the collections.

Times Open all year, Tue-Sat 10-5, Sun 2-5. Closed Mon, Etr, Xmas & New Year. **Fees** Free entrance. Charges for study days, workshop & group tours **Facilities** 🅿 ♿ toilets for disabled shop ⊗

HAMPTON COURT

Hampton Court Palace

KT8 9AU
☎ 0870 752 7777 📠 020 8781 9669
e-mail: hamptoncourt@hrp.org.uk
web: www.hrp.org.uk
dir: A3 to Hook underpass then A309. Train from Waterloo - Hampton Court, 2mins walk from station

Step into a living Tudor world at Henry VIII's favourite palace, celebrating the 500 years since his accession to the throne. As part of the Henry VIII: heads and hearts festivities the palace is hosting a fantastic variety of events for all ages. Creep along the eerie Haunted Gallery, relax in the acres of beautiful gardens running alongside the River Thames, and lose yourself in the world famous Maze.

Times Open all year, palace & maze 29 Mar-24 Oct, daily 10-6. Last ticket sold at 5, last entry into the maze 5.15 ; 25 Oct -27 Mar, daily 10-4.30. Last ticket sold at 3.30, last entry into the maze: 3.45. Closed 24-26 Dec.* **Fees** £14 (ch £7 under 5's free, children must be accompanied by an adult, concessions full-time student, over 60 with ID £11.50). Family ticket (2ad+3ch) £38.* **Facilities** 🅿 🅿 ⎚ ⍾⎚ licensed 🛋♿ toilets for disabled shop ⊗

Kew Gardens (Royal Botanic Gardens)

TW9 3AB

☎ 020 8332 5655   📄 020 8332 5197
e-mail: info@kew.org
web: www.kew.org
dir: 1m from M4 on South Circular (A205)

Kew Gardens is a paradise throughout the seasons. Lose yourself in the magnificent glasshouses and discover plants from the world's deserts, mountains and oceans. Wide-open spaces, stunning vistas, listed buildings and wildlife contribute to the Gardens' unique atmosphere. As well as being famous for its beautiful gardens, Kew is world renowned for its contribution to botanical and horticultural science.

Times Open all year, Gardens daily 9.30. Closing times vary (seasonal, phone to verify). Closed 24-25 Dec.* **Fees** £13 (ch under 17 free, concessions £11).* **Facilities** 🅿 🅿 �🍽 licensed ♿ (partly accessible) (access restricted in Palm House basement & galleries, Temperate House & steps to upper level in the Princess of Wales Conservatory) toilets for disabled shop ⊗

Kew Palace

Royal Botanic Gardens TW9 3AB

☎ 0870 751 5179
e-mail: kewpalace@hrp.org.uk
web: www.hrp.org.uk
dir: Underground - Kew Bridge

A fairly modest red-brick building, built in the Dutch style with gables, Kew Palace was built in 1631 and used until 1818 when Queen Charlotte died. Visitors can see artefacts that belonged to George III and his family, and gain access to the second floor, which has never before been open to the public. There are also rooms on the second floor, faithfully recreated with décor and furnishings as George III and his family would have known them in the early 1800s.

Times Open 10 Apr-27 Sep, Mon 11-5, Tue-Sun 10-5 (last admission 4.15).* **Fees** £5 (ch under 16 free, concessions full-time student, over 60 with ID £4.50) Admission ticket to Kew Gardens must be purchased in order to access Kew Palace* **Facilities** 🅿 🅿 ♿ toilets for disabled shop ⊗

LIVERPOOL

The Beatles Story

Britannia Pavilion, Albert Dock L3 4AD
☎ 0151 709 1963 🗎 0151 203 3089
e-mail: info@beatlesstory.com
web: www.beatlesstory.com
dir: follow signs to Albert Dock. Located outside
Britannia Pavilion, next to Premier Inn

Located within Liverpool's historic Albert Dock,
the Beatles Story is a unique visitor attraction
that transports you on an enlightening and
atmospheric journey into the life, times, culture
and music of The Beatles. White Feather: the
spirit of Lennon, a new exclusive exhibition telling
the emotional personal story of the life of the
Lennon family is open until December 2010.

Times Open all year, daily 9-7 (last admission
5). Closed 25-26 Dec.* **Fees** £12.25 (ch 5-16
yrs £6.35 & concessions £8.30). Family ticket
(2ad+2ch) £32 (2ad+3ch) £37.* **Facilities** 🅿
🅿 ☕🕹 toilets for disabled shop ⊗

LIVERPOOL

The Grand National Experience &
Visitor Centre

Aintree Racecourse, Ormskirk Rd L9 5AS
☎ 0151 523 2600
e-mail: aintree@jockeyclubracecourses.com
web: www.aintree.co.uk
dir: Aintree Racecourse on A59 (Liverpool to
Preston road), clearly signed

A fascinating look at Britain's most famous
horserace, the Grand National. Visitors can sit
in the jockeys' weighing-in chair, walk around
the dressing rooms, watch video presentations,
and view a gallery of paintings and photography
depicting the race.

Times Open late May-mid Oct, Tue-Fri, 10-5.*
Fees Please telephone for details.* **Facilities** 🅿
🍽 licensed 🍴 (indoor & outdoor) 🕹 toilets for
disabled ⊗

LIVERPOOL

International Slavery Museum
FREE

Albert Dock L3 4AQ
☎ 0151 478 4499 📠 0151 478 4590
web: www.liverpoolmuseums.org.uk
dir: enter Albert Dock from the Strand

2007 saw the bicentenary of the abolition of the
slave trade in Britain, and this museum was
opened at Albert Dock. It looks at the impact
of the transatlantic slave trade and includes
thought-provoking displays on issues such
as freedom, identity, human rights, racial
discrimination and cultural change.

Times Open all year, daily 10-5 & 24 Dec 10-2.
Closed 25-26 Dec & 1 Jan.* **Facilities** 🅿 🅿 ⛾
🍽 licensed toilets for disabled shop ⊗

LIVERPOOL

Mendips

251 Menlove Av, Woolton L25 7SA
☎ 0151 427 7231 & 0844 800 4791
e-mail: mendips@nationaltrust.org.uk
web: www.nationaltrust.org.uk/beatles
dir: No direct access by car or on foot. Visits are
by combined minibus tour only with 20 Forthlin
Road, childhood home of Sir Paul McCartney

Visit Mendips and 20 Forthlin Road as part of a
combined minibus tour. The childhood home of
John Lennon, Mendips is a 1930s semi where his
passion for music began and where some of his
early songs were written. The house evokes the
time he spent here during his formative years.

Times Open 28 Feb-15 Mar & 7-29 Nov, Wed-Sun
10, 12.30 & 3; 18 Mar-1 Nov, 10, 10.50, 2.30 &
3.20.* **Fees** Joint ticket Mendips & Forthlin Road
£16.80 (ch £3.15, NT members £7.90) **Facilities**
♿ (partly accessible) toilets for disabled ⊗ 🚐

LIVERPOOL

Merseyside Maritime Museum
FREE

Albert Dock L3 4AQ
☎ 0151 478 4499 📄 0151 478 4590
web: www.liverpoolmuseums.org.uk
dir: enter Albert Dock from the Strand

Discover the story behind one of the world's greatest ports and the people who used it. For many, Liverpool was a gateway to a new life in other countries. For others its importance to the slave trade had less happy consequences. From slavers to luxury liners, submarine hunters to passenger ferries, explore Liverpool's central role.

Times Open all year, daily 10-5 & 24 Dec 10-2. Closed 25-26 Dec & 1 Jan.* **Facilities** 🅿 💻 🍴 licensed 🍴 (outdoor) toilets for disabled shop ⊗

LIVERPOOL

20 Forthlin Road

L24 1YP
☎ 0844 8004791
e-mail: 20forthlinroad@nationaltrust.org.uk
web: www.nationaltrust.org.uk/beatles
dir: No direct access by car or on foot. Visits are by combines minibus tour only with Mendips, childhood home of John Lennon

Visit 20 Forthlin Road and Mendips as part of a combined minibus tour. 20 Forthlin Road is the former home of the McCartney family, a 1950s terraced house where the Beatles met, rehearsed and wrote many of their earliest songs. Displays include contemporary photographs by Michael McCartney and early Beatles memorabilia.

Times Open 28 Feb-15 Mar & 7-29 Nov, Wed-Sun 10, 12.30 & 3; 18 Mar-1 Nov, 10, 10.50, 2.30 & 3.20.* **Fees** Joint ticket Forthlin Road & Mendips £16.80 (ch £3.15, NT members £7.90) **Facilities** ♿ (partly accessible) toilets for disabled ⊗ 🌿

GREAT YARMOUTH

Great Yarmouth Row 111 Houses & Greyfriars' Cloister

South Quay NR30 2RQ
☎ 01493 857900
web: www.english-heritage.org.uk
dir: follow signs to dock and south quay

Visit these 17th-century houses unique to Great Yarmouth, and the remains of a Franciscan friary with rare early wall paintings. Guided tours explain how the rich and poor lived in these properties through history.

Times Open Apr-Sep, daily 12-5. **Fees** £3.90 (concessions £3.30, ch £2). Family ticket £9.80. Prices and opening times are subject to change in March 2010. Please call 0870 333 1181 for the most up to date prices and opening times when planning your visit. **Facilities** shop ⊗ ♯

GRIMES GRAVES

Grimes Graves

IP26 5DE
☎ 01842 810656
web: www.english-heritage.org.uk
dir: 7m NW of Thetford off A134

These unique and remarkable Neolithic flint mines are the earliest major industrial site in Europe.

Times Open Mar & Oct-1 Nov, Thu-Mon 10-5; Apr-Jun & Sep, daily 10-5; Jul-Aug, daily 10-6. Closed 2 Nov-Feb. **Fees** £3 (concessions £2.60, ch £1.50). Family ticket £7.50.(No entry to mines for children under 5). Prices and opening times are subject to change in March 2010. Please call 0870 333 1181 for the most up to date prices and opening times when planning your visit. **Facilities** ℗ ♿ (partly accessible) (exhibition area only; access track rough) shop ♯

HOUGHTON

Houghton Hall

PE31 6UE

☎ 01485 528569 📠 01485 528167
e-mail: administrator@houghtonhall.com
web: www.houghtonhall.com
dir: 1.25m off A148. 13m E of King's Lynn & 10m
W of Fakenham on A148

Houghton Hall, built in the 1720s by Sir Robert
Walpole, Britain's first Prime Minister, is one
of the grandest surviving Palladian Houses in
England. Now owned by the 7th Marquess of
Cholmondeley. who restored the spectacular
5-acre walled garden. A collection of Model
Soldiers contains over 20,000 models laid out in
various battle formations. Look out for the herd
of fallow deer that live in the grounds, and also
a collection of contemporary sculpture. There are
musical events in the summer, and the Houghton
International Horse Trials in May.

Times Open Park, Walled Garden, Soldier Museum
4 Apr-Sep, Wed, Thu, Sun & BHs 11.30-5.30.
House open 1.30-5 (last entry 4.30). Fees £8.80
(ch £3.50). Family ticket £22. Grounds only (not
house) £6 (ch £2.50) Family ticket £15. Facilities
🅿 🍽️ licensed 🍴 (outdoor) ♿ toilets for
disabled shop ⊗

NORWICH

Air Defence Radar Museum

RAF Neatishead NR12 8YB

☎ 01692 631485
e-mail: curator@radarmuseum.co.uk
web: www.radarmuseum.co.uk
dir: follow brown signs from A1062 at Horning

This multi-award winning Museum, housed in
the original 1942 Radar Operations building,
features the Battle of Britain Room, 1942 Ground
Controlled Interception Room, Radar Engineering,
Military Communications Systems, Cold War
Operations Room, Royal Observer Corps, Space
Defence, Bloodhound Missiles and Original
Mobile Radar Vehicles. The newest addition is the
RAF Coltishall Memorial Room.

Times Open year round 2nd Sat each month; Apr-
Oct, Tue & Thu & BH Mons 10-5* Fees £4.50 (ch
£3.50, under 13 free, concessions £4)* Facilities
🅿 🍽️🍴 (outdoor) ♿ (partly accessible) (two
rooms not accessible to wheelchairs) toilets for
disabled shop ⊗

SANDRINGHAM

Sandringham House, Gardens & Museum

PE35 6EN
☎ 01553 612908 🖷 01485 541571
e-mail: visits@sandringhamestate.co.uk
web: www.sandringhamestate.co.uk
dir: off A148

The private country retreat of Her Majesty The Queen, this neo-Jacobean house was built in 1870 for King Edward VII. The main rooms used by the Royal Family when in residence are all open to the public. Sixty acres of glorious grounds surround the House and offer beauty and colour throughout the season. Sandringham Museum contains fascinating displays of Royal memorabilia. The ballroom exhibition changes each year.

Times Open Etr Sat-mid Jul & early Aug-Oct. House open 11-4.45, Museum 11-5 & Grounds 10.30-5.* **Fees** House, Museum & Grounds: £10 (ch £5, pen £8). Family ticket £25. **Facilities** Ⓟ ☕ 🍽 licensed ⛩ (outdoor) ♿ toilets for disabled shop ⊗

ALTHORP

Althorp

NN7 4HQ
☎ 01604 770107 & 0870 167 9000
🖷 01604 770042
e-mail: mail@althorp.com
web: www.althorp.com
dir: from S, exit M1 junct 16, & N junct 18, follow signs towards Northampton until directed by brown signs

Althorp House has been the home of the Spencer family since 1508. The house was built in the 16th century, but has been changed since, most notably by Henry Holland in the 18th century. Restored by the present Earl, the house is carefully maintained and in immaculate condition. The award-winning exhibition 'Diana, A Celebration' is located in six rooms and depicts the life and work of Diana, Princess of Wales. There is in addition, a room which depicts the work of the Diana, Princess of Wales Memorial Fund.

Times Open Jul-30 Aug, daily 11-5. **Fees** £12.50 (ch £5.50 & pen £10.50). Family ticket £29.50. Tickets discounted if pre-booked.* **Facilities** Ⓟ ☕ ⛩ (outdoor) ♿ (partly accessible) (no assisted access to upstairs rooms, but alternative arrangements can be made) toilets for disabled shop ⊗

NORTHAMPTON

Northampton Museum & Art Gallery
FREE

Guildhall Rd NN1 1DP

☎ 01604 838111 ▤ 01604 838720
e-mail: museums@northampton.gov.uk
web: www.northampton.gov.uk/museums
dir: situated in town centre, in Guildhall Rd

Home to the world's largest collection of shoes, Northampton Museum and Art Gallery displays shoes that have been in fashion through the ages, from Ferragamo to Vivienne Westwood. 'Life and Sole' tells the history of footwear, and other displays detail the history of Northampton, and British and Oriental ceramics and glass. There is also a gallery of Italian paintings depicting scenes from the Bible and ancient mythology. There is a changing programme of exhibitions.

Times Open all year, Tue-Sat 10-5, Sun 2-5. (closed 25-26 Dec & 1 Jan). **Facilities** ℗ ㅤ toilets for disabled shop ⊗

ALNWICK

Alnwick Castle

NE66 1NQ

☎ 01665 510777 ▤ 01665 510876
e-mail: enquiries@alnwickcastle.com
web: www.alnwickcastle.com
dir: off A1 on outskirts of town, signed

Set in a stunning landscape, Alnwick Castle overlooks the historic market town of Alnwick. Although it was originally built for the Percy family, who have lived here since 1309, -the current Duke and Duchess of Northumberland being the current tenants- the castle is best known as one of the locations that served as Hogwarts School in the Harry Potter movies. The castle is full of art and treasures and there are plenty of activities for all the family.

Times Open Etr-Oct, daily 10-6 (last admission 4.30). **Fees** £11.95 (ch 5-16yrs £4.95, concessions £9.95). Family ticket (2ad+4ch) £29.95. Party 14+ £7.95.* **Facilities** ℗ ㅤ ⊧◯ㅣ licensed ⊣ (outdoor) ㅤ (partly accessible) (Some areas not suitable for wheelchair users) toilets for disabled shop ⊗

BAMBURGH

Bamburgh Castle

NE69 7DF

☎ 01668 214515 & 214208
web: www.bamburghcastle.com
dir: A1 Belford by-pass, E on B1342 to Bamburgh

Rising dramatically from a rocky outcrop, Bamburgh Castle is a huge, square Norman castle. Last restored in the 19th century, it has an impressive hall and an armoury with a large collection of armour from the Tower of London. These formidable stone walls have witnessed dark tales of royal rebellion, bloody battles, spellbinding legends and millionaire benefactors. Experience the sights, stories and atmosphere of over two thousand years of exhilarating history.

Times Open Mar-Oct, daily 10-5 (last admission 4).* **Fees** £8 (ch under 5 free, ch 5-15yrs £4 & pen £7). **Facilities** ❷ ℗ ⏝⏛ (outdoor) ♿ (partly accessible) (5 castle rooms accessible to wheelchairs) toilets for disabled shop ⊗

BARDON MILL

Vindolanda (Chesterholm)

Vindolanda Trust NE47 7JN

☎ 01434 344277 ▤ 01434 344060
e-mail: info@vindolanda.com
web: www.vindolanda.com
dir: signed from A69 or B6318

Vindolanda was a Roman fort and frontier town. It was started well before Hadrian's Wall, and became a base for 500 soldiers. The civilian settlement lay just west of the fort and has been excavated. The excellent museum in the country house of Chesterholm nearby has displays and reconstructions. There are also formal gardens and an open-air museum with Roman Temple, shop, house and Northumbrian croft.

Times Open Feb-Mar, daily 10-5; Apr-Sep, 10-6; Oct & Nov 10-5. Limited winter opening, please contact site for further details.* **Facilities** ❷ ⏝⏛ (outdoor) ♿ (partly accessible) (please contact for further info) toilets for disabled shop ⊗

GREENHEAD

Roman Army Museum

Carvoran CA8 7JB

☎ 016977 47485

e-mail: info@vindolanda.com

web: www.vindolanda.com

dir: follow brown tourist signs from A69 or B6318

Situated alongside the Walltown Grags Section of Hadrian's Wall, the museum is a great introduction to the Roman Army. Find out about Roman weapons, training, pay, off-duty activities and much more. See if you can be persuaded to join up by watching the recruitment film, or view the Eagle's Eye film and soar with the eagle over Hadrian's Wall.

Times Open Feb-Mar & Oct-Nov, 10-5; Apr-Sep 10-6 (closed mid Nov-mid Feb)* **Facilities** Ⓟ Ⓟ ⊑ ⎍ (outdoor) ♿ toilets for disabled shop ⊗

HOLY ISLAND (LINDISFARNE)

Lindisfarne Castle

TD15 2SH

☎ 01289 389244   ▤ 01289 389909

e-mail: lindisfarne@nationaltrust.org.uk

web: www.nationaltrust.org.uk

dir: 8m S Berwick from A1 on Holy Island via 3m tidal causeway

This 16th-century fort was restored by Sir Edwin Lutyens in 1903. The austere outside walls belie the Edwardian comfort within, which includes antique Flemish and English furniture, porcelain and polished brass. A small walled garden designed by Gertrude Jekyll is set on the southward facing slope, some 500 metres to the north of the castle. Spectacular views from the ramparts to the Farne Islands, Bamburgh Castle and beyond.

Times Open 13 Mar-Oct, daily (closed Mon ex BHs). As Lindisfarne is a tidal island, the Castle opening times will vary. Garden open all year (10-dusk). **Fees** Castle & garden £6.30 (ch £3.10) Family ticket £15.70. Garden only £1.* **Facilities** Ⓟ shop ⊗ 🐾

HOLY ISLAND (LINDISFARNE)

Lindisfarne Priory

TD15 2RX

☎ 01289 389200

web: www.english-heritage.org.uk

dir: can only be reached at low tide across a causeway. Tide tables posted at each end of the causeway

One of the holiest Anglo-Saxon sites in England, renowned for the original burial place of St Cuthbert whose corpse was discovered 11 years after his burial and found to be mysteriously undecayed. An award-winning museum.

Times Open all year, Apr-Sep, daily 9.30-5; Oct-1 Nov, daily 9.30-4; 2 Nov-Jan, Sat-Mon 10-2; Feb-Mar, daily 10-4. Closed 24-26 Dec & 1 Jan. **Fees** £4.20 (concessions £3.60, ch £2.10). Prices and opening times are subject to change in March 2010. Please call 0870 333 1181 for the most up to date prices and opening times when planning your visit. **Facilities** toilets for disabled shop ⌗

HOUSESTEADS

Housesteads Roman Fort

Haydon Bridge NE47 6NN

☎ 01434 344363

web: www.english-heritage.org.uk

dir: 2.5m NE of Bardon Mill on B6318

The jewel in the crown of Hadrian's Wall and the most complete Roman fort in Britain, these superb remains offer a fascinating glimpse into the past glories of one of the world's greatest empires.

Times Open all year, Apr-Sep, daily 10-6; Oct-Mar, daily 10-4. Closed 24-26 Dec & 1 Jan. **Fees** £4.50 (concessions £3.80, ch £2.30). Free entry to NT members. Prices and opening times are subject to change in March 2010. Please check web site or call 0870 333 1181 for the most up to date prices and opening times when planning your visit. **Facilities** ℗ ⌓ shop ⌗

WALWICK

Chesters Roman Fort

Chollerford NE46 4EP
☎ 01434 681379
web: www.english-heritage.org.uk
dir: 0.5m W of Chollerford on B6318

The best-preserved Roman cavalry fort in Britain. The museum holds displays of carved stones, altars and sculptures from all along Hadrian's Wall.

Times Open all year, Apr-Sep, daily 10-6; Oct-Mar, daily 10-4. Closed 24-26 Dec & 1 Jan. **Fees** £4.50 (concessions £3.80, ch £2.30). Prices and opening times are subject to change in March 2010. Please check web site or call 0870 333 1181 for the most up to date prices and opening times when planning your visit. **Facilities** ℗ ☕ shop ♿

WARKWORTH

Warkworth Castle & Hermitage

NE66 0UJ
☎ 01665 711423
web: www.english-heritage.org.uk

The magnificent eight-towered keep of Warkworth Castle stands on a hill high above the River Coquet, dominating all around it. A complex stronghold, it was home to the Percy family, which at times wielded more power in the North than the King himself.

Times Open all year. Castle: Apr-Sep, daily 10-5; Oct-1 Nov, daily 10-4; 2 Nov-Mar, Sat-Mon 10-4. Hermitage: Apr-Sep, Wed, Sun & BH 11-5. Closed 24-26 Dec & 1 Jan. **Fees** Castle: £4.20 (concessions £3.60, ch £2.10). Family ticket £10.50. Hermitage: £3 (concessions £2.60, ch £1.50). Prices and opening times are subject to change in March 2010. Please check web site or call 0870 333 1181 for the most up to date prices and opening times when planning your visit. **Facilities** ℗ ♿ (partly accessible) (limited access, steps) toilets for disabled shop ♿

WYLAM

George Stephenson's Birthplace

NE41 8BP

☎ 01661 853457

e-mail: georgestephensons@nationaltrust.org.uk

web: www.nationaltrust.org.uk

dir: 1.5m S of A69 at Wylam

Birthplace of the world famous railway engineer, this small stone tenement was built around 1760 to accommodate mining families. The furnishings reflect the year of Stephenson's birth here in 1781, his whole family living in one room.

Times Open 15 Mar-2 Nov, Thu-Sun, 12-5 & BH Mons.* **Facilities** ⓟ ⌷ ⅍ toilets for disabled ⊗ �

NEWSTEAD

Newstead Abbey, Historic House & Gardens

Newstead Abbey Park NG15 8NA

☎ 01623 455900   📄 01623 455904

e-mail: sally.winfield@nottinghamcity.gov.uk

web: www.newsteadabbey.org.uk

dir: off A60, between Nottingham & Mansfield, at Ravenshead

This beautiful house is best known as the home of poet Lord Byron. Visitors can see Byron's own rooms, mementoes of the poet and other splendidly decorated rooms. The grounds of over 300 acres include waterfalls, ponds, water gardens and Japanese gardens. Special events include outdoor theatre and opera, Christmas events and Ghost Tours. Please telephone for details of events running throughout the year.

Times Open: Grounds all year, daily 9-dusk or 6 whichever is earliest (ex last Fri in Nov & 25 Dec); House Apr-Sep, Fri-Mon 12-5. (Last admission 4).* **Fees** House & Grounds £7 (ch £2, concessions £3) Family ticket £17.50. Grounds only £3.50 (concessions £3) Family ticket £9.50. Subject to change.* **Facilities** ⓟ ⌷ 🎋 (outdoor) ⅍ (partly accessible) (grounds & ground floor of house accessible) toilets for disabled shop ⊗

NOTTINGHAM

Galleries of Justice

The Shire Hall, High Pavement, Lace Market
NG1 1HN

☎ 0115 952 0555 🖹 0115 993 9828
e-mail: info@nccl.org.uk
web: www.nccl.org.uk
dir: follow signs to city centre, brown heritage
signs to Lace Market & Galleries of Justice

The Galleries of Justice are located on the site
of an original Court and County Gaol. Recent
developments include the arrival of the HM Prison
Service Collection, which will now be permanently
housed in the 1833 wing. Never before seen
artefacts from prisons across the country
offer visitors the chance to experience some of
Britain's most gruesome, yet often touching,
reminders of what prison life would have been
for inmates and prison staff over the last three
centuries.

Times Open all year, Tue-Sun & BH Mon 10-5
(also open Mon in school hols). (Last admission
one hour before closing). Contact for Xmas
opening times.* Facilities ℗ ⊔ 🎮 (indoor)
toilets for disabled shop ⊗

SOUTHWELL

The Workhouse

Upton Rd NG25 0PT
☎ 01636 817250 🖹 01636 817251
e-mail: theworkhouse@nationaltrust.org.uk
web: www.nationaltrust.org.uk
dir: 13m from Nottingham on A612

Discover the most complete workhouse in
existence. Immerse yourself in the unique
atmosphere evoked by the audio guide. Based on
real archive records, the guide helps bring the
19th-century inhabitants back to life. Discover
how society dealt with poverty through the
centuries. Explore the segregated work yards,
day rooms, dormitories, master's quarters
and cellars, then see the recreated working
19th-century garden and find out what food the
paupers would have eaten.

Times Open 28 Feb-15 Mar, Sat -Sun 11-5; 18
Mar-1 Nov, Wed-Sun 12-5. Open BH Mons &
Good Fri. (Last admission 1hr before closing,
normal house admission from noon)* Fees With
Gift Aid donation: £6.10 (ch £3.15). Family
ticket (2ad+3ch) £15.35. Family ticket (1ad)
£9.25.* Facilities ℗ ℗ ♿ (partly accessible)
(Ground floor accessible, stairs to other floors.
Not suitable for motorised wheelchairs. Grounds
partly accessible, loose gravel paths) toilets for
disabled ⊗ ⅏

DIDCOT

Didcot Railway Centre

OX11 7NJ
☎ 01235 817200 📠 01235 510621
e-mail: info@didcotrailwaycentre.org.uk
web: www.didcotrailwaycentre.org.uk
dir: M4 junct 13, A34, located on A4130 at Didcot Parkway Station

Based around the original GWR engine shed, the Centre is home to the biggest collection anywhere of Great Western Railway steam locomotives, carriages and wagons. A typical GWR station has been re-created and a section of Brunel's original broad gauge track relaid, with a replica of Fire Fly locomotive of 1840. There is a full programme of steamdays, including the now-traditional Thomas the Tank and Santa specials. Contact for a timetable.

Times Open all year, Sat-Sun; daily 14-22 Feb; 4-19 Apr ; 23-31 May; 20 Jun-6 Sep; 24 Oct-1 Nov; 27 Dec-3 Jan. Day out with Thomas 6-8 Mar, 2-4 Oct & 5-23 Dec, Fri-Sun.* **Fees** £5-£10 depending on event (ch £4-£9, concessions £4.50-£9.50).* **Facilities** Ⓟ ☕ 🍴 licensed (outdoor) ♿ (partly accessible) (18 awkward steps at entrance) toilets for disabled shop

OXFORD

Ashmolean Museum of Art & Archaeology **FREE**

Beaumont St OX1 2PH
☎ 01865 278000 📠 01865 278018
web: www.ashmolean.org
dir: city centre, opposite The Randolph Hotel

The oldest museum in the country, opened in 1683, the Ashmolean contains Oxford University's priceless collections. Many important historical art pieces and artefacts are on display, including work from Ancient Greece through to the twentieth century. The museum has undergone a massive redevelopment, including the building of 39 new galleries, an education centre, conservation studios and a walkway.

Times Open all year, Tue-Sun 10-5, BH Mons 10-5. Closed during St.Giles Fair (7-9 Sept) Xmas & 1 Jan. **Facilities** Ⓟ ☕ 🍴 licensed ♿ toilets for disabled shop

OXFORD

Museum of the History of Science FREE

Broad St OX1 3AZ
☎ 01865 277280 📄 01865 277288
e-mail: museum@mhs.ox.ac.uk
web: www.mhs.ox.ac.uk
dir: next to Sheldonian Theatre in city centre, on Broad St

The first purpose-built museum in Britain, containing the world's finest collection of early scientific instruments used in astronomy, navigation, surveying, physics and chemistry. Various events through the year.

Times Open all year, Tue-Fri 12-5, Sat 10-5, Sun 2-5. Closed Xmas and Etr Sun. **Facilities** Ⓟ ⅙ (partly accessible) (lift to basement) toilets for disabled shop ⊗

OXFORD

Oxford University Museum of Natural History FREE

Parks Rd OX1 3PW
☎ 01865 272950 📄 01865 272970
e-mail: info@oum.ox.ac.uk
web: www.oum.ox.ac.uk
dir: opposite Keble College

Built between 1855 and 1860, this museum of "the natural sciences" was intended to satisfy a growing interest in biology, botany, archaeology, zoology, entomology and so on. The museum reflects Oxford University's position as a 19th-century centre of learning, with displays of early dinosaur discoveries, Darwinian evolution and Elias Ashmole's collection of preserved animals. Although visitors to the Pitt-Rivers Museum must pass through the University Museum, the two should not be confused.

Times Open daily 10-5. Times vary at Xmas & Etr. **Facilities** Ⓟ ⅿ (outdoor) ⅙ toilets for disabled shop ⊗

OXFORD

Pitt Rivers Museum **FREE**

South Parks Rd OX1 3PP
☎ 01865 270927 📄 01865 270943
e-mail: prm@prm.ox.ac.uk
web: www.prm.ox.ac.uk
dir: 10 min walk from city centre, visitors
entrance on Parks Rd through the Oxford
University Museum of Natural History

The museum is one of the city's most popular
attractions. It is part of the University of Oxford
and was founded in 1884. The collections held at
the museum are internationally acclaimed, and
contain many objects from different cultures of
the world and from various periods, all grouped
by type, or purpose. The upper gallery, housing
the weapons and armour displays, will reopen in
Spring 2010.

Times Open all year, Tue-Sun & BH Mon 10-4.30,
Mon 12-4.30. Contact museum at Christmas &
Easter to check times. **Facilities** Ⓟ ♿ toilets
for disabled shop ⊗

OXFORD

St Edmund Hall **FREE**

College of Oxford University OX1 4AR
☎ 01865 279000 📄 01865 279090
e-mail: bursary@seh.ox.ac.uk
web: www.seh.ox.ac.uk
dir: Queen's Lane Oxford at end of High St

This is the only surviving medieval academic hall
and has a Norman crypt, 17th-century dining
hall, chapel and quadrangle. Other buildings are
of the 18th and 20th centuries.

Times Open all year. Closed 20-30 Mar, 23-26
Aug, 21 Dec-5 Jan* **Facilities** ⊑ ♿ (partly
accessible) toilets for disabled ⊗

OXFORD

University of Oxford Botanic Garden

Rose Ln OX1 4AZ
☎ 01865 286690 📠 01865 286693
e-mail: postmaster@obg.ox.ac.uk
web: www.botanic-garden.ox.ac.uk
dir: E end of High St on banks of River Cherwell

Founded in 1621, this botanic garden is the oldest in the United Kingdom. There is a collection of over 6000 species of plants from all over the world. Consisting of three sections, the Glasshouses contain plants that need protection from the British weather. The area outside the Walled Garden contains a water garden and rock garden as well as the spring border and autumn border. Within the Walled Garden plants are grouped by country of origin, botanic family or economic use.

Times Open all year daily: 9-4.30 Jan-Feb & Nov-Dec (last admission 4.15). Mar-Apr, Sep-Oct 9-5 (last admission 4.15) May-Aug 9-6 (last admission 5.15) Closed Good Fri & 25 Dec*
Fees £3.50 (ch free, disabled with 1 carer free, concessions £3). Annual pass to be confirmed.
Facilities ℗ ♿ toilets for disabled shop ⊗ 🚭

UFFINGTON

Uffington Castle, White Horse & Dragon Hill **FREE**

☎ 01793 762209
web: www.nationaltrust.org.uk
dir: S of B4507

The 'castle' is an Iron Age fort on the ancient Ridgeway Path. It covers about eight acres and has only one gateway. On the hill below the fort is the White Horse, a 375ft prehistoric figure carved in the chalk hillside and thought to be about 3000 years old.

Times Open at any reasonable time.* **Facilities** ℗ 🌲 (outdoor) ♿ (partly accessible) (disabled car parking and access to view points) 🐾

WOODSTOCK

Blenheim Palace

OX20 1PP

☎ 08700 602080   📠 01993 810570
e-mail: operations@blenheimpalace.com
web: www.blenheimpalace.com
dir: M40 junct 9, follow signs to Blenheim Palace,
on A44 8m N of Oxford

Home of the Duke and Duchess of Marlborough
and birthplace of Sir Winston Churchill, Blenheim
Palace is an English Baroque masterpiece. Fine
furniture, sculpture, paintings and tapestries
are set in magnificent gilded staterooms that
overlook sweeping lawns and formal gardens.
'Capability' Brown landscaped the 2100-acre
park, which is open to visitors for pleasant walks
and beautiful views.

Times Open Palace & Gardens 13 Feb-12 Dec
(ex Mon-Tue in Nov & Dec) daily 10.30-6 (last
admission 4.45). Park daily all year 9-6 (last
admission 4.45) Closed 25 Dec. **Fees** Palace,
Park & Gardens £12.30-£17.50 (ch £6.75-£10,
concessions £10.80-£14). Familly £46. Park &
Gardens £6.90-£10 (ch £3.30-£5, concessions
£5.70-£7.50). Family £25. **Facilities** 🅿 ⓟ ⊡
🍽 licensed 🎋 (outdoor) ♿ (partly accessible)
(Wheelchair access via lift in Palace) toilets for
disabled shop ⊗

COSFORD

The Royal Air Force Museum

TF11 8UP

☎ 01902 376200   📠 01902 376211
e-mail: cosford@rafmuseum.org
web: www.rafmuseum.org
dir: on A41, 1m S of M54 junct 3

The Royal Air Force Museum Cosford has one of
the largest aviation collections in the UK, with 70
historic aircraft on display. Visitors will be able
to see Britain's V bombers - Vulcan, Victor and
Valiant and other aircraft suspended in flying
attitudes in the national Cold War exhibition,
housed in a landmark building covering
8000sqm.

Times Open all year daily, 10-6 (last admission
4). Closed 24-26 Dec & 1 Jan, 7-11 Jan.*
Facilities 🅿 ⊡ 🍽 licensed 🎋 (outdoor) ♿
toilets for disabled shop ⊗

IRONBRIDGE

Ironbridge Gorge Museums

Coach Rd TF8 7DQ
☎ 01952 884391 & 0800 590258
📠 01952 884391
e-mail: tic@ironbridge.org.uk
web: www.ironbridge.org.uk
dir: M54 junct 4, signed

Ironbridge is the site of the world's first iron bridge. It was cast and built here in 1779, to span a narrow gorge over the River Severn. Now Ironbridge is the site of a remarkable series of museums relating the story of the bridge, recreating life in Victorian times and featuring ceramics and social history displays.

Times Open all year, 10-5. Some small sites closed Nov-Mar. Telephone for exact winter details. **Fees** A passport ticket allowing repeat visits to all museums for 12 months is available call 01952 884391 or see website for details.*
Facilities 🅿🅿 ⬜🍴 licensed 🛱 (outdoor) ♿ toilets for disabled shop 🚫

WESTON-UNDER-REDCASTLE

Hawkstone Historic Park & Follies

SY4 5UY
☎ 01948 841700 📠 01939 200335
e-mail: enquiries@hawkstone.co.uk
web: www.principal-hayley.co.uk
dir: 3m from Hodnet off A53, follow brown heritage signs

Created in the 18th century by the Hill family, Hawkstone is one of the greatest historic parklands in Britain. After almost 100 years of neglect it has been restored and designated a Grade I historic landscape. Visitors can once again experience the magical world of intricate pathways, arches and bridges, towering cliffs and follies, and an awesome grotto. The park covers nearly 100 acres of hilly terrain and visitors are advised to wear sensible shoes and clothing and to bring a torch. Allow 3-4 hours for the tour, which is well signposted - a route map is included in the admission price.

Times Open from 10 Mar, Sat & Sun; Apr-May, & Sep-Oct, Wed-Sun; Jun-Aug, daily. Closed Nov-Mar.* **Fees** Wkdays £6 (ch £4 pen & students £5). Family ticket £17.* **Facilities** 🅿 ⬜🍴 licensed 🛱 (outdoor) ♿ (partly accessible) (access to tearooms, gift shop and grand valley) toilets for disabled shop

BATH

American Museum in Britain

Claverton Manor BA2 7BD
☎ 01225 460503 📄 01225 469160
e-mail: info@americanmuseum.org
web: www.americanmuseum.org
dir: Signed from city centre & A36 Warminster road

Claverton Manor is just two miles south east of Bath, in a beautiful setting above the River Avon. The house was built in 1820 by Sir Jeffrey Wyatville, and is now a museum of American decorative arts. The gardens are well worth seeing, and include an American arboretum and a replica of George Washington's garden at Mount Vernon. Each year the museum holds special exhibitions and runs a full programme of special events with kids' activities, live music, living history events and Quilting Bees.

Times Open 13 Mar-Oct, Tue-Sun 12-5. Open Mon in Aug & BHs. Also open 26 Nov-19 Dec Tue-Sun 12-4.30. **Fees** £8 (ch £4.50, concessions £7). Family ticket £21.50. **Facilities** 🅿 🍴 🍴 (outdoor) ♿ (partly accessible) (grounds not fully accessible) toilets for disabled shop

BATH

Bath Postal Museum

27 Northgate St BA1 1AJ
☎ 01225 460333 📄 01225 460333
e-mail: info@bathpostalmuseum.org
web: www.bathpostalmuseum.org
dir: On entering city fork left at mini rdbt. After all lights into Walcot St. Podium car park facing

The first letter sent with a stamp was sent from Bath, and this museum helps you to discover how 18th-century Bath influenced and developed the Postal System, including the story of the Penny Post. Visitors can explore the history of written communication from ancient Egyptian clay tablets, to the first Airmail flight from Bath to London in 1912. See the Victorian Post Office and watch continuous video films including the in-house production entitled 'History of Writing'. The museum is full of hands-on and interactive features to engage the whole family.

Times Open all year, Mon-Sat 11-5. (Last admission Mar-Oct 4.30, Nov-Feb 4).* **Fees** £3.50 (ch under 5 free, ch £1.50, concessions £3, students £1.50). Family and Party 10+ tickets available.* **Facilities** 🅿 ♿ shop ⊗

BATH

Fashion Museum

Bennett St BA1 2QH
☎ 01225 477173 📠 01225 477743
e-mail: fashion_bookings@bathnes.gov.uk
web: www.fashionmuseum.co.uk
dir: Museum near city centre. Parking in Charlotte Street Car park.

The Fashion Museum showcases a world-class collection of historical and contemporary dress and includes opportunities to try on replica corsets and crinolines. It is housed in Bath's famous 18th-century Assembly Rooms designed by John Wood the Younger in 1771. Entrance to the Assembly Rooms is free. Special exhibitions are held every summer in the Ballroom.

Times Open all year, daily Jan-Feb 10.30-4; Mar-Oct, 10.30-5; Nov-Dec, 10.30-4. Closed 25-26 Dec.* **Fees** £7 (ch £5). Family ticket £20. Combined ticket with Roman Baths, £14.50 (ch £8.70).* **Facilities** Ⓟ ☕ ♿ toilets for disabled shop 🚭

BATH

The Jane Austen Centre

40 Gay St, Queen Square BA1 2NT
☎ 01225 443000 📠 01225 443018
e-mail: jackie@janeausten.co.uk
web: www.janeausten.co.uk
dir: in heart of Bath by Queen Square

Celebrating Bath's most famous resident, the centre offers a snapshot of life during Regency times and explores how living in this city affected Jane Austen's life and writing. Every September, Bath holds a Jane Austen festival.

Times Open all year, daily 9.45-5.30; Jul-Aug, Thu-Sat 9.45-7; Nov-Mar, Sun-Fri 11-4.30, Sat 9.45-5.30.* **Fees** £6.95 (ch £3.95, concessions £5.50). Family ticket (2 ad+up to 4 ch) £18.* **Facilities** Ⓟ ☕ 🍽 licensed ♿ (partly accessible) (access to exhibition on ground floor only) shop 🚭

BATH

No 1 Royal Crescent

No 1 Royal Cresent BA1 2LR

☎ 01225 428126 📠 01225 481850

e-mail: no1musuem@bptrust.org.uk

web: www.bath-preservation-trust.org.uk

dir: 1st house in Royal Crescent situated above Victoria Ave & Victoria Park, Charlotte St car park

Bath is very much a Georgian city, but most of its houses have been altered over the years to suit changing tastes and lifestyles. Built in 1768 by John Wood the Elder, No 1 Royal Crescent has been restored to look as it would have done some 200 years ago. Visitors can see a grand townhouse of the late 18th century with authentic furniture, paintings and carpets. On the ground floor are the study and dining room, and on the first floor a lady's bedroom and drawing room. In the basement there is a period kitchen and the museum shop.

Times Open 13 Feb-23 Oct, 10.30-5; 24 Oct-12 Dec, 10.30-4. Open BH Mon. (Last admission 30 mins before closing). **Fees** £5 (concessions £4). Family ticket £12. Group rate 10+ £3 each. Schools £2.50 each. **Facilities** ℗ ♿ (partly accessible) shop ⊗

BATH

Roman Baths & Pump Room

Abbey Church Yard BA1 1LZ

☎ 01225 477785 📠 01225 477743

e-mail: romanbaths_bookings@bathnes.gov.uk

web: www.romanbaths.co.uk

dir: M4 junct 18, A46 into city centre

The remains of the Roman baths and temple give a vivid impression of life nearly 2,000 years ago. Built next to Britain's only hot spring, the baths served the sick, and the pilgrims visiting the adjacent Temple of Sulis Minerva. Above the Temple Courtyard, the Pump Room became a popular meeting place in the 18th century. The site still flows with natural hot water and no visit is complete without a taste of the famous hot spa water. Costumed characters every day.

Times Open all year, Mar-Jun & Sep-Oct, daily 9-5; Jul & Aug, daily 9am-9pm; Jan-Feb & Nov-Dec, daily 9.30-4.30. Closed 25-26 Dec. (Last exit 1hr after these times).* **Fees** £11 (£11.50 Jul-Aug) (ch £7.20). Family ticket £32. Combined ticket with Fashion Museum £14.50 (ch £8.70).* **Facilities** ℗ 🍽 licensed ♿ (partly accessible) (lift to lower museum) toilets for disabled shop ⊗

GLASTONBURY

Glastonbury Abbey

Abbey Gatehouse, Magdalene St BA6 9EL
☎ 01458 832267 📄 01458 836117
e-mail: info@glastonburyabbey.com
web: www.glastonburyabbey.com
dir: M5 junct 23 to A39, on A361 between Frome
& Taunton

Few places in Britain are as rich in myth and
legend as Glastonbury. Tradition maintains
that the impressive ruins mark the birthplace
of Christianity in Britain. Joseph of Arimathea
is said to have founded a chapel here in AD61,
planting his staff in the ground where it flowered
both at Christmas and Easter. Later, it is said,
King Arthur and Guinevere were buried here, and
the abbey has been a place of pilgrimage since
the Middle Ages. The present abbey ruins date
mostly from the 12th and 13th centuries. The
display area contains artefacts and a model of
the Abbey as it might have been in 1539.

Times Open all year, daily, Jun-Aug 9-6; Sep-May
9.30-6 or dusk, whichever is the earliest. Dec-Feb
open at 10. Closed 25 Dec.* Fees £5.50 (ch 5-15
£3.50, pen £5). Family ticket £16.50 Facilities
❷Ⓟ ⊑🗖 (outdoor) ♿ (partly accessible)
toilets for disabled shop ⊗

SPARKFORD

Haynes International Motor Museum

BA22 7LH
☎ 01963 440804 📄 01963 441004
e-mail: info@haynesmotormuseum.co.uk
web: www.haynesmotormuseum.co.uk
dir: from A303 follow A359 towards Castle Cary

An excellent day out for everyone - with more
than 400 cars and bikes stunningly displayed,
dating from 1886 to the present day, this is the
largest international motor museum in Britain.
If you want a nostalgic trip down memory lane
the museum offers a host of familiar names
such as Austin, MG and Morris, while for those
seeking something more exotic there is a vast
array of performance cars, from modern classics
such as the Dodge Viper, Jaguar XJ220 and the
Ferrari 360, plus the classic Jaguar E Type and
AC Cobra. Also on show is a large collection of
American cars, including the jewels in the Haynes
crown, the V16 Cadillac, and the million-dollar
Duesenberg.

Times Open all year, Apr-Sep, daily 9.30-5.30;
Oct-Mar, 10-4.30. Closed 24-26 Dec & 1 Jan.
Fees £7.95 (ch £4.25, concessions £6.95). Family
£10.95 (1ad+1ch), £25.75 (2ad+3ch). Facilities
❷ ⊑🗖 (outdoor) ♿ toilets for disabled shop ⊗

WESTON-SUPER-MARE

The Helicopter Museum

The Heliport, Locking Moor Rd BS24 8PP
☎ 01934 635227 📠 01934 645230
e-mail: helimuseum@btconnect.com
web: www.helicoptermuseum.co.uk
dir: outskirts of town on A371, nr M5 junct 21, follow propellor signs

The world's largest rotary-wing collection and the only helicopter museum in Britain, home of the Queen's Royal flight helicopters. More than 70 helicopters and autogyros are on display - including examples from France, Germany, Poland, Russia and the United States, from 1935 to the present day - with displays of models, engines and other components explaining the history and development of the rotorcraft. Special events include 'Open Cockpit Days', when visitors can learn more about how the helicopter works. Helicopter flights available on set dates throughout the year.

Times Open all year, Nov-Mar, Wed-Sun 10-4.30; Apr-Oct 10-5.30. Open daily during Etr & summer school hols 10-5.30. Closed 24-26 Dec & 1 Jan. **Fees** £5.50 (ch under 5 free, ch 5-16 £3.50, concessions £4.50). Family ticket (2ad+2ch) £15.50, (2ad+3ch) £17.50. Party 12+.* **Facilities** 🅿 ⛲ 🍴 (outdoor) ♿ toilets for disabled shop

YEOVILTON

Fleet Air Arm Museum

Royal Naval Air Station BA22 8HT
☎ 01935 840565 📠 01935 842630
e-mail: info@fleetairarm.com
web: www.fleetairarm.com
dir: on B3151, just off junct of A303 and A37

The Fleet Air Arm Museum is where museum meets theatre! You'll 'fly' by helicopter to the replica flight deck of aircraft carrier HMS Ark Royal. You'll see fighter aircraft and two enormous projection screens showing jet fighters taking off and landing, and even a nuclear bomb. The Museum has Europe's largest collection of naval aircraft and the first British-built Concorde. Go on board and visit the cockpit. There's an adventure playground, and the museum is located alongside Europe's busiest military air station at RNAS Yeovilton.

Times Open all year: Apr-Oct, daily 10-5.30; Nov-Mar, Wed-Sun 10-4.30 (Closed 24-26 Dec)* **Fees** £11 (ch under 17 £8, under 5 free, concessions £9). Family (2ad+3ch) £35.* **Facilities** 🅿🅿 ⛲🍴 licensed 🍴 (outdoor) ♿ toilets for disabled shop ⊗

LICHFIELD

Samuel Johnson Birthplace Museum
FREE

Breadmarket St WS13 6LG
☎ 01543 264972 📠 01543 258441
e-mail: sjmuseum@lichfield.gov.uk
web: www.samueljohnsonbirthplace.org.uk
dir: located in city centre market place

Dr Samuel Johnson, author of the famous English dictionary of 1755, lexicographer, poet, critic, biographer and personality was born in this house in 1709. The birthplace now houses a museum dedicated to his extraordinary life, work and personality. Five floors of exhibits featuring period room settings, introductory video and personal items owned by Johnson, his family and his famous friends. Johnson's birthday is celebrated annually in September. Please see the website for special events.

Times Open all year, daily Apr-Sep 10.30-4.30; Oct-Mar 11-3.30. **Facilities** Ⓟ ♿ (partly accessible) (Grade 1 listed & many unavoidable stairs) shop ⊗

SHUGBOROUGH

Shugborough Estate

ST17 0XB
☎ 01889 881388 📠 01889 881323
e-mail: shugborough.promotions@staffordshire.gov.uk
web: www.shugborough.org.uk
dir: 6m E of Stafford off A513, signed from M6 junct 13

Costumed living history characters bring the past to life - in the walled garden meet the gardeners of 1805 and find out how fruit and vegetables are grown on the estate. At the farm the servants are busy making butter and cheese and the farm hands tend to the animals. The story continues in the Servants' Quarters where cooks and kitchen maids prepare food on the range, starch the whites in the laundry and brew ale in the wood-fired brewery. The Mansion House completes the story, where the 1805 Viscount and Lady Anson are often present.

Times Open 18 Mar-28 Oct, daily 11-5. Site open all year to pre-booked parties.* **Fees** £12 (ch £7, under 5 free, concessions £9.50). Family ticket (2ad+3ch) £30, (1ad+1ch £15). **Facilities** Ⓟ ⊡ ᴓ licensed ⋒ (outdoor) ♿ (partly accessible) (steps to house, stairclimber available) toilets for disabled shop ⊗ ⋇

STOKE-ON-TRENT

Gladstone Working Pottery Museum

Uttoxeter Rd, Longton ST3 1PQ
☎ 01782 237777 📄 01782 237076
e-mail: gladstone@stoke.gov.uk
web: www.stoke.gov.uk/gladstone
dir: A50 then follow brown heritage signs

Located at the heart of the Potteries, Gladstone Pottery Museum is the last remaining Victorian Pottery industry. Whilst touring the original factory building discover what it was like for the men, women and children to live and work in a potbank during the era of the coal firing bottle ovens. In original workshops working potters can be found demonstrating traditional pottery skills. There are also lots of opportunities for you to have a go at pottery making, throw your own pot on the potters wheel, make china flowers and decorate pottery items to take home. Also explore Flushed with Pride, dedicated to the story of the development of the toilet, and The Tile Gallery, a fine collection which traces the development of decorative tiles.

Times Open all year, daily 10-5 (last admission 4). Limited opening Xmas & New Year.* **Facilities** 🅿 ☕ 🍽 licensed 🪑 toilets for disabled shop ⊗

STOKE-ON-TRENT

Wedgwood Visitor Centre

Barlaston ST12 9ER
☎ 01782 282986 📄 01782 223063
e-mail: bookings@wedgwood.com
web: www.wedgwoodvisitorcentre.com
dir: From M1, via A50 follow tourist signs to Stoke. From M6 junct 15 follow brown tourist signs

Set in 250 acres of lush parkland in the heart of Staffordshire, visitors can take a fascinating trip behind the scenes at one of the world's famous pottery companies. The award winning tour allows visitors to enjoy the entire experience at their own pace. Hands on activities such as throwing your own pot or painting your own plate are available in the demonstration area, where individuals craft artisans demonstrate their skills including Coalport painter, Jewellery Maker, Hand painter and Flower Maker. Add to this, exhibition areas, film theatre and an exclusive Wedgwood shop, the centre offers an all-inclusive day for everyone.

Times Open all year, Mon-Fri 9-5, Sat & Sun 10-5. Shop open Sun 10-4 (ex Etr Sun). Closed Xmas week. **Fees** £4.75 (concessions £3.75). Family £16. **Facilities** 🅿 ☕ 🍽 licensed ♿ toilets for disabled shop ⊗

WALL

Wall Roman Site FREE

Watling St WS14 0AW
☎ 01543 480768
web: www.english-heritage.org.uk
dir: off A5

Explore the haunting remains of a 2,000 year old wayside staging post situated along Watling Street, the famous Kent to North Wales Roman road.

Times Site open: Mar-Oct, daily 10-5; Museum 21 Mar-Oct, last Sun & Mon of each month 10-5. Closed Nov-Feb.* **Facilities** ⓟ shop ♯ ⛾

WHITTINGTON

Staffordshire Regiment Museum

Whittington Barracks WS14 9PY
☎ 01543 434394 & 434395
🖹 01543 434391
e-mail: curator@staffordshireregimentmuseum.com
dir: on A51 between Lichfield/Tamworth

Located next to Whittington Barracks, the museum tells the story of the soldiers of the Staffordshire Regiment and its predecessors. Exhibits include vehicles, uniforms, weapons, medals and memorabilia relating to three hundred years of regimental history, including distinguished service in the First and Second World Wars and the Gulf War. Visitors can experience a World War I trench system with sound effects and a World War II Anderson shelter.

Times Open all year, Mon-Fri 10-4.30 (last admission 4); also Apr-Oct wknds and BH 12.30-4.30. Closed Xmas-New Year. Parties at other times by arrangement.* **Facilities** ⓟⓟ ⊓ (outdoor) ♿ toilets for disabled shop ⊗

FLIXTON

Norfolk & Suffolk Aviation Museum FREE

Buckeroo Way, The Street NR35 1NZ
☎ 01986 896644
e-mail: nsam.flixton@tesco.net
web: www.aviationmuseum.net
dir: off A143, take B1062, 2m W of Bungay

Situated in the Waveney Valley, the museum
has over 60 historic aircraft. There is also a
Bloodhound surface-to-air missile, the 446th
Bomb Group Museum, RAF Bomber Command
Museum, the Royal Observer Corps Museum,
RAF Air-Sea Rescue and Coastal Command and
a souvenir shop. Among the displays are Decoy
Sites and Wartime Deception, Fallen Eagles -
Wartime Luftwaffe Crashes and an ex-Ipswich
airport hangar made by Norwich company
Boulton and Paul Ltd.

Times Open all year, Apr-Oct, Sun-Thu 10-5 (last
admission 4); Nov-Mar, Tue, Wed & Sun 10-4
(last admission 3). Closed late Dec-early Jan.*
Facilities ❶❷ ⌑ ㅠ (outdoor) ♿ toilets for
disabled shop ⊗

LAVENHAM

Lavenham The Guildhall of Corpus Christi

Market Place CO10 9QZ
☎ 01787 247646   ▤ 01787 246345
e-mail: lavenhamguildhall@nationaltrust.org.uk
web: www.nationaltrust.org.uk/lavenham
dir: Lavenham Market Place. A1141 & B1071

The Guildhall of Corpus Christi is one of the finest
timber framed buildings in Britain. It was built
around 1530 by the prosperous Corpus Christi
Guild, for religious rather than commercial
reasons. The hall now houses a local history
museum telling the story of Lavenham's 15th-
and 16th-century cloth-trade riches. Visitors can
also see the walled garden with its 19th-century
lock-up and mortuary.

Times Open 7 Mar-29 Mar, Wed-Sun, 11-4; Apr-1
Nov, Mon-Sun 11-5; 7 Nov-29 Nov, Sat-Sun
11-4.* Fees Gift Aid admission prices £4.20 (ch
£1.55). Family ticket £10.15 Gift aid admission
includes a voluntary donation but visitors can
choose to pay the standard prices displayed at
the property and on the website.* Facilities ℗
⌑♿ (partly accessible) shop ⊗ ♨

LOWESTOFT

East Anglia Transport Museum

Chapel Rd, Carlton Colville NR33 8BL
☎ 01502 518459 📠 01502 584658
e-mail: enquiries@eatm.org.uk
web: www.eatm.org.uk
dir: 3m SW of Lowestoft, follow brown signs from
A12, A146 & A1117

A particular attraction of this museum is the
reconstructed 1930s street scene which is used
as a setting for working vehicles: visitors can ride
by tram, trolley bus and narrow gauge railway.
Other motor, steam and electrical vehicles are
exhibited. There is also a woodland picnic area
served by trams.

Times Open: Apr-Sep, Sun and BH 11-5. From
Jun, Thu and Sat, 2-5.* **Facilities** 🅿 ⛄ 🎪
(outdoor) ♿ (partly accessible) toilets for
disabled shop

NEWMARKET

National Horseracing Museum and Tours

99 High St CB8 8JH
☎ 01638 667333 📠 01638 665600
web: www.nhrm.co.uk
dir: located in centre of High St

This friendly award-winning museum tells the
story of the people and horses involved in racing
in Britain. Have a go on the horse simulator in
the hands-on gallery and chat to retired jockeys
and trainers about their experiences. Special mini
bus tours visit the gallops, a stable and horses'
swimming pool.

Times Open Etr-Oct, daily 11-5 (also BH
Mons). 10am on race days.* **Fees** £6 (ch £3,
concessions £5). Family (2ad+2ch) £13.*
Facilities 🅿 ⛄ 🍽 licensed 🎪 (outdoor) ♿
toilets for disabled shop ⊗

STOWMARKET

Museum of East Anglian Life

IP14 1DL

☎ 01449 612229 📄 01449 672307
e-mail: enquiries@eastanglianlife.org.uk
web: www.eastanglianlife.org.uk
dir: in centre of Stowmarket, signed from A14
& B1115

This 70-acre, all-weather museum is set in
an attractive river-valley site with 3km of
woodland and riverside nature trails. There are
reconstructed buildings, including a working
water mill, a smithy and also a wind pump, and
the Boby Building houses craft workshops. There
are displays on Victorian domestic life, gypsies,
farming and industry. These include working
steam traction engines, the only surviving pair
of Burrell ploughing engines of 1879, and a
Suffolk Punch horse. The William Bone Building
illustrates the history of Ransomes of Ipswich.

Times Open late March-end Oct.* **Fees** £6.50 (ch
4-16 £3.50, concessions £5.50). Family ticket
(2ad+2/3ch) £17.50. 1ad family £11. Party
10+.* **Facilities** ℗ ⌴ 卅 (outdoor) toilets for
disabled shop

SUDBURY

Gainsborough's House

46 Gainsborough St CO10 2EU

☎ 01787 372958 📄 01787 376991
e-mail: mail@gainsborough.org
web: www.gainsborough.org
dir: in centre of Sudbury. Follow pedestrian signs
from town centre car parks or from train stn

The birthplace of Thomas Gainsborough RA
(1727-88). The Georgian-fronted town house,
with an attractive walled garden, displays
more of the artist's work at any one time than
any other gallery, together with 18th-century
furniture and memorabilia. A varied programme
of temporary exhibitions on British art is shown
throughout the year, with sculpture in the garden
during the summer.

Times Open all year, Mon-Sat 10-5. Closed
Sun, Good Fri & Xmas-New Year. **Fees** £4.50
(concessions £3.60, ch and students £2). Family
£10. **Facilities** ℗ ⌴ & (partly accessible) (2nd
floor not accessible) toilets for disabled shop ⊗

137

WEST STOW

West Stow Anglo Saxon Village

West Stow Country Park, Icklingham Rd
IP28 6HG
☎ 01284 728718 📄 01284 728277
e-mail: weststow@stedsbc.gov.uk
web: www.weststow.org
dir: off A1101, 7m NW of Bury St Edmunds.
Follow brown heritage signs

The village is a reconstruction of a pagan Anglo-Saxon settlement dated 420-650 AD. Seven buildings have been reconstructed on the site of the excavated settlement. There is a Visitors' Centre which includes a new archaeology exhibition, DVD area and a children's play area. A new Anglo-Saxon Centre houses the original objects found on the site. Located in the 125 acre West Stow Country Park with river, lake, woodland and heath, plus many trails and paths.

Times Open all year, daily 10-5. Last entry 4 (3.30 in Winter) except Xmas period.* **Facilities** ℗℗ ⬛ 🎋 (outdoor) ♿ (partly accessible) toilets for disabled shop ⊗

WOODBRIDGE

Sutton Hoo

IP12 3DJ
☎ 01394 389700 📄 01394 389702
e-mail: suttonhoo@nationaltrust.org.uk
web: www.nationaltrust.org.uk/suttonhoo
dir: off B1083 Woodbridge to Bawdsey road.
Follow signs from A12 avoiding Woodbridge itself

Discovered in 1939 and described as 'page one of English history', this is the site of one of the most important archaeological finds in Britain: the complete 7th-century ship burial of an Anglo-Saxon king, missed by grave-robbers, and undisturbed for 1300 years. The centre-piece is a full sized replica of an Anglo-Saxon warrior king's burial chamber. Sutton Hoo changed forever our perceptions of the 'Dark Ages', by revealing a culture rich in craftsmanship, trade and legend.

Times Open all year: Jun, Wed-Sun, 10.30-5; Jul-Aug, daily 10.30-5; Sep-Oct, Wed-Sun, 10.30-5; Nov-Feb, Sat-Sun, 11-4. Open: BHs.* **Fees** Gift Aid Admission prices £6.50, (ch £3.40). Family tickets £16.45. Gift aid admission includes a voluntary donation but visitors can choose to pay the standard prices displayed at the property and on the website.* **Facilities** ℗ 🍽 licensed 🎋♿ (partly accessible) (Grounds partly access, slopes, burial mound tours not accessible to w/chairs or PMV) toilets for disabled shop ⊗ 🐾

WOODBRIDGE

Woodbridge Tide Mill

Tide Mill Way IP12
☎ 01728 746959 📠 01728 748226
e-mail: wtm@terina.booker@btinternet.com
web: www.tidemill.org.uk
dir: follow signs for Woodbridge off A12, 7m E of
Ipswich-Tide Mill is on riverside

The machinery of this 18th-century mill has been
completely restored. There are photographs and
working models on display. Situated on a busy
quayside, the unique building looks over towards
the historic site of the Sutton Hoo Ship Burial.
Every effort is made to run the machinery for a
while whenever the mill is open and the tides are
favourable.

Times Open Etr, then daily May-Sep; Apr, Oct
wknds only, 11-5.* **Fees** £2.50 (accompanied
ch free (ex school groups) concessions £2).*
Facilities ℗ ♿ (partly accessible) (ground floor
& viewing area only accessible) shop ⊗

ASH VALE

Army Medical Services Museum FREE

Keogh Barracks GU12 5RQ
☎ 01252 868612 📠 01252 868832
e-mail: armymedicalmuseum@btinternet.com
web: www.ams-museum.org.uk
dir: M3 junct 4 on A331 to Mytchett then follow
tourist signs

The museum traces the history of Army medicine,
nursing, dentistry and veterinary science from
1660 until the present day. Medical equipment
and ambulances complement displays including
uniforms and medals.

Times Open all year, Mon-Fri 10-3.30. Closed
Xmas, New Year & BH. Wknds by appointment
only.* **Facilities** ℗℗ toilets for disabled shop
⊗

GREAT BOOKHAM

Polesden Lacey

RH5 6BD

☎ 01372 452048 📠 01372 452023
e-mail: polesdenlacey@nationaltrust.org.uk
web: www.nationaltrust.org.uk/polesdenlacey
dir: 2m S off A246 from village of Bookham

King George VI and Queen Elizabeth the Queen Mother spent part of their honeymoon here, and photographs of other notable guests can be seen. The house is handsomely furnished and full of charm, and it is set in spacious grounds. There is also a summer festival, where concerts and plays are performed. Please phone for details of special events.

Times Open all year; Grounds & Garden: daily 10-5. House: 15 Mar-25 Oct,11-5 (last admission 30 mins before closing).* **Fees** Gift Aid donation: Garden £7 (ch £3.50). Family ticket £17.50. House & Garden £11 (ch £5.50). Family £27.50. Group rates 15+. Includes a voluntary donation of 10% or more. Visitors can however, choose to pay the standard admission which is displayed at the property and on NT website.* **Facilities** 🅿 ➰ 🍴 licensed 🍴 (outdoor) ♿ (partly accessible) (no access for w/chairs to house upper floors. Some steps & uneven paths in garden. Courtesy shuttle from car park to front of house) toilets for disabled shop 🌱

WEYBRIDGE

Brooklands Museum

Brooklands Rd KT13 0QN
☎ 01932 857381 📠 01932 855465
e-mail: info@brooklandsmuseum.com
web: www.brooklandsmuseum.com
dir: M25 junct 10/11, museum off B374, follow brown signs

Brooklands racing circuit was the birthplace of British motorsport and aviation. From 1907 to 1987 it was a world-renowned centre of engineering excellence. The Museum features old banked track and the 1-in-4 Test Hill. Many of the original buildings have been restored including the Clubhouse, the Shell and BP Petrol Pagodas, and the Malcolm Campbell Sheds in the Motoring Village. Many motorcycles, cars and aircraft are on display. Ring for details of special events.

Times Open all year, daily & BHs 10-5 (4 in winter).* **Facilities** 🅿 ➰ 🍴 (outdoor) ♿ (partly accessible) (no wheelchair access to aircraft) toilets for disabled shop ⊗

WISLEY

RHS Garden Wisley

GU23 6QB

☎ 01483 224234   📄 01483 211750
web: www.rhs.org.uk
dir: on A3, close to M25 junct 10

With over 100 years of gardening, Wisley is the flagship garden of the Royal Horticultural Society. The garden stretches over 200 acres and there are countless opportunities for visitors to draw inspiration and gather new ideas. A 'must see' is the new glasshouse, one of the highlights, with exotics from around the world in two climate zones. The mixed borders and vegetable garden are glories of summer, while the country garden, Battleston Hill and wild garden are magnificent in spring. Whatever the season the garden is full of interest.

Times Open all year, Mon-Fri 10-6 (4.30 Nov-Feb), Sat-Sun, 9-6 (4.30 Nov-Feb). Closed 25 Dec.* **Facilities** 🅿 ⛾ ⑩ licensed 🎋 (outdoor) ♿ (partly accessible) (garden partly accessible, some difficult paths) toilets for disabled shop ⊗

BATTLE

1066 Battle of Hastings Abbey & Battlefield

TN33 0AD

☎ 01424 773792   📄 01424 775059
web: www.english-heritage.org.uk
dir: A21 onto A2100

Explore the site of the Battle of Hastings, where on 14th October 1066, one of the most famous events in English history took place. Free interactive wand tour of the battlefield and atmospheric abbey ruins.

Times Open all year, Apr-Sep, daily 10-6; Oct-Mar, daily 10-4. Closed 24-26 Dec & 1 Jan. **Fees** £6.70 (concessions £5.70, ch £3.40). Family £16.80. Opening times and prices are subject to change from March 2010, for further details please phone 0870 333 118. **Facilities** 🅿♿ (partly accessible) (steps to enter all abbey buildings) toilets for disabled shop ⊞

BATTLE

Yesterday's World

89-90 High St TN33 0AQ
☎ 01424 893938 & 774269
🖷 01424 893316
e-mail: shop@yesterdaysworld.co.uk
web: www.yesterdaysworld.co.uk
dir: M25 junct 5, A21 onto A2100 towards Battle, opposite Battle Abbey Gatehouse

Go on a magical time-travel adventure from the reign of Queen Victoria to the psychedelic 1970s. Explore five floors of displays with over 100,000 artefacts, virtual and interactive exhibits, sounds and smells. See an English country garden, a children's play village, the 1930s Nippy's Tea Room, nostalgic gift shop and traditional English sweet shop.

Times Open all year, Winter, daily 9.30-5.30; Summer, daily 9.30-6. Closed 25-26 Dec & 1 Jan.* Fees £7 (ch £3.95, concession £5). Family ticket (2ad+2ch - extra child £3) £20. Discount for groups of 15+.* Facilities ℗ ⊒ ☲ (outdoor) ♿ (partly accessible) toilets for disabled shop ⊗

BODIAM

Bodiam Castle

TN32 5UA
☎ 01580 830196 🖷 01580 830398
e-mail: bodiamcastle@nationaltrust.org.uk
web: www.nationaltrust.org.uk/bodiamcastle
dir: 2m E of A21 Hurst Green

With its tall round drum towers at each corner, Bodiam is something of a fairytale castle. It was built in 1386 by Sir Edward Dalyngrigge, for comfort and defence. The ramparts rise dramatically above a broad moat and the great gatehouse contains the original portcullis - a very rare example of its kind.

Times Open all year, Jan-12 Feb, Sat-Sun 10.30-4; 13 Feb-Oct, daily 10.30-5.30; Nov-19 Dec, Wed-Sun 10.30-4 (last entry 30 mins before closing). Fees Gift Aid donation: £6.20 (ch £3.10). Family ticket £15.50. Group 15+ £5.10 (ch £2.55). Includes a voluntary donation of 10% or more. Visitors can however, choose to pay the standard admission which is displayed at the property and on NT website. Facilities ℗ ⊒♿ (partly accessible) (ground floor level is fully accessible, spiral staircase to upper levels) toilets for disabled shop ⊗ ⚘

BRIGHTON

Royal Pavilion

BN1 1EE

☎ 03000 290900 📄 03000 292871
e-mail: visitor.services@brighton-hove.gov.uk
web: www.royalpavilion.org.uk
dir: M23/A23 from London. In city centre near seafront. 15 min walk from rail station

Acclaimed as one of the most exotically beautiful buildings in the British Isles, the Royal Pavilion was the magnificent seaside residence of George IV. This breathtaking Regency palace is decorated in Chinese style, with a romanticised Indian exterior, and surrounded by restored Regency gardens.

Times Open all year, Apr-Sep, daily 9.30-5.45 (last admission 5); Oct-Mar, daily 10-5.15 (last admission 4.30). Closed 25-26 Dec. **Fees** £9 (ch £5.20, concessions £7). Family ticket (1ad+2ch) £14.20, (2ad+2ch) £23.20. Group rates available 15+. **Facilities** ℗ ♥ ⵏ◎⵩ licensed 🎋 (outdoor) ♿ (partly accessible) (ground floor only accessible) toilets for disabled shop ⊗

BURWASH

Bateman's

TN19 7DS

☎ 01435 882302 📄 01435 882811
e-mail: batemans@nationaltrust.org.uk
web: www.nationaltrust.org.uk
dir: 0.5m SW off A265

Rudyard Kipling lived for over 34 years in this 17th-century manor house and it remains much the same as it was during his lifetime. His 1928 Rolls Royce Phantom is on display, and the watermill at the bottom of the garden grinds wheat into flour on Saturday afternoons and Wednesdays.

Times Open 13 Mar-Oct, Sat-Wed 11-5, also open Good Fri, (last admission 4.30). House closes at 5. **Fees** Gift Aid donation: £8.20 (ch £4.10). Family ticket £20.50. Party £6.45 (ch £3.15). Includes a voluntary donation of 10% or more. Visitors can however, choose to pay the standard admission which is displayed at the property and on NT website. **Facilities** ℗ ♥ ⵏ◎⵩ licensed 🎋 (outdoor) ♿ (partly accessible) (access to first floor & water mill restricted) toilets for disabled shop ⊗ ⵚ

EASTBOURNE

"How We Lived Then" Museum of Shops & Social History

20 Cornfield Ter BN21 4NS
☎ 01323 737143
e-mail: howwelivedthen@btconnect.com
web: www.how-we-lived-then.co.uk
dir: just off seafront, between town centre & theatres, signed

Over the last 50 years, Jan and Graham Upton have collected over 100,000 items which are now displayed on four floors of authentic old shops and room-settings, transporting visitors back to their grandparents' era. Other displays, such as seaside souvenirs, wartime rationing and Royal mementoes, help to capture 100 years of social history.

Times Open all year, daily, 10-5 (last entry 4.30). Winter times subject to change, telephone establishment.* Fees £4.50 (ch 5-15 £3.50, under 5's free, concession £4). Party 10+.*
Facilities Ⓟ ♿ (partly accessible) (ground floor access only) shop

HASTINGS

1066 Story in Hastings Castle

Castle Hill Rd, West Hill TN34 3RG
☎ 01424 781111 & 781112 (info line)
📄 01424 781186
e-mail: bookings@discoverhastings.co.uk
web: www.hastings.gov.uk
dir: close to A259 seafront, 2m from B2093

The ruins of the Norman castle stand on the cliffs, close to the site of William the Conqueror's first motte-and-bailey castle in England. It was excavated in 1825 and 1968, and old dungeons were discovered in 1894. An unusual approach to the castle can be made via the West Hill Cliff Railway.

Times Open daily, 27 Mar-Sep 10-5; Oct-26 Mar 11-3.30. Closed 24-26 Dec.* Facilities Ⓟ ⊼ shop ⊗

HERSTMONCEUX

The Observatory Science Centre

BN27 1RN

☎ 01323 832731 📠 01323 832741
e-mail: info@the-observatory.org
web: www.the-observatory.org
dir: 0.75m N of Wartling village

From the 1950s to the 1980s this was part of the Royal Greenwich Observatory, and was used by astronomers to observe and chart movements in the night sky. Visitors can learn about not only astronomy, but also other areas of science in a series of interactive and engaging displays. There are also exhibitions, a discovery park, and a collection of unusual giant exhibits.

Times Open daily from 26 Jan-Nov. Open wknd of Dec 6-7.* Fees £7.23 (ch 4-15 £5.41). Family ticket (2ad+3ch or 1ad+4ch) £22.27. Family of 5 £25.40.* Facilities ❷ ⊑ 🛱 (indoor & outdoor) ♿ (partly accessible) toilets for disabled shop ⊗

LEWES

Lewes Castle & Barbican House Museum

169 High St BN7 1YE

☎ 01273 486290 📠 01273 486990
e-mail: castle@sussexpast.co.uk
web: www.sussexpast.co.uk
dir: N of High St off A27/A26/A275

One of the oldest castles in England, built soon after the Norman Conquest, and one of only two in England to be built on two mounds. The views over Lewes, the River Ouse and surrounding Downs are worth the climb up the Keep. Barbican House Museum tells the story of Sussex from the Stone Age to the end of the medieval period, and displays include flint tools, pottery, weapons, jewellery and other archaeological discoveries, as well as a model of Lewes in about 1870. Special events include a Medieval Day in May and open-air theatre.

Times Open all year, daily, Tue-Sat 10-5.30, Sun, Mon & BHs 11-5.30. (Last admission 30 mins before closing). Closed Xmas & Mon in Jan.* Fees £5.20 (ch 5-15 £2.60, concessions £4.55). Family ticket (2ad+2ch) £14.30, (1ad+4ch) £14.30. Carer £1.95 each.* Facilities ℗ ♿ (partly accessible) (Wheelchair access is limited to the lower Gun Garden of the Castle) shop ⊗

PEVENSEY

Pevensey Castle

BN24 5LE

☎ 01323 762604
web: www.english-heritage.org.uk
dir: off A259

William the Conqueror landed here in 1066 and established his first stronghold. Discover the history of the Norman castle and the remains of an unusual keep through the free audio tour.

Times Open all year, Apr-Sep, daily 10-6; Oct-1 Nov, daily 10-4; 2 Nov-Mar, Sat-Sun 10-4. Closed 24-26 Dec & 1 Jan. **Fees** £4.30 (concessions £3.70, ch £2.20). Family £10.80. Prices and opening times are subject to change in March 2010. Please check web site or call 0870 333 1181 for the most up to date prices and opening times when planning your visit. **Facilities** ❷ ◻ shop ⌗

ARUNDEL

Arundel Castle

BN18 9AB

☎ 01903 882173 🖷 01903 884581
e-mail: info@arundelcastle.org
web: www.arundelcastle.org
dir: on A27 between Chichester & Worthing

Set high on a hill in West Sussex, this magnificent castle and stately home, seat of the Dukes of Norfolk for nearly 1000 years, commands stunning views across the river Arun and out to sea. Climb to the keep and battlements; marvel at a fine collection of 16th-century furniture; portraits by Van Dyke, Gainsborough, Canaletto and others; tapestries and the personal possessions of Mary, Queen of Scots; wander in the grounds and renovated Victorian flower and vegetable gardens.

Times Open Apr-Oct, Sun-Fri 11-5, Castle open 12-5. (Last admission 4). Closed Sat.* **Facilities** ❷℗ ◻ toilets for disabled shop ⊗

BIGNOR

Bignor Roman Villa & Museum

RH20 1PH

☎ 01798 869259 📄 01798 869259
e-mail: enquiries@bignorromanvilla.co.uk
web: www.bignorromanvilla.co.uk
dir: 6m S of Pulborough & 6m N of Arundel on A29, signed. 8m S of Petworth on A285, signed

Rediscovered in 1811, this Roman house was built on a grand scale. It is one of the largest known, and has spectacular mosaics. The heating system can also be seen, and various finds from excavations are on show. The longest mosaic in Britain (82ft) is on display here in its original position.

Times Open Mar-Apr, Tue-Sun & BH 10-5; May daily 10-5; Jun-Sep daily 10-6, Oct daily 10-5* **Fees** £5.50 (ch under 16 £2.50, pen £4). Family £14. Party 10+ 20% discount. Guided tours by arrangement.* **Facilities** 🅿 ⬚ 🎌 (outdoor) ♿ (partly accessible) (most areas accessible) shop ⊗

FISHBOURNE

Fishbourne Roman Palace

Salthill Rd PO19 3QR

☎ 01243 785859 📄 01243 539266
e-mail: adminfish@sussexpast.co.uk
web: www.sussexpast.co.uk
dir: off A27 onto A259 into Fishbourne. Turn right into Salthill Rd & right into Roman Way

The remains of the Roman Palace at Fishbourne were discovered in 1960. Here you can see Britain's largest collection of in-situ Roman floor mosaics. More everyday Roman objects found during the excavations are displayed in the museum gallery. An audio-visual presentation uses computer-generated images to interpret the site. Outside the garden has been replanted to its original plan, using plants that may have grown there when the palace was inhabited. The Collections Discovery Centre displays more artefacts from both Fishbourne and Chichester district. Join a 'behind the scenes' tour for an opportunity to handle some of these.

Times Open all year, daily Feb-15 Dec. Feb, Nov-mid Dec 10-4; Mar-Jul & Sep-Oct 10-5; Aug 10-6. Winter wknds 10-4.* **Facilities** 🅿 ⬚ 🎌 (outdoor) ♿ toilets for disabled shop ⊗

SINGLETON

Weald & Downland Open Air Museum

PO18 0EU

☎ 01243 811348   📠 01243 811475
e-mail: office@wealddown.co.uk
web: www.wealddown.co.uk
dir: 6m N of Chichester on A286

A showcase of English architectural heritage, where historic buildings have been rescued from destruction and rebuilt in a parkland setting. Vividly demonstrating the evolution of building techniques and use of local materials, these fascinating buildings bring to life the homes, farms and rural industries of the south east of the past 500 years. See also working Shire horses, cattle and traditional breeds of farm animals.

Times Open daily all year, during BST, 10.30-6 & 10.30-4 the rest of year. Winter opening days vary, see website for details. **Fees** £8.95 (ch £4.70, pen £7.95). Family ticket (2ad+3ch) £24.25.* **Facilities** 🅿 ♿ 🚻 (indoor & outdoor) ♿ (partly accessible) (some areas of museum not suitable for disabled visitiors, but most key areas and exhibits are accessible) toilets for disabled shop

JARROW

Bede's World

Church Bank NE32 3DY

☎ 0191 489 2106   📠 0191 428 2361
e-mail: visitor.info@bedesworld.co.uk
web: www.bedesworld.co.uk
dir: off A185 near S end of Tyne tunnel

Bede's World is an ambitious museum based around the extraordinary life and work of the Venerable Bede (AD673-735) early Medieval Europe's greatest scholar and England's first historian. Attractions include an 'Age of Bede' exhibition in the museum, which displays finds excavated from the site of St Paul's monastery. Alongside the museum, Bede's World has developed Gyrwe, an Anglo-Saxon demonstration farm, which brings together the animals, timber buildings, crops and vegetables that would have featured in the Northumbrian Landscape of Bede's Day.

Times Open all year, Apr-Oct, Mon-Sat 10-5.30, Sun noon-5.30; Nov-Mar, Mon-Sat 10-4.30 & Sun 12-4.30. Please contact for Xmas/New Year opening times.* **Facilities** 🅿🅿 ♿ 🍽 licensed 🚻 (outdoor) toilets for disabled shop ⊗

SOUTH SHIELDS

Arbeia Roman Fort & Museum

Baring St NE33 2BB

☎ 0191 456 1369 📠 0191 427 6862

web: www.twmuseums.org.uk

dir: 5 mins' walk from town centre

In South Shields town are the extensive remains of Arbeia, a Roman fort in use from the 2nd to 4th century. It was the supply base for the Roman army's campaign against Scotland. On site there are full size reconstructions of a fort gateway, a barrack block and part of the commanding officer's house. Archaeological evacuations are in progress throughout the summer.

Times Open all year, Apr-Oct, Mon-Sat 10-5.30, Sun 1-5; Nov-Mar, Mon-Sat 10-3.30. Closed 25-26 Dec & 1 Jan* **Fees** Fort & Museum free of charge ex for 'Timequest' Archaeological Interpretation Gallery £1.50 (ch & concessions 80p).* **Facilities** ℗ 🅿 (outdoor) ♿ (partly accessible) toilets for disabled shop

WALLSEND

Segedunum Roman Fort, Baths & Museum

Buddle St NE28 6HR

☎ 0191 236 9347 📠 0191 295 5858

e-mail: segedunum@twmuseums.org.uk

web: www.twmuseums.org.uk/sege

dir: A187 from Tyne Tunnel, signposted

Hadrian's Wall was built by the Roman Emperor Hadrian in 122AD, Segedunum was built as part of the Wall, serving as a garrison for 600 soldiers until the collapse of Roman rule around 410AD. This major historical venture shows what life would have been like then, using artefacts, audio-visuals, reconstructed buildings and a 34m high viewing tower. Plenty of special events including craft activities and re-enactments from Roman cavalry and soldiers. Contact for details.

Times Open all year, Apr-Oct 10-5; Nov-Mar, 10-3. **Fees** £4.25 (ch, pen & concessions £2.50). (ch 16 and under free) **Facilities** ℗🅿 ♿🅿 (outdoor) ♿ toilets for disabled shop ⊗

WHITBURN

Souter Lighthouse & The Leas

Coast Rd SR6 7NH
☎ 0191 529 3161 & 01670 773966
🖷 0191 529 0902
e-mail: souter@nationaltrust.org.uk
web: www.nationaltrust.org.uk
dir: on A183 coast road, 2m S of South Shields,
3m N of Sunderland

When it opened in 1871, Souter was the most advanced lighthouse in the world, and warned shipping off the notorious rocks in the river approaches of the Tyne and the Wear. Painted red and white and standing at 150ft high, it is a dramatic building and hands-on displays and volunteers help bring it to life. Visitors can explore the whole building with its engine room and lighthouse keeper's cottage. You can take part in activities concerning shipwrecks and the workings of the lighthouse. Climb to the top of the lighthouse, or walk along the Leas, a 2.5 mile stretch of spectacular coastline.

Times Open 13 Mar-Oct daily (ex Fri but open Good Fri) 11-5. **Fees** £4.85 (ch £3.15) Family ticket £12.65. Group 10+ £4.* **Facilities** 🅿 Ⓟ
🍽 licensed 🚻 toilets for disabled shop ⊗ 🐾

GAYDON

Heritage Motor Centre

Banbury Rd CV35 0BJ
☎ 01926 641188 🖷 01926 641555
e-mail: enquiries@heritage-motor-centre.co.uk
web: www.heritage-motor-centre.co.uk
dir: M40 junct 12 and take B4100. Attraction signed

The Heritage Motor Centre is home to the world's largest collection of historic British cars. The museum boasts exciting and interactive exhibitions which uncover the story of the British motor industry from the 1890s to the present day. Fun for all the family with children's activity packs, special school holiday and lecture programs, plus free guided tours twice a day, onsite café and gift shop and a selection of outdoor activities including children's play area, picnic site, 4x4 Experience and Go-Karts.

Times Open all year, daily 10-5. (Closed over Xmas, check website or call 01926 641188 for details) **Fees** £9 (ch 5-16 £7, under 5 free, & concessions £8). Family ticket £28. (Additional charges apply to outdoor activities). Group & education rates available.* **Facilities** 🅿 ⊒ 🍴
(outdoor) ♿ toilets for disabled shop ⊗

KENILWORTH

Kenilworth Castle

CV8 1NE

☎ 01926 852078   📠 01926 851514
web: www.english-heritage.org.uk

Explore the largest and most extensive castle ruin in England, with a past rich in famous names and events. Its massive red sandstone towers, keep and wall glow brightly in the sunlight. Discover the history of Kenilworth through the interactive model in Leicester's Barn.

Times Open all year, Mar-1 Nov, daily 10-5; 2 Nov-Feb, daily 10-4. Closed 24-26 Dec & 1 Jan.
Fees £7 (concessions £6, ch £3.50). Family ticket £17.50. Prices and opening times are subject to change in March 2010. Please check web site or call 0870 333 1181 for the most up to date prices and opening times when planning your visit. **Facilities** 🅿 ⬜ 🎋 ♿ (partly accessible) (uneven surfaces, steep slopes, steps) toilets for disabled shop ♯

KENILWORTH

Stoneleigh Abbey

CV8 2LF

☎ 01926 858535 & 858585
📠 01926 850724
e-mail: enquire@stoneleighabbey.org
web: www.stoneleighabbey.org
dir: entrance off B4115 close to junct of A46 and A452

Stoneleigh Abbey is one of the finest country house estates in the Midlands and has been the subject of considerable restoration work. The abbey, founded in the reign of Henry II, is now managed by a charitable trust. Visitors will experience a wealth of architectural styles spanning more than 800 years. The magnificent state rooms and chapel, the medieval Gatehouse and the Regency stables are some of the major areas to be admired.

Times Open Good Fri-Oct, Tue-Thu, Sun & BHs for guided tours at 11, 1 & 3. Grounds open 10-5.
Fees Grounds only, £3. Guided tour of house, £6.50 (1ch 5-12 free, additional ch £3) pen £5.50. **Facilities** 🅿 ⬜ ♿ (partly accessible) (access over exterior gravel paths will require assistance & lift access to state rooms) toilets for disabled shop ⊗

RUGBY

The Webb Ellis Rugby Football Museum **FREE**

5 Saint Matthew's St CV21 3BY
☎ 01788 567777 📄 01788 537400
e-mail: sales@webb-ellis.co.uk
web: www.webb-ellis.co.uk
dir: on A428 opposite Rugby School

An intriguing collection of Rugby football memorabilia is housed in the shop in which rugby balls have been made since 1842. Visitors can watch a craftsman at work, hand-stitching the footballs. Situated near to Rugby School and its famous playing field.

Times Open all year, Mon-Sat 9-5. Phone for holiday opening times.* **Facilities** ℗ ♿ (partly accessible) shop ⊗

SHOTTERY

Anne Hathaway's Cottage

Cottage Ln CV37 9HH
☎ 01789 292100 📄 01789 263138
e-mail: info@shakespeare.org.uk
web: www.shakespeare.org.uk
dir: House in Shottery Village, 1m from Stratford

This world-famous thatched cottage was the childhood home of Anne Hathaway, William Shakespeare's wife. The cottage still contains many family items including the beautiful 'Hathaway Bed'. In the stunning grounds there is a quintessential English cottage garden, orchard, sculpture garden, a romantic willow cabin and a maze.

Times Open all year, Apr-May & Oct-Nov, Mon-Sat 9.30-5, Sun 10-5; Jun-Aug, Mon-Sat 9-5, Sun 9.30-5; Nov-Mar, daily 10-4;.* **Facilities** ℗ ☕ toilets for disabled shop ⊗

STRATFORD-UPON-AVON

Shakespeare's Birthplace

Henley St CV37 6QW
☎ 01789 204016 📠 01789 263138
e-mail: info@shakespeare.org.uk
web: www.shakespeare.org.uk
dir: in town centre

Visit the house where the world's most famous playwright was born and grew up. Discover the fascinating story of William Shakespeare's life and see it brought to life by the costumed guides. There is a new exhibition entitled 'Life, Love and Legacy'.

Times Open all year, daily Apr-Oct 9-5, Nov-Mar 10-4.* **Fees** Birthplace including Nash's/Halls Croft £12 (ch £7, concessions £11) Family ticket £31. All five Shakespeare Houses £17 (ch £10, concessions £15.50) Family ticket £44.50. Mary Arden's Farm £8 (ch £5, concessions £7) Family ticket £21. **Facilities** Ⓟ ♿ (partly accessible) toilets for disabled shop ⊗

WARWICK

Warwick Castle

CV34 4QU
☎ 0870 442 2000 📠 0870 442 2394
e-mail: customer.information@warwick-castle.com
web: www.warwick-castle.com
dir: 2m from M40 junct 15

From the days of William the Conqueror to the reign of Queen Victoria, Warwick Castle has provided a backdrop for many turbulent times. Today it offers family entertainment with a medieval theme. Attractions include the world's largest siege engine, thrilling jousting tournaments, birds of prey, daredevil knights, and entire castleful of colourful characters. The newest addition is the immersive and interactive "Dream of Battle".

Times Open all year, daily 10-6 (5pm Nov-Mar). Closed 25 Dec.* **Facilities** 🅟 Ⓟ ☕ 🍽 licensed ⛩ toilets for disabled shop ⊗

COVENTRY

Coventry Transport Museum FREE

Millennium Place, Hales St CV1 1JD
☎ 024 7623 4270 🖷 024 7623 4284
e-mail: enquiries@transport-museum.com
web: www.transport-museum.com
dir: just off junct 1, Coventry ring road, Tower St
in city centre

Coventry is the traditional home of the British
motor industry, and the museum's world-
renowned collection displays over 150 years of its
history. You can design your own car, feel what
its like to break the sound barrier at 763mph
and even travel into the future. The Festival of
Motoring takes place over the fist weekend in
September and features vintage, veteran and
classic vehicles with family activities and stunt
show riders culminating in a car and motorcycle
rally around the region.

Times Open all year, daily 10-5. Closed 24-26
Dec & 1 Jan **Facilities** ℗ 🖵 ♿ toilets for
disabled shop ⊗

DUDLEY

Black Country Living Museum

Tipton Rd DY1 4SQ
☎ 0121 557 9643 & 520 8054
🖷 0121 557 4242
e-mail: info@bclm.co.uk
web: www.bclm.co.uk
dir: on A4037, near Showcase cinema

A recreated canal-side village, with shops,
houses and workshops. Find out what life
was like around 1900. Ride on a tramcar,
explore the underground mine, venture into
the limestone caverns or visit the fairground
(additional charge). There are demonstrations
of chainmaking, glass engraving and sweet-
making. Watch a silent movie in the Limelight
cinema, taste fish and chips cooked on a 1930s
range, and finish your visit with a glass of real
ale or dandelion and burdock in the inn.

Times Open all year, Mar-Oct, Mon-Sun 10-5;
Nov-Feb, Wed-Sun 10-4. (Telephone for Xmas
closing)* **Fees** £12.95 (ch & student with NUS
card £6.95, pen £10.50). Family (1ad+1ch)
£18 & (2ad+3ch) £34.95* **Facilities** ℗ 🖵
🍽 licensed 🪑 (indoor & outdoor) ♿ (partly
accessible) (access to most buildings requires
use of temporary ramp. Staff will assist visitors
with restricted mobility) toilets for disabled
shop ⊗

SOLIHULL

National Motorcycle Museum

Coventry Rd, Bickenhill B92 0EJ
☎ 01675 443311 📄 0121 711 3153
web: www.nationalmotorcyclemuseum.co.uk
dir: M42 junct 6, off A45 near NEC

The National Motorcycle Museum is recognised as the finest and largest motorcycle museum in the world, with machines always being added to the collection. It is a place where legends live on and it is a tribute to and a living record of this once great British industry that dominated world markets for some sixty years. The museum records for posterity the engineering achievements of the last century.

Times Open all year, daily 10-6. Closed 24-26 Dec. **Fees** £6.95 (ch 12 & pen £4.95). Party 20+ £5.95. **Facilities** 🅿 🍽 licensed 🚻 toilets for disabled shop ⊗

ALUM BAY

The Needles Old Battery & New Battery

West High Down PO30 0JH
☎ 01983 754772 📄 01983 756978
e-mail: isleofwight@nationaltrust.org.uk
web: www.nationaltrust.org.uk/isleofwight
dir: at Needles Headland, W of Freshwater Bay and Alum Bay, B3322

The threat of a French invasion prompted the construction in 1862 of this spectacularly sited fort, which now contains exhibitions on the Battery's involvement in both World Wars. Two of the original gun barrels are displayed in the parade ground and a 60-yard tunnel leads to a searchlight emplacement perched above the Needles Rocks giving magnificent views of the Dorset coastline beyond. Opening times vary, phone for details.

Times Old battery open: 13 Mar-Oct, daily 10.30-5 (last admission 4.30). New battery 13 Mar-Oct, Sat-Sun & Tue 11-4 (both properties close in high winds). **Fees** Old battery with Gift Aid: £4.85 (ch £2.45). Family ticket £12.10. New battery free.* **Facilities** 🅿 🖵🚻 (partly accessible) (Access to the tunnel at Old Battery via spiral staircase. Uneven surfaces & steep paths. Access to New battery via steps to exhibition room) toilets for disabled shop 🦌

OSBORNE HOUSE

Osborne House

PO32 6JY

☎ 01983 200022 📠 01983 281380
web: www.english-heritage.org.uk
dir: 1m SE of East Cowes

The beloved seaside retreat of Queen Victoria offers a glimpse into the private life of Britain's longest reigning monarch. The royal apartments are full of treasured mementos; and Queen Victoria's role as Empress of India is celebrated in the decoration of the Durbar Room. Visit the gardens and the charming Swiss Cottage.

Times Open all year, Apr-Sep, daily 10-6 (house 10-5); Oct-1 Nov, daily 10-4; 4 Nov-Mar, Wed-Sun 10-4 (pre-booked guided tours, last tour 2.30. Xmas tour season 18 Nov-3 Jan). May close early for special events on occasional days in Jul & Aug. **Fees** House & Grounds: £10.20 (concessions £8.70, ch £5.10). Family £25.50. Grounds only: £8.40 (concessions £7.20, ch £4.20). Family £21. Prices and opening times are subject to change in March 2010. Please check web or call 0870 333 1181 for the most up to date prices and opening times. **Facilities** 🅿 ⊑ 🍴 shop ⊗ ♯

AVEBURY

Alexander Keiller Museum

High St SN8 1RF

☎ 01672 539250 📠 01672 538038
e-mail: avebury@nationaltrust.org.uk
web: www.nationaltrust.org.uk
dir: 6m W of Marlborough. 1m N of Bath Rd (A4) on A4361 and B4003

Avebury is one of the most important megalithic monuments in Europe, and was built before Stonehenge. The museum, including an exhibition in the 17th-century threshing barn, presents the full archaeological story of the stones using finds from the site, along with interactive and audio-visual displays.

Times Open all year, Feb-Oct, daily 10-5; Nov-Feb, 10-4. Closed 24-26 Dec.* **Facilities** 🅿🅿 ⊑ 🍴 licensed ♯ toilets for disabled shop ⊗ ♨

LACOCK

Lacock Abbey, Fox Talbot Museum & Village

SN15 2LG

☎ 01249 730227 (abbey) & 730459

🖷 01249 730501

e-mail: lacockabbey@nationaltrust.org.uk

web: www.nationaltrust.org.uk

dir: 3m S of Chippenham, E of A350, car park signed

Lacock Abbey is the former home of William Henry Fox Talbot, who invented the photographic negative process. The oldest negative in existence is of a photograph of Lacock Abbey. As well as the museum there are newly-restored botanic gardens and greenhouse and a well-preserved country village. The Abbey has also been used as a film location, and can be seen in Harry Potter, Pride and Prejudice, Cranford, The Other Boleyn Girl and Wolfman.

Times Cloisters & Grounds, Mar-2 Nov, daily 11-5.30. Closed Good Fri. Abbey, 15 Mar-2 Nov, daily, ex Tue, 1-5.30. Closed Good Fri. Museum 23 Feb-2 Nov, daily 11-5.30; 8 Nov-21 Dec, Sat & Sun 11-4; 3-31 Jan, Sat & Sun 11-4* **Facilities** ❷ 🛱 (outdoor) toilets for disabled shop ⊗ 🐾

LONGLEAT

Longleat

The Estate Office BA12 7NW

☎ 01985 844400　🖷 01985 844885

e-mail: enquiries@longleat.co.uk

web: www.longleat.co.uk

dir: turn off A36 Bath-Salisbury road onto A362 Warminster-Frome road

Nestling within magnificent 'Capability' Brown landscaped grounds, Longleat House is widely regarded as one of the most beautiful stately homes open to the public. Built by Sir John Thynne and completed in 1580, it has remained the home of the same family ever since. Many treasures are contained within the house: paintings by Tintoretto and Wootton, exquisite Flemish tapestries, fine French furniture and elaborate ceilings by John Dibblee Crace. Longleat is also renowned for its safari park, which was the first of its kind in the UK. Among the most magnificent sights are the famous pride of lions, wolves, rhesus monkeys and zebra.

Times Open daily 14-22 Feb, wknds only 28 Feb-29 Mar; daily 4 Apr-1 Nov. Longleat House open daily (ex 25 Dec).* **Facilities** ❷ 🖵 🍽 licensed 🛱 (outdoor) ♿ (partly accessible) toilets for disabled shop

MARLBOROUGH

Crofton Beam Engines

Crofton Pumping Station, Crofton SN8 3DW
☎ 01672 870300
e-mail: enquiries@croftonbeamengines.org
web: www.croftonbeamengines.org
dir: signed from A4/A338/A346 & B3087 at Burbage

The oldest working beam engine in the world still in its original building and still doing its original job, the Boulton and Watt 1812, can be found in this rural spot. Its companion is a Harvey's of Hayle of 1845. Both are steam driven, from a hand-stoked, coal-fired boiler, and pump water into the summit level of the Kennet and Avon Canal with a lift of 40ft.

Times Open daily Etr-Sep, 10.30-5 (last entry 4.30). 'In Steam' Etr, BH wknds & last wknd of Jun, Aug & Sep.* **Fees** In Steam wknd: £7 (ch £2.50, under 5 free & pen £6). Family ticket £16. Non-In Steam days £4.50 (ch £2.50, pen £4) Family £11.* **Facilities** ℗ ⬚ ⌂ (outdoor) ♿ (partly accessible) (access restricted to ground floor pumphouse) shop ⊗

STONEHENGE

Stonehenge

SP4 7DE
☎ 0870 333 1181 & 01722 343834
🖷 01722 343831
web: www.english-heritage.org.uk
dir: 2m W of Amesbury on junct A303 and A344/A360

Britain's greatest prehistoric monument and a World Heritage Site. What visitors see today are the substantial remains of the last in a series of monuments erected between around 3000 and 1600BC.

Times Open all year, 16 Mar-May & Sep-15 Oct, daily 9.30-6; Jun-Aug, daily 9-7; 16 Oct-15 Mar, daily 9.30-4; 26 Dec & 1 Jan, 10-4. Closed 24-25 Dec (opening times may vary around Summer Solstice 20-22 Jun). **Fees** £6.60 (concessions £5.60, ch £3.30). Family ticket £16.50. NT members free. Prices and opening times are subject to change in March 2010. Please check web site or call 0870 333 1181 for the most up to date prices and opening times when planning your visit. **Facilities** ℗ ⬚ shop ⊗ ⌗

SWINDON

STEAM - Museum of the Great Western Railway

Kemble Dr SN2 2TA
☎ 01793 466646   📄 01793 466615
e-mail: steampostbox@swindon.gov.uk
web: www.steam-museum.org.uk
dir: from M4 junct 16 & A420 follow brown signs to 'Outlet Centre' & Museum

This fascinating day out tells the story of the men and women who built, operated and travelled on the Great Western Railway. Hands-on displays, world-famous locomotives, archive film footage and the testimonies of ex-railway workers bring the story to life. A reconstructed station platform, posters and holiday memorabilia recreate the glamour and excitement of the golden age of steam. Good value group packages, special events, exhibitions and shop.

Times Open daily 10-5. Closed 25-26 Dec & 1 Jan* **Facilities** ℗ toilets for disabled shop ⊗

BROMSGROVE

Avoncroft Museum of Historic Buildings

Stoke Heath B60 4JR
☎ 01527 831886 & 831363
📄 01527 876934
e-mail: admin@avoncroft.org.uk
web: www.avoncroft.org.uk
dir: 2m S, off A38

A visit to Avoncroft takes you through nearly 700 years of history. Here you can see 25 buildings rescued from destruction and authentically restored on a 15 acre rural site. There are 15th and 16th-century timber framed buildings, 18th-century agricultural buildings and a cockpit. There are industrial buildings and a working windmill from the 19th century, and from the 20th a fully furnished pre-fab.

Times Open all year, Apr-Oct, Tue-Sun 10.30-5, daily Jul-Aug; Nov-Dec & Mar, Fri-Sun 10.30-4.30; Closed Mon (except BHs), 24-26 Dec.* **Fees** £6.60 (ch £3, concessions £5.50). Family (2ad+3ch) £16.50. Members free.* **Facilities** ℗ ⊡ ⋒ (outdoor) ♿ (partly accessible) (some building interiors may not be fully accessible) toilets for disabled shop

WORCESTER

The Elgar Birthplace Museum

Crown East Ln, Lower Broadheath WR2 6RH
☎ 01905 333224 📄 01905 333426
e-mail: birthplace@elgarmuseum.org
web: www.elgarmuseum.org
dir: 3m W of Worcester, signed off A44 to Leominster

In 2000, the Elgar Centre was opened to complement the historic Birthplace Cottage and to provide additional exhibition space for more treasures from this unique collection, telling the story of Elgar's musical development and inspirations. Listen to his music as the audio tour guides you round the easily accessible displays.

Times Open Feb-23 Dec, daily 11-5 (last admission 4.15). Closed Xmas-end Jan. **Fees** £6 (ch £2, pen £5, concessions £3.50).* **Facilities** 🅿🅿 ㅈ (outdoor) ♿ (partly accessible) (Elgar centre fully accessible, Birthplace Cottage has steps & narrow stairs/doorways) toilets for disabled shop ⊗

WORCESTER

Worcester Porcelain Museum

Severn St WR1 2ND
☎ 01905 21247 📄 01905 617807
e-mail:
info.admin@worcesterporcelainmuseum.org
web: www.worcesterporcelainmuseum.org
dir: M5 junct 7, follow signs to city centre, at 7th set of lights take 1st left into Edger St & bear left with road into Severn St. At T-junct bear right & after 700yds take 1st left. Museum on left

Worcester Porcelain Museum is situated amidst the city's Historic Quarter within two minutes walk, the Cathedral, Commandery, Birmingham Canal and River Severn. An informative and entertaining audio tour featuring Henry Sandon and skilled craftsmen is free with entry and tells the story of the factory's history, its famous customers, the talented workforce and everyday life. Gallery displays from1751 to the 20th century include Oriental simplicity and Victorian extravaganza and offer a glimpse of times past, taking the visitor on a memorable journey through over 200 years of history.

Times Open all year, Etr-Oct, Mon-Sat 10-5; Nov-Etr, Tue-Sat, 10-4. Closed Sun & BHs. **Fees** Museum £5 (concessions £4.25).* **Facilities** 🅿🅿 ⊑ 🍽 licensed ♿ toilets for disabled shop ⊗

GOOLE

The Yorkshire Waterways Museum

Dutch River Side DN14 5TB
☎ 01405 768730   📄 01405 769868
e-mail: info@waterwaysmuseum.org.uk
web: www.waterwaysmuseum.org.uk
dir: M62 junct 36, enter Goole, turn right at next
3 sets of lights onto Dutch River Side. 0.75m and
follow brown signs

Discover the story of the Aire & Calder Navigation
and the growth of the 'company town' of Goole
and its busy port. Find out how to sail and, in
the interactive gallery, see how wooden boats
were built. Enjoy the unique 'Tom Pudding' story,
brought to life through the vessels on the canal
and the boat hoist in South Dock. Rediscover
the Humber keels and sloops, and Goole's
shipbuilding history through the objects, photos
and memories of Goole people.

Times Open all year Mon-Fri 9-4, Sat-Sun 10-4.
(Closed Xmas & New Year).* Fees Free entry
to museum. Boat trip £4 (ch under 12 £3).*
Facilities 🅿 ⎁ 🍴 (outdoor) ♿ toilets for
disabled shop ⊗

KINGSTON UPON HULL

'Streetlife' - Hull Museum of Transport FREE

High St HU1 1PS
☎ 01482 613902   📄 01482 613710
e-mail: museums@hullcc.gov.uk
web: www.hullcc.gov.uk
dir: A63 from M62, follow signs for Old Town

This purpose-built museum uses a 'hands-on'
approach to trace 200 years of transport history.
With a vehicle collection of national importance,
state-of-the-art animatronic displays and
authentic scenarios, you can see Hull's Old Town
brought vividly to life. The mail coach ride uses
the very latest in computer technology to recreate
a Victorian journey by four-in-hand.

Times Open all year, Mon-Sat 10-5, Sun
1.30-4.30. Closed 24-25 Dec & Good Fri*
Facilities 🅿 🍴♿ toilets for disabled shop ⊗

161

KINGSTON UPON HULL

Maritime Museum FREE

Queen Victoria Square HU1 3DX
☎ 01482 613902 📄 01482 613710
e-mail: museums@hullcc.gov.uk
web: www.hullcc.gov.uk
dir: A63 to town centre, museum is within pedestrian area

Hull's maritime history is illustrated here, with displays on whales and whaling, ships and shipping, and other aspects of this Humber port. There is also a Victorian court room which is used for temporary exhibitions. The restored dock area, with its fine Victorian and Georgian buildings, is well worth exploring too.

Times Open all year, Mon-Sat 10-5 & Sun 1.30-4.30. Closed 25 Dec-2 Jan & Good Fri*
Facilities ℗ ♿ (partly accessible) shop ⊗

KINGSTON UPON HULL

Wilberforce House FREE

23-25 High St HU1 1NE
☎ 01482 613902 📄 01482 613710
e-mail: museums@hullcc.gov.uk
web: www.hullcc.gov.uk
dir: A63 from M62 or A1079 from York, follow signs for Old Town

The early 17th-century Merchant's house was the birthplace of William Wilberforce, who became a leading campaigner against slavery. Re-opened in 2007 after full refurbishment the House tells the story of slavery, abolition, the triangular trade and explores modern issues surrounding slavery.

Times Open all year, Mon-Sat 10-5 & Sun 1.30-4.30. Closed 25-26 Dec, 1 Jan & Good Fri.*
Facilities ℗ ☂ (outdoor) ♿ shop ⊗

ELVINGTON

Yorkshire Air Museum & Allied Air Forces Memorial

Halifax Way YO41 4AU

☎ 01904 608595 📠 01904 608246

e-mail: museum@yorkshireairmuseum.co.uk

web: www.yorkshireairmuseum.co.uk

dir: from York take A1079 then immediate right onto B1228, museum is signposted on right

This award-winning museum and memorial is based around the largest authentic former WWII Bomber Command Station open to the public. There is a restored tower, an air gunners museum, archives, an Airborne Forces display, Squadron memorial rooms, and much more. Among the exhibits are replicas of the pioneering Cayley Glider and Wright Flyer, along with the Halifax Bomber and modern jets like the Harrier GR3, Tornado GR1 and GR4. A new exhibition 'Against The Odds' tells the story of the RAF Bomber Command.

Times Open all year, daily, 10-5 (summer); 10-3.30 (winter). Closed 25-26 Dec.* **Fees** £7 (ch £4 & pen £6). Prices under review **Facilities** 🅿 🖵 🍴 licensed 🎋 (outdoor) ♿ toilets for disabled shop

HARROGATE

The Royal Pump Room Museum

Crown Place HG1 2RY

☎ 01423 556188 📠 01423 556130

e-mail: museums@harrogate.gov.uk

web: www.harrogate.gov.uk/museums

dir: A61 into town centre and follow brown heritage signs

Housed in the pump room, the museum tells the glory of Harrogate's Spa heyday. Also see the stunning Egyptian collection and temporary exhibitions of social history.

Times Open all year, Mon-Sat 10-5, Sun 2-5, (Nov-Mar close at 4). Closed 24-27 Dec, 1 Jan, 4-6 Jan. Open Aug, Sun 12-5.* **Fees** £3.20 (ch £1.60, concessions £1.80). Family rate £8.50 (2ad+2ch). Party. Combined seasonal tickets available for The Royal Pump Room Museum & Knaresborough Castle & Museum £15.* **Facilities** 🅿 ♿ toilets for disabled shop ⊗

163

HAWES

Dales Countryside Museum & National Park Centre

Station Yard DL8 3NT
☎ 01969 666210 📠 01969 666239
e-mail: hawes@yorkshiredales.org.uk
web: www.yorkshiredales.org.uk
dir: off A684 in Old Station Yard

Fascinating museum telling the story of the people and landscape of the Yorkshire Dales. Static steam loco and carriages with displays. Added features include hands-on interactive displays for children, temporary exhibitions and special events. Free family exhibition every summer with activities for visitors of all ages!

Times Open all year daily 10-5. Closed 24-26 Dec 1 Jan & Jan following Xmas hol period.
Fees Museum: £3 (ch free, concessions £2). National park centre, temporary exhibitions free.*
Facilities 🅿 🅟 🍴 (outdoor) ♿ toilets for disabled shop ⊗

KNARESBOROUGH

Knaresborough Castle & Museum

Castle Yard HG5 8AS
☎ 01423 556188 📠 01423 556130
e-mail: museums@harrogate.gov.uk
web: www.harrogate.gov.uk/museums
dir: off High St towards Market Square, right at police station into Castle Yard

Towering high above the town of Knaresborough, the remains of this 14th-century castle look down over the gorge of the River Nidd. This imposing fortress was once the hiding place of Thomas Becket's murderers and a summer home for the Black Prince. Visit the King's Tower, the secret underground tunnel and the dungeon. Discover Knaresborough's history in the museum and find out about 'Life in a Castle' in the hands-on gallery. Play the new computer game "Time Gate: The Prisoner of Knaresborough Castle". Special events include a Medieval Day annually on the third Sunday in June.

Times Open Good Fri-4 Oct, daily 10.30-5. Guided tours regularly available* **Fees** £2.80 (ch £1.50, concessions £1.80). Family ticket (2ad+3ch) £7.50 Party 10+. Annual season tickets available for Knaresborough Castle & Museum & The Royal Pump Room Museum.* **Facilities** 🅿 🅟 ♿ (partly accessible) (ground floor of King's Tower accessible) toilets for disabled shop ⊗

MALTON

Castle Howard

YO60 7DA

☎ 01653 648333   🖹 01653 648529
e-mail: house@castlehoward.co.uk
web: www.castlehoward.co.uk
dir: off A64, follow brown heritage signs

A magnificent 18th-century house situated in breathtaking parkland. House guides share the history of the house, family and collections, while outdoor guided tours reveal the secrets of the gardens and architecture. Visitors can also enjoy a changing programme of exhibitions and events; boat trips, adventure playground and various cafes and shops including a farm shop and a chocolate shop. New exhibition "Brideshead Restored" - telling the story of restoration of Castle Howard and the filming of both the TV and movie versions of Brideshead Revisited.

Times House: Mar-Oct open Mar-1 Nov & 28 Nov-20 Dec, daily from 11. Gardens, shops & cafes open all year from 10.* Fees £10.50 (ch £6.50, concessions £9.50). Grounds only £8 (ch £5.50, concessions £7.50).* Facilities 🅿 ⊡ ⭢○⭠ licensed ♿ (partly accessible) toilets for disabled shop ⊗

MALTON

Eden Camp Modern History Theme Museum

Eden Camp YO17 6RT

☎ 01653 697777   🖹 01653 698243
e-mail: admin@edencamp.co.uk
web: www.edencamp.co.uk
dir: junct of A64 & A169, between York & Scarborough

In the unique setting of an original prisoner of war camp built in 1942 to house Italian and German POWs, this award-winning museum presents the most comprehensive display of British civilian life during WWII. The period is brought to life through life size tableaux and dioramas which incorporate sound, light and even smells to create the atmosphere of the 1940s. Other sections of the museum cover military and political events of WWII and British military history of the 20th century from WWI to the war in Iraq and Afghanistan. The museum also houses an extensive collection of military vehicles, artillery and associated equipment.

Times Open 2nd Mon in Jan-23 Dec, daily 10-5. (Last admission 4) Fees £5.50 (ch & concessions £4.50). Party 10+, £1 discount on individual admission prices. Facilities 🅿 ⊡ 🎏 (indoor & outdoor) toilets for disabled shop

MIDDLESBROUGH

Captain Cook Birthplace Museum **FREE**

Stewart Park, Marton TS7 8AT
☎ 01642 311211 📄 01642 515659
e-mail: captcookmuseum@middlesbrough.gov.uk
web: www.captcook-ne.co.uk
dir: 3m S on A172

Opened to mark the 250th anniversary of the birth of the voyager in 1728, this museum illustrates the early life of James Cook and his discoveries with permanent and temporary exhibitions. Located in spacious and rolling parkland, the site also offers outside attractions for the visitor. The museum has a special resource centre which has fresh approaches to presentation with computers, films, special effects, interactives and educational aids.

Times Open all year: Mar-Oct, Tue-Sun, 10-5.30. Nov-Feb 9-4. (Last entry 45 mins before closure). Closed Mon & some BH, 24-26 Dec,1 Jan & 1st full week Jan.* **Facilities** 🅿🅿 ⛻ 🍽 licensed 🍴 (outdoor) ♿ toilets for disabled shop ⊗

RIPLEY

Ripley Castle

HG3 3AY
☎ 01423 770152 📄 01423 771745
e-mail: enquiries@ripleycastle.co.uk
web: www.ripleycastle.co.uk
dir: off A61, Harrogate to Ripon road

Ripley Castle has been home to the Ingilby family for 26 generations and stands at the heart of an estate with deer park, lakes and Victorian walled gardens. The Castle has a rich history and a fine collection of Royalist armour housed in the 1555 tower. There are also tropical hot houses, a children's play trail, tearooms, woodland walks, pleasure grounds and the National Hyacinth Collection in spring.

Times Open Nov-8 Mar, Tue, Thu, Sat & Sun 10.30-3; Apr-Oct, daily 10.30-3; Dec-Feb wknds only, also BH and school hols. Groups all year by prior arrangement. Gardens open daily 9-5.* **Fees** Castle & Gardens £8 (ch £5, pen £7). Gardens only £5.50 (ch £3.50, concessions £5). Party £5.* **Facilities** 🅿 ⛻ 🍽 licensed ♿ (partly accessible) (two of the rooms in the castle on view are upstairs) toilets for disabled shop ⊗

RIPON

Fountains Abbey & Studley Royal

HG4 3DY

☎ 01765 608888   📠 01765 601002
e-mail: fountainsenquiries@nationaltrust.org.uk
web: www.fountainsabbey.org.uk
dir: 4m W of Ripon off B6265

A World Heritage Site comprising the ruin of a
12th-century Cistercian abbey and monastic
watermill, an Elizabethan mansion and one
of the best surviving examples of a Georgian
water garden. Elegant ornamental lakes, canals,
temples and cascades provide eye-catching
vistas. The site also contains the Victorian St
Mary's Church and medieval deer park.

Times Open all year, daily, Nov-Feb 10-4, Mar-Oct
10-5. Closed Fri Nov-Jan & 24-25 Dec.* **Facilities**
🅿 ⛄ 🍽 licensed 🎍 (outdoor) ♿ (partly
accessible) toilets for disabled shop ⊗ 🐾

SKIPTON

Skipton Castle

BD23 1AW

☎ 01756 792442   📠 01756 796100
e-mail: info@skiptoncastle.co.uk
web: www.skiptoncastle.co.uk
dir: in town centre at head of High Street

Skipton Castle is one of the most complete and
well-preserved medieval castles in England.
Some of the castle dates from the 1650s when
it was rebuilt after being partially damaged
following the Civil War. However, the original
castle was erected in Norman times and became
the home of the Clifford family in 1310 and
remained so until 1676. Illustrated tour sheets
are available in a number of languages. Please
see website for special events.

Times Open all year, daily from 10, (Sun from
noon). Last admission 6 (4pm Oct-Feb). Closed
25 Dec. **Fees** £6 (incl illustrated tour sheet) (ch
under 18 £3.50, under 5 free, concessions £5.40).
Family ticket £18.90. Party 15+.* **Facilities** 🅿
⛄ 🎍 (indoor & outdoor) ♿ (partly accessible)
(access to grounds, shops, tea room) shop ⊗

WHITBY

Whitby Abbey

YO22 4JT

☎ 01947 603568 📠 01947 825561
web: www.english-heritage.org.uk
dir: on clifftop E of Whitby town centre

Uncover the full story of these atmospheric ruins in their impressive clifftop location above the picturesque fishing town with associations ranging from Victorian jewellery and whaling, to Count Dracula.

Times Open all year, Apr-Sep, daily 10-6; Oct-Mar, Thu-Mon 10-4. Closed 24-26 Dec & 1 Jan. Fees £5.50 (concessions £4.70, ch £2.80). Family ticket £13.80. Prices and opening times are subject to change in March 2010. Please check web site or call 0870 333 1181 for the most up to date prices and opening times when planning your visit. Facilities ⓟ ⛾ ⊼ shop ⚏

YORK

Jorvik Viking Centre

Coppergate YO1 9WT

☎ 01904 615505 📠 01904 627097
e-mail: jorvik@yorkat.co.uk
web: www.jorvik-viking-centre.com
dir: follow A19 or A64 to York. Jorvik in Coppergate shopping area (city centre) signed

Explore York's Viking history on the very site where archaeologists discovered remains of the city of Jorvik. See over 800 of the items discovered on site and meet the famous Jorvik Vikings in three exciting exhibitions, learn what life was like here more than 1000 years ago, and journey through a reconstruction of actual Viking streets. 'Are You A Viking?'uses scientific evidence to discover if you have Viking ancestors. 'Unearthed' tells how the people of ancient York lived and died, as revealed by real bone material. Special events throughout the year.

Times Open all year, summer, daily 10-5; winter, daily 10-4. Closed 24-26 Dec. Opening times subject to change. Fees £8.50 (ch 5-15 £6, under 5 free, concessions £7) Family of 4 £26 & family of 5 £29. Telephone bookings on 01904 615505 (£1 booking fee per person at peak times).* Facilities ⓟ ⛾ ♿ (partly accessible) (wheelchair users are advised to pre-book) toilets for disabled shop ⊗

YORK

Merchant Adventurers' Hall

Fossgate YO1 9XD
☎ 01904 654818   🖹 01904 616150
e-mail: enquiries@theyorkcompany.co.uk
web: www.theyorkcompany.co.uk
dir: located in town centre, between Piccadilly and Fossgate

Construction of the Merchant Adventurers' Hall began in 1357 and it is one of the best preserved medieval guild halls in the world. Explore the Great Hall, Undercroft, and Chapel, along with unique collections of art, silver and furniture. Fully accessible to all from Fossgate.

Times Open all year, Etr-Sep, Mon-Thu, 9-5, Fri & Sat, 9-3.30. Sun 12-4. Oct-Etr, Mon-Sat, 9-3.30, Closed Sun & Xmas period. **Fees** £3 (ch under 7 free, ch 7-16yrs £1, concessions £2.50). Family (2ad+2 or more ch) £7.* **Facilities** ℗ ㅠ (outdoor) ♿ toilets for disabled ⊗

YORK

National Railway Museum

Leeman Rd YO26 4XJ
☎ 01904 621261   🖹 01904 611112
e-mail: nrm@nrm.org.uk
web: www.nrm.org.uk
dir: behind rail station. Signed from all major roads and city centre

The National Railway Museum is the world's largest railway museum. From record breakers to history makers the museum is home to a vast collection of locomotives, carriages and wagons, including The Royal Trains, a replica of Stephenson's Rocket, the Japanese Bullet Train and the elegant Duchess. With three enormous galleries, interactive exhibits and daily events, the National Railway Museum mixes education with fun. This attraction is also free. NB: There is a charge for certain special events.

Times Open all year 10-6. Closed 24-26 Dec. **Fees** Admission is free but there may be charges for special events and rides. **Facilities** ℗℗ ⊡ ⋈ licensed ㅠ (outdoor) ♿ toilets for disabled shop ⊗

YORK

York Castle Museum

The Eye of York YO1 1RY
☎ 01904 687687
e-mail: castle.museum@ymt.org.uk
web: www.yorkcastlemuseum.org.uk
dir: city centre, next to Clifford's Tower

Fascinating exhibits that bring memories to life, imaginatively displayed through reconstructions of period rooms and Victorian indoor streets, complete with cobbles and a Hansom cab. The museum is housed in the city's former prison and is based on an extensive collection of 'bygones' acquired at the beginning of the 20th century. The Victorian street includes a pawnbroker, a tallow candle factory and a haberdasher's. An extensive collection of many other items ranging from musical instruments to costumes. The museum also has one of Britain's finest collections of Militaria. A special exhibition called 'Seeing it Through' explores the life of York citizens during the Second World War. Please contact the museum for details of exhibitions and events.

Times Open all year, daily 9.30-5 **Fees** £7.50 (ch £4 under 5's free, concessions £6.50). Family tickets available* **Facilities** ℗ ☐ ﴾ (partly accessible) (main galleries accessible, no access up stairs) toilets for disabled shop ⊗

YORK

Yorkshire Museum

Museum Gardens YO1 7FR
☎ 01904 551800   📄 01904 551802
e-mail: yorkshire.museum@york.gov.uk
web: http://www.york.gov.uk
dir: park & ride service from 4 sites near A64/A19/A1079 & A166, also 3 car parks within short walk

The Yorkshire Museum is set in 10 acres of botanical gardens in the heart of the historic City of York, and displays some of the finest Roman, Anglo-Saxon, Viking and Medieval treasures ever discovered in Britain. The Middleham jewel, a fine example of English Gothic jewellery, is on display, and in the Roman Gallery, visitors can see a marble head of Constantine the Great. The Anglo-Saxon Gallery houses the delicate silver-gilt Ormside bowl and the Gilling sword.

Times Open all year, daily 10-5.* **Facilities** ℗ ⌨ toilets for disabled shop ⊗

CONISBROUGH

Conisbrough Castle

DN12 3HH
☎ 01709 863329
web: www.english-heritage.org.uk
dir: NE of town centre off A630

The white, circular keep of this 12th-century castle is a spectacular structure. Made of magnesian limestone, it is the oldest of its kind in England. Recently restored, with two new floors and a roof, it is a fine example of medieval architecture and was the inspiration for Sir Walter Scott's classic novel Ivanhoe.

Times Open all year, Apr-Sep, daily 10-5 (last admission 4.20); Oct-Mar, Thu-Mon 10-4, please call site for details. Closed 24-26 Dec & 1 Jan.
Facilities ℗ ⛾ shop ⊗ ♯

SHEFFIELD

Millennium Gallery

Arundel Gate S1 2PP
☎ 0114 278 2600 🖹 0114 278 2604
e-mail: info@museums-sheffield.org.uk
web: www.museums-sheffield.org.uk
dir: Follow signs to city centre, then follow the brown signs marked M.

With four different galleries under one roof, the Millennium Gallery has something for everyone. Enjoy new blockbuster exhibitions drawn from the collections of Britain's national galleries and museums, including the Victoria & Albert Museum and Tate Gallery. See the best of contemporary craft and design in a range of exhibitions by established and up-and-coming makers. Be dazzled by Sheffield's magnificent and internationally important collection of decorative and domestic metalwork and silverware. Discover the Ruskin Gallery with its wonderful array of treasures by Victorian artist and writer John Ruskin.

Times Open all year, daily Mon-Sat 10-5, Sun 11-5.* **Fees** Admission prices apply for some special exhibitions (concessions available).
Facilities ℗ ⛾🍴 licensed toilets for disabled shop ⊗

BRADFORD

Bradford Industrial Museum and Horses at Work **FREE**

Moorside Mills, Moorside Rd, Eccleshill
BD2 3HP
☎ 01274 435900 🖹 01274 636362
web: www.bradfordmuseums.org
dir: off A658

Moorside Mills is an original spinning mill, now part of a museum that brings vividly to life the story of Bradford's woollen industry. There is the machinery that once converted raw wool into cloth, and the mill yard rings with the sound of iron on stone as shire horses pull trams, haul buses and give rides. Daily demonstrations and changing exhibitions.

Times Open all year, Tue-Sat 10-5, Sun 12-5. Closed Mon ex BH, Good Fri & 25-26 Dec*
Facilities 🅿 ⛁ toilets for disabled shop ⊗

BRADFORD

National Media Museum

Pictureville BD1 1NQ
☎ 01274 202030 🖹 01274 723155
e-mail: talk@nationalmediamuseum.org.uk
web: www.nationalmediamuseum.org.uk
dir: 2m from end of M606, follow signs for city centre

Journey through popular photography and visit IMAX - the world's powerful giant screen experience, discover the past, present and future of television in Experience TV, watch your favourite TV moments in TV Heaven, play with light, lenses and colour in the Magic Factory and explore the world of animation - watch a real animator at work in the Animation Gallery. There are also temporary exhibitions and various special events are planned, please see the website for details.

Times Open all year, Tue-Sun 10-6, BH Mon & school hols. Closed 24-26 Dec.* **Fees** Admission to permanent galleries free, IMAX Cinema £6.95 (concessions £4.95). DMR (Feature length films) £8 (£6 concesssions). Groups 20% discount.*
Facilities 🅿🅿 ⛁🍽 licensed ⊼ (Indoor) ♿ toilets for disabled shop ⊗

HALIFAX

Eureka! The National Children's Museum

Discovery Rd HX1 2NE
☎ 01422 330069 📄 01422 330275
e-mail: info@eureka.org.uk
web: www.eureka.org.uk
dir: M62 junct 24 follow brown heritage signs to Halifax centre - A629

With over 400 'must touch' exhibits, interactive activities and challenges, visitors are invited to embark upon a journey of discovery through six main gallery spaces. They can find out how their bodies and senses work, discover the realities of daily life, travel from the familiar 'backyard' to amazing and faraway places and experiment with creating their own sounds and music.

Times Open all year, daily 10-5. Closed 24-26 Dec* **Fees** £7.25 (ch 1-2 £2.25, ch under 1 free) Family Saver ticket £31. Special group rates available.* **Facilities** ⓟⓟ ⌴⊼ (indoor & outdoor) ♿ toilets for disabled shop ⊗

HAWORTH

Brontë Parsonage Museum

Church St BD22 8DR
☎ 01535 642323 📄 01535 647131
e-mail: bronte@bronte.org.uk
web: www.bronte.info
dir: A629 & A6033 follow signs for Haworth, take Rawdon Rd, pass 2 car parks, next left, then right

Haworth Parsonage was the lifelong family home of the Brontës. An intensely close-knit family, the Brontës saw the parsonage as the heart of their world and the moorland setting provided them with inspiration for their writing. The house contains much personal memorabilia, including the furniture Charlotte bought with the proceeds of her literary success, Branwell's portraits of local worthies, Emily's writing desk and Anne's books and drawings. The museum is currently holding a two year exhibition focusing on Branwell Brontë, who as a child was considered the greatest genius of the family. Branwell declined into alcoholism while his sisters went on to write great novels.

Times Open all year, Apr-Sep, daily 10-5.30; Oct-Mar, daily 11-5 (final admission 30 min before closing). Closed 24-27 Dec & 2-31 Jan. **Fees** £6 (ch 5-16 £3, concessions £4.50). Family ticket £15.* **Facilities** ⓟⓟ ♿ (partly accessible) (please contact the museum for info) shop ⊗

173

LEEDS

Leeds Industrial Museum at Armley Mills

Canal Rd, Armley LS12 2QF
☎ 0113 263 7861
web: www.leeds.gov.uk/armleymills
dir: 2m W of city centre, off A65

Once the world's largest woollen mill, Armley Mills evokes memories of the 18th-century woollen industry, showing the progress of wool from the sheep to knitted clothing. The museum has its own 1930s cinema illustrating the history of cinema projection, including the first moving pictures taken in Leeds. The Museum is set in some lovely scenery, between the Leeds & Liverpool Canal and the River Aire. There are demonstrations of static engines and steam locomotives, a printing gallery and a journey through the working world of textiles and fashion.

Times Open all year, Tue-Sat 10-5, Sun 1-5. Last entry 4pm. Closed Mon ex BHs.* **Facilities** ℗ ⊼ (indoor & outdoor) ﾖ (partly accessible) toilets for disabled shop ⊗

LEEDS

Royal Armouries Museum **FREE**

Armouries Dr LS10 1LT
☎ 0113 220 1999 & 0990 106 666
🖹 0113 220 1955
e-mail: enquiries@armouries.org.uk
web: www.royalarmouries.org
dir: off A61 close to Leeds centre, follow brown heritage signs.

The museum is an impressive contemporary home for the renowned national collection of arms and armour. The collection is divided between five galleries: War, Tournament, Self-Defence, Hunting and Oriental. The Hall of Steel features a 100ft-high mass of 3000 pieces of arms and armour. Visitors are encouraged to take part in and handle some of the collections. Live demonstrations and interpretations take place throughout the year.

Times Open all year, daily, from 10-5. Closed 24-25 Dec* **Facilities** ℗ ⊐ ⎮◎⎮ licensed ⊼ (indoor) toilets for disabled shop ⊗

LEEDS

Temple Newsam Estate

Temple Newsam Rd, Off Selby Rd, Halton
LS15 0AE

☎ 0113 264 7321 (House) & 264 5535
(Estate) 🖷 0113 232 6485
e-mail: temple.newsam.house@leeds.gov.uk
web: www.leeds.gov.uk/templenewsam
dir: 4m from city centre on A63 or 2m from M1
junct

Temple Newsam is celebrated as one of the
country's great historic houses and estates.
Set in 1500 acres of stunning parkland,
Temple Newsam House is home to outstanding
collections of fine and decorative art, many
of national importance. The Estate includes a
working Rare Breeds farm and national plant
collections.

Times Open all year. House: Tue-Sun 10.30-5,
Nov-28 Dec & Mar, Tue-Sat 10.30-4. Open BHs.
Home Farm: Tue-Sun, 10-5 (4 in winter), also
open Mon in school hols; Gardens: 10-dusk.
Estate: daily, dawn-dusk.* **Facilities** 🅿 ⚏ 🎌
(outdoor) ♿ toilets for disabled shop ⊗

MIDDLESTOWN

National Coal Mining Museum for England **FREE**

Caphouse Colliery, New Rd WF4 4RH
☎ 01924 848806 🖷 01924 844567
e-mail: info@ncm.org.uk
web: www.ncm.org.uk
dir: on A642 between Huddersfield & Wakefield

A unique opportunity to go 140 metres
underground down one of Britain's oldest working
mines. Take a step back in time with one of the
museum's experienced local miners who will
guide parties around the underground workings,
where models and machinery depict methods
and conditions of mining from the early 1800s
to present day. Other attractions include the
Hope Pit, pithead baths, Victorian steam winder,
nature trail and adventure playground and meet
the last ever working pit ponies. You are strongly
advised to wear sensible footwear and warm
clothing.

Times Open all year, daily 10-5. Closed 24-26
Dec & 1 Jan.* **Facilities** 🅿 ⚏ 🍽 licensed 🎌
(outdoor) ♿ toilets for disabled shop ⊗

175

FOREST

German Occupation Museum

GY8 0BG

☎ 01481 238205

dir: Behind Forest Church near the airport

The museum has the Channel Islands' largest collection of Occupation items, with tableaux of a kitchen, bunker rooms and a street during the Occupation. 2010 sees the 65th anniversary of Liberation Day on the 9th May and will be celebrated with special events, exhibitions and the opening of a new extension.

Times Open all year, daily Apr-Oct 10-4.30; Nov-Mar 10-12.30 (Closed Mon Nov-Mar) **Fees** £4 (ch £2). Free admission for disabled. **Facilities** ℗ ⛴ 🌳 (outdoor) ♿ (partly accessible) (Steps to street level alternative route available) ⊗

ST PETER PORT

Castle Cornet

GY1 1AU

☎ 01481 721657   📄 01481 715177

e-mail: admin@museums.gov.gg

web: www.museums.gov.gg

dir: 5 mins walk from St Peter Port bus terminus

The history of this magnificent castle spans eight centuries and its buildings now house several museums, the Refectory Cafe and a shop. Soldiers fire the noonday gun in a daily ceremony. Look for the Maritime Museum that charts Guernsey's nautical history, the 'Story of Castle Cornet' with its mystery skeleton and the 201 squadron RAF Museum. A refurbished Regimental Museum of the Royal Guernsey Militia and Royal Guernsey Light Infantry is now open. A programme of living history, theatre, music and family events take place throughout the year.

Times Open 26 Mar-Oct, daily 10-5. **Fees** £7.25 (ch over 7, students & adults after 4 pm £1, pen £5.75). Season ticket available. **Facilities** ℗ ⛴ shop ⊗

ST PETER PORT

Guernsey Museum & Art Gallery

Candie Gardens GY1 1UG
☎ 01481 726518 📠 01481 715177
e-mail: admin@museums.gov.gg
web: www.museums.gov.gg
dir: On the outskirts of St Peter Port set in the
Victorian 'Candie gardens'

The museum, designed around a Victorian
bandstand, tells the story of Guernsey and its
people. There is an audio-visual theatre and an
art gallery, and special exhibitions are arranged
throughout the year. It is surrounded by beautiful
gardens with superb views over St Peter Port
harbour.

Times Open Feb-Dec, daily 10-5 (winter 10-4)
Fees £4.50 (ch over 7 & students £1, pen £3.75).
Season ticket available. Facilities ℗ ☐&
toilets for disabled shop ⊗

ST HELIER

Maritime Museum & Occupation Tapestry Gallery

New North Quay JE2 3ND
☎ 01534 811043 📠 01534 874099
e-mail: marketing@jerseyheritagetrust.org
web: www.jerseyheritagetrust.org
dir: alongside Marina, opposite Liberation Square

This converted 19th-century warehouse houses
the tapestry consisting of 12 two-metre panels
that tells the story of the occupation of Jersey
during World War II. Each of the 12 parishes
took responsibility for stitching a panel, making
it the largest community arts project ever
undertaken on the island. The Maritime Museum
celebrates the relationship of islanders and
the sea, including an award winning hands-on
experience, especially enjoyed by children.

Times Open all year, daily summer 9.30-5; winter
10-4.* Facilities ℗ & toilets for disabled
shop ⊗

ST LAWRENCE

Jersey War Tunnels

Les Charrieres Malorey JE3 1FU
☎ 01534 860808 📠 01534 860886
e-mail: info@jerseywartunnels.com
web: www.jerseywartunnels.com
dir: bus route 8A from St Helier

On 1 July 1940 the Channel Islands were occupied by German forces, and this vast complex dug deep into a hillside is the most evocative reminder of that Occupation. A video presentation, along with a large collection of memorabilia, illustrates the lives of the islanders at war and a further exhibition records their impressions during 1945, the year of liberation.

Times Open 14 Feb-19 Dec, daily 9.30-5.30 (last admission 4).* **Facilities** 🅿 🅟 ☕ 🍴 licensed toilets for disabled shop 🚫

ST OUEN

The Channel Islands Military Museum

Five Mile Rd
☎ 07797 732072
e-mail: damienhorn@jerseymail.co.uk
dir: N end of Five Mile Rd, at rear of Jersey Woollen Mill & across road from Jersey Pearl

The museum is housed in a German coastal defence bunker, which formed part of Hitler's Atlantic Wall. It has been restored, as far as possible, to give the visitor an idea of how it looked. The visitor can also see German uniforms, weapons, documents, photographs, other items from the 1940-45 occupation as well as a large collection of civilian items from the time, many of which have not been on display before.

Times Open Mon before Good Fri-Oct. **Fees** £4 (ch £2) Groups by arrangement. **Facilities** 🅿 🅟 ☕ 🍴 (outdoor) ♿ toilets for disabled shop 🚫

CASTLETOWN

Castle Rushen

The Quay IM9 1LD
☎ 01624 648000 📠 01624 648001
e-mail: enquiries@mnh.gov.im
web: www.storyofmann.com
dir: centre of Castletown

One of the world's best preserved medieval castles, Castle Rushen is a limestone fortress rising out of the heart of the old capital of the Island, Castletown. Once the fortress of the Kings and Lords of Mann, Castle Rushen is brought alive with rich decorations, and the sounds and smells of a bygone era.

Times Open daily, Etr-Oct, 10-5.* **Fees** £5 (ch £2.50) Family £12. Group from £4.50 each.* **Facilities** ℗ shop ⊗

CASTLETOWN

Old Grammar School **FREE**

IM9 1LE
☎ 01624 648000 📠 01624 648001
e-mail: enquiries@mnh.gov.im
web: www.storyofmann.com
dir: centre of Castletown, opposite the castle

Built around 1200AD, the former capital's first church, St Mary's, has had a significant role in Manx education. It was a school from 1570 to 1930 and evokes memories of Victorian school life.

Times Open daily, Etr-late Oct, 10-5.* **Facilities** ℗ ℗ 🎋 (outdoor) ♿ (partly accessible) (restricted access narrow door, 3 steps) shop ⊗

CASTLETOWN

The Old House of Keys

IM9 1LA

☎ 01624 648000 📠 01624 648001
e-mail: enquiries@mnh.gov.im
web: www.storyofmann.com
dir: opposite Castletown Rushen in centre of
Castletown

The Old House of Keys is a portrayal of the long
and often turbulent history of Manx politics. It
has been restored to its appearance in 1866
and visitors are invited to participate in a lively
debate with interactive Members of Tynwald, the
Manx parliament.

Times Open daily, Apr-late Oct, 10-5.* **Facilities**
Ⓟ ⊗

DOUGLAS

Manx Museum FREE

IM1 3LY

☎ 01624 648000 📠 01624 648001
e-mail: enquiries@mnh.gov.im
web: www.storyofmann.com
dir: signed in Douglas

The Island's treasure house provides an exciting
introduction to the "Story of Mann" where a
specially produced film portrayal of Manx history
complements the award-winning displays.
Galleries depict natural history, archaeology
and the social development of the Island. There
are also examples of famous Manx artists in the
National Art Gallery, together with the Island's
National archive and reference library. Events
and exhibitions throughout the year, please visit
website for details.

Times Open all year, Mon-Sat, 10-5. Closed
25-26 Dec & 1 Jan.* **Facilities** 🅿 Ⓟ 🖵 🍽
licensed 🍴 (outdoor) ♿ toilets for disabled
shop ⊗

LAXEY

Great Laxey Wheel & Mines Trail

☎ 01624 648000 📄 01624 648001
e-mail: enquiries@mnh.gov.im
web: www.storyofmann.com
dir: signed in Laxey village

Built in 1854, the Great Laxey Wheel, 22 metres in diameter, is the largest working water wheel in the world. It was designed to pump water from the lead and zinc mines, and is an acknowledged masterpiece of Victorian engineering. The wheel is also known as 'Lady Isabella', after the wife of the then Lieutenant Governor of the Isle of Man.

Times Open Etr-Oct 10-5* **Fees** £3.50 (ch £1.80) Family £8.50. Group rates from £2.80* **Facilities** 🅿 ℗ 🍴 (outdoor) shop ⊗

ABERDEEN

Aberdeen Maritime Museum
FREE

Shiprow AB11 5BY
☎ 01224 337700 📄 01224 213066
e-mail: info@aagm.co.uk
web: www.aberdeencity.gov.uk
dir: located in city centre

The award-winning Maritime Museum brings the history of the North Sea to life. Featuring displays and exhibitions on the offshore oil industry, shipbuilding, fishing and clipper ships.

Times Open all year, Tue-Sat, 10-5, Sun 2-5.*
Facilities ℗ 🖵 🍴 licensed ♿ (partly accessible) (2 rooms in Provost Ross's house not accessible due to stairs) toilets for disabled shop ⊗

BALMORAL

Balmoral Castle Grounds & Exhibition

AB35 5TB

☎ 013397 42534 📄 013397 42034
e-mail: info@balmoralcastle.com
web: www.balmoralcastle.com
dir: on A93 between Ballater & Braemar

Queen Victoria and Prince Albert first rented Balmoral Castle in 1848, and Prince Albert bought the property four years later. He commissioned William Smith to build a new castle, which was completed by 1856 and is still the Royal Family's Highland residence. Explore the exhibitions, grounds, gardens and trails as well as the magnificent Castle Ballroom.

Times Open Apr-Jul, daily 10-5 (last admission 4.30)* **Fees** £7 (ch £3, concessions £6). Family (2ad+4ch) £15.* **Facilities** 🅿 🖵 🎡 (outdoor) ♿ toilets for disabled shop

MINTLAW

Aberdeenshire Farming Museum FREE

Aden Country Park AB42 5FQ

☎ 01771 624590 📄 01771 623558
e-mail: museums@aberdeenshire.gov.uk
web: www.aberdeenshire.gov.uk/museums
dir: 1m W of Mintlaw on A950

Housed in 19th-century farm buildings, once part of the estate which now makes up the Aden Country Park. Two centuries of farming history and innovation are illustrated, and the story of the estate is also told. The reconstructed farm of Hareshowe shows how a family in the north-east farmed during the 1950s - access by guided tour only.

Times Open May-Sep, daily 11-4.30; Apr & Oct, wknds only noon-4.30. (Last admission 30 mins before closing). Park open all year, Apr-Sep 7-10; winter 7-7.* **Facilities** 🅿 🅟 🖵 🎡 (outdoor) ♿ (partly accessible) (1st floor not accessible) toilets for disabled shop ⊗

OYNE

Archaeolink Prehistory Park

Berryhill AB52 6QP
☎ 01464 851500   📄 01464 851544
e-mail: info@archaeolink.co.uk
web: www.archaeolink.co.uk
dir: 1m off A96 on B9002

A stunning audio-visual show, a Myths and Legends Gallery and a whole range of interpretation techniques help visitors to explore what it was like to live 6000 years ago. In addition there are landscaped walkways, and outdoor activity areas including an Iron Age farm, Roman marching camp and Stone Age settlement in the 40-acre park. Enjoy daily hands-on activities for all ages, guided tours with costumed guides or relax in the coffee shop. Special weekend events held regularly.

Times Open Apr-Oct, daily 10-5 Fees £5.75 (ch £3.70, concessions £4.90) Family from £12.15*
Facilities ❷ ⓟ ⌴ ⦿ licensed ⦚ (outdoor) toilets for disabled shop ⊗

ARBROATH

Arbroath Abbey

DD11 1EG
☎ 01241 878756
web: www.historic-scotland.gov.uk

The `Declaration of Arbroath' - declaring Robert the Bruce as king - was signed at the 12th-century abbey on 6 April 1320. The abbot's house is well preserved, and the church remains are also interesting.

Times Open all year, Apr-Sep, daily, 9.30-5.30; Oct-Mar, daily 9.30-4.30. Closed 25-26 Dec & 1-2 Jan.* Fees £4.70 (ch £2.35, concessions £3.70). Please phone or check website for further details.* Facilities ❷ ⊗ ⦚

BRECHIN

Pictavia Visitor Centre

Brechin Castle Centre, Haughmuir DD9 6RL
☎ 01356 626241 ▤ 01307 467357
e-mail: ecdev@angus.gov.uk
web: www.pictavia.org.uk
dir: off A90 at Brechin

Find about more about the ancient pagan nation of the Picts, who lived in Scotland nearly 2000 years ago. Visitors can learn about Pictish culture, art and religion through film, interactive displays and music. There are also nature and farm trails, a pets' corner, and an adventure playground in the adjacent country park (operated by Brechin Castle Centre). 2010 will see the introduction of new interactive computer games, a temporary exhibition and re-enactment weekends. For details please check website.

Times Open all year, Mar-Oct, Mon-Sat 9-5, Sun 10-5; Nov-Feb, Sat 9-5, Sun 10-5. **Fees** £3.25 (ch & concessions £2.25, ch under 5 free). Family ticket £10. Group rates available for large parties & educational groups. **Facilities** ❷ ☑ ⁏◉⁏ licensed ⋤ (outdoor) � toilets for disabled shop ⊗

GLAMIS

Glamis Castle

DD8 1RJ
☎ 01307 840393 ▤ 01307 840733
e-mail: enquiries@glamis-castle.co.uk
web: www.glamis-castle.co.uk
dir: 5m W of Forfar on A94

Glamis Castle is the family home of the Earls of Strathmore and Kinghorne and has been a royal residence since 1372. It is the childhood home of the late Queen Mother, the birthplace of her daughter the late Princess Margaret, and the setting for Shakespeare's play 'Macbeth'. Though the Castle is open to visitors it remains the home of the Strathmore family. Each year there are Highland games, a transport extravaganza, the Scottish Prom Weekend, and a countryside festival. Contact venue for exact dates.

Times Open all year, Mar-Oct, 10-6 (last admission 4.30), Nov-Dec 10.30-5 (last admission 3.30).* **Facilities** ❷ ℗ ⁏◉⁏ licensed ⋤ (outdoor) ৬ (partly accessible) toilets for disabled shop ⊗

KILMARTIN

Kilmartin House Museum

PA31 8RQ

☎ 01546 510278 🖻 01546 510330
e-mail: museum@kilmartin.org
web: www.kilmartin.org
dir: in centre of village, adjacent to church

People have lived in the Kilmartin area for thousands of years, gradually shaping the extraordinary landscape you see today. More than 350 prehistoric and historic sites lie within six miles of this quiet village; burial cairns, rock-carvings, standing stones, stone circles and the fortress of the earliest Scottish Kings, medieval castles, ancient gravestones depicting warriors, early Christian crosses and deserted croft houses. This remarkable concentration and diversity of ancient sites is celebrated at Kilmartin House Museum. Explore enigmatic monuments, see ancient objects and learn more about the people who made them.

Times Open Mar-Oct, daily, 10-5.30. Nov-Xmas 11-4.* **Fees** £4.60 (ch £1.70, concessions £3.90). Family ticket £6 or £10.* **Facilities** 🅿 🅟 ⬛ 🍽 licensed 🛱 (outdoor) ♿ (partly accessible) (stairs to audio visual theatre) toilets for disabled shop ⊗ ▱

DUMFRIES

Robert Burns Centre

Mill Rd DG2 7BE

☎ 01387 264808 🖻 01387 265081
e-mail: dumfriesmuseum@dumgal.gov.uk
web: www.dumgal.gov.uk/museums
dir: on Westbank of River Nith

This award-winning centre explores the connections between Robert Burns and the town of Dumfries. Situated in the town's 18th-century watermill, the centre tells the story of Burns' last years spent in the busy streets and lively atmosphere of Dumfries in the 1790s. In the evening the centre shows feature films in the Film Theatre.

Times Open all year, Apr-Sep Mon-Sat 10-8, Sun 2-5, Oct-Mar, Tue-Sat 10-1 & 2-5. **Fees** Free admission to museum, audio-visual theatre £1.80 (concessions 90p).* **Facilities** 🅿 🅟 ⬛ 🍽 licensed 🛱 (outdoor) ♿ toilets for disabled shop

DUMFRIES

Robert Burns House

Burns St DG1 2PS
☎ 01387 255297   📠 01387 265081
e-mail: dumfriesmuseum@dumgal.gov.uk
web: www.dumgal.gov.uk/museums
dir: signed from Brooms Rd [ATS] car park

It was in this house that Robert Burns spent the last three years of his short life; he died here in 1796. It retains much of its 18th-century character and contains many fascinating items connected with the poet. There is the chair in which he wrote his last poems, many original letters and manuscripts, and the famous Kilmarnock and Edinburgh editions of his work.

Times Open all year, Apr-Sep, Mon-Sat 10-5, Sun 2-5; Oct-Mar, Tue-Sat 10-1 & 2-5.* **Fees** Free admission but donations welcome **Facilities** ℗ shop

NEW ABBEY

National Museum of Costume Scotland

Shambellie House DG2 8HQ
☎ 0131 247 4030
e-mail: info@nms.ac.uk
web: www.nms.ac.uk/costume
dir: 7m S of Dumfries, on A710

Become a dedicated follower of fashion. Shambellie House, a 19th-century country home in wooded grounds, is the perfect setting for discovering 100 years of costume, from the 1850s through to the 1950s. Put yourself in the shoes of those who wore the trends of the time. The museum holds special events and activities throughout the year.

Times Open Apr-Oct, daily, 10-5. **Fees** £3.50 (ch under 12 & members free, concessions £2.50). **Facilities** ℗ ⊑ ⩕ (outdoor) ♿ (partly accessible) (ramp & wheelchair lift provide access to ground floor of museum, tearoom & toilets) shop ⊗

RUTHWELL

Savings Banks Museum FREE

DG1 4NN

☎ 01387 870640

e-mail: savingsbanksmuseum@tiscali.co.uk
web: www.lloydstsb.com/savingsbankmuseum
dir: off B724, 10m E of Dumfries & 7m W of
Annan

Housed in the building where Savings Banks
first began, the museum traces their growth
and development from 1810 up to the present
day. The museum also traces the life of Dr Henry
Duncan, father of savings banks, and restorer
of the Ruthwell Cross. Multi-lingual leaflets
available.

Times Open all year, Apr-Sep, Tue-Sat; Oct-Mar,
Thu-Sat 10-4. Open on BHs except Xmas Day &
New Year.* **Facilities** 🅿 🅟 🕭 🛇

WANLOCKHEAD

Hidden Treasures Museum of Lead Mining

ML12 6UT

☎ 01659 74387   📄 01659 74481

e-mail: miningmuseum@hotmail.com
web: www.leadminingmuseum.co.uk
dir: signed from M74 and A76

Wanlockhead is Scotland's highest village, set
in the beautiful Lowther Hills. Visitors can see
miners' cottages, and the miners' library as well
as the 18th-century lead mine. Visitors can also
pan for gold.

Times Open Apr-Nov, daily 11-4.30; Jul-Aug &
BHs 10-5.* **Fees** £6.25 (ch & concessions £4.50).
Family tickets available.* **Facilities** 🅿 🅟 🍵
🍴 licensed 🎪 (outdoor) 🕭 toilets for disabled
shop 🛇

187

WHITHORN

Whithorn-Cradle of Christianity

45-47 George St DG8 8NS

☎ 01988 500508

e-mail: enquiries@whithorn.com

web: www.whithorn.com

dir: follow directions S from junct at Newton Stewart & Glenluce A75. Centre on main street in centre of Whithorn

The Whithorn Story tells the story of the first Christian settlement in Scotland - the Candida Casa (or White House) built by St Ninian circa 397AD. There is an audio-visual element, an exhibition, Priory ruins and a Historic Scotland Museum. The Festival of St Ninian takes place from the end of July to mid-September.

Times Open daily, Apr or Etr-Oct 10.30-5.*
Facilities ℗ ☐ ⊟ (outdoor) ⑤ toilets for disabled shop

WHITHORN

Whithorn Priory

DG8 8PY

☎ 01988 500700

web: www.historic-scotland.gov.uk

dir: on A746

The first Christian church in Scotland was founded here by St Ninian in 397AD, but the present ruins date from the 12th century. These ruins are sparse but there is a notable Norman door, the Latinus stone of the 5th century and other early Christian monuments.

Times Open Apr-Oct, daily 10.30-5.* **Fees** £3.70 (ch £1.85, concessions £2.70). Please phone or check website for further details.* **Facilities** ℗ ⊗ 具

DUNDEE

Discovery Point & RRS Discovery

Discovery Quay DD1 4XA
☎ 01382 309060 📠 01382 225891
e-mail: info@dundeeheritage.co.uk
web: www.rrsdiscovery.com
dir: follow brown heritage signs for Historic Ships

Discovery Point is the home of *RRS Discovery*, Captain Scott's famous Antarctic ship. Spectacular lighting, graphics and special effects re-create key moments in the Discovery story. The restored bridge gives a captain's view over the ship and the River Tay. Learn what happened to the ship after the expedition, during the First World War and the Russian Revolution, and find out about her involvement in the first survey of whales' migratory patterns.

Times Open all year, Apr-Oct, Mon-Sat 10-6. Sun 11-6; Nov-Mar, Mon-Sat 10-5, Sun 11-5.* **Fees** £7.50 (ch £4.50, concessions £5.75). Family ticket £20.* **Facilities** ℗ ℗ ☑ 🍽 licensed ☶ (outdoor) ♿ (partly accessible) (access to exhibition on top deck, no access to lower deck, but virtual tour available) toilets for disabled shop ⊗

DUNDEE

HM Frigate Unicorn

Victory Dock DD1 3BP
☎ 01382 200900 & 200893
e-mail: mail@frigateunicorn.org
web: www.frigateunicorn.org
dir: from W follow A85 from A90 at Invergowrie. From E follow A92. Near N end of Tay Road Bridge. Follow signs for City Quay.

The *Unicorn* is the oldest British-built warship afloat, and Scotland's only example of a wooden warship. Today she houses a museum of life in the Royal Navy during the days of sail, with guns, models and displays.

Times Open all year Apr-Oct, daily 10-5; Nov-Mar, Wed-Fri 12-4, Sat-Sun 10-4. Closed Mon-Tue & 2 weeks at Xmas & New Year. **Fees** £4 (concessions £3). Family ticket £9-£11. Groups 10+ £2.50 each.* **Facilities** ℗ ☑ ♿ (partly accessible) (wheelchair access to main gun deck only) shop ⊗

EAST FORTUNE

National Museum of Flight Scotland

East Fortune Airfield EH39 5LF

☎ 0131 247 4238

e-mail: info@nms.ac.uk

web: www.nms.ac.uk

dir: signed from A1 near Haddington. Onto B1347, past Athelstaneford, 20m E of Edinburgh

Situated on 63 acres of one of Britain's best preserved wartime airfields, the museum has four hangars, with more than 50 aeroplanes, plus engines, rockets and memorabilia. Items on display include two Spitfires, a Vulcan bomber and Britain's oldest surviving aeroplane, built in 1896; recent exhibits also include a Phantom jet fighter, and a Harrier jump-jet. The Concorde Experience (boarding passes are limited) explores the story of this historic plane through the lives of those who worked or travelled on it.

Times Open all year, Apr-Oct, daily, 10-5. Nov-Mar, wknds only, 10-4. (Contact for details of seasonal variations in opening times) Fees £8.50 (ch under 12 & NMS members free, concessions £6.50). Facilities ♿ ⏛ ⻌ (outdoor) ♿ (partly accessible) (no wheelchair access to Concorde's passenger cabin, most display areas are on ground floor) toilets for disabled shop ⊗

PRESTONPANS

Prestongrange Museum   FREE

Prestongrange

☎ 0131 653 2904   📄 01620 828201

e-mail: elms@eastlothian.gov.uk

web: www.prestongrange.org

dir: on B1348 coast road between Prestonpans & Musselburgh

The oldest documented coal mining site in Scotland, with 800 years of history, this museum shows a Cornish Beam Engine and on-site evidence of associated industries such as brickmaking and pottery. It is located next to a 16th-century customs port. Contact for details of special events or see website.

Times Open Apr-Oct, daily, 11-4.30. Facilities ♿ ⏛ ⻌ (outdoor) ♿ (partly accessible) (grounds partly accessible) toilets for disabled shop ⊗

EDINBURGH

Edinburgh Castle

EH1 2NG
☎ 0131 225 9846
web: www.historic-scotland.gov.uk

This historic stronghold stands on the precipitous crag of Castle Rock. One of the oldest parts is the 11th-century chapel of the saintly Queen Margaret, but most of the present castle evolved later, during its stormy history of sieges and wars, and was altered again in Victorian times. The Scottish crown and other royal regalia are displayed in the Crown Room. Also notable is the Scottish National War Memorial.

Times Open all year, Apr-Sep, daily, 9.30-6; Oct-Mar 9.30-5; 1 Jan, 11-4.30. Closed 25-26 Dec.* **Fees** £10.30 (ch £4.50, concessions £8.50). Please phone or check website for further details.* **Facilities** ℗ ⊡ ᝥ licensed toilets for disabled shop ⊗ 🗮

EDINBURGH

John Knox House

Scottish Story Telling Centre, 43-45 High St
EH1 1SR
☎ 0131 556 9579 ▤ 0131 557 5224
e-mail: reception@scottishstorytellingcentre.com
web: www.scottishstorytellingcentre.co.uk
dir: Between The Castle and Holyrood House, halfway along Edinburgh's Royal Mile

John Knox the Reformer is said to have died in the house, which was built by the goldsmith to Mary, Queen of Scots. Renovation work has revealed the original floor in the Oak Room, and a magnificent painted ceiling. Audio tour available.

Times Open all year, Mon-Sat 10-6. Jul-Aug, Sun 12-6. Closed 25-26 Dec and 1-2 Jan. **Fees** £3.50 (ch £1, under 7's free, concessions £3).* **Facilities** ℗ ⊡ ᝤ (partly accessible) (access to ground floor only, virtual computer tour for rest of house) toilets for disabled shop ⊗

EDINBURGH

National Museum of Scotland **FREE**

Chambers St EH1 1JF
☎ 0131 225 7534
e-mail: info@nms.ac.uk
web: www.nms.ac.uk
dir: situated in Chambers St in Old Town. A few mins walk from Princes St and The Royal Mile

Scotland - past, present and future. The Museum's collections tell you the story of Scotland - land, people and culture. What influence has the world had on Scotland, and Scotland on the world? Your journey of discovery starts here. For generations the museum has collected key exhibits from all over Scotland and beyond. Viking brooches, Pictish stones, ancient chessmen and Queen Mary's clarsach. There's more! Connect with Dolly the sheep, design a robot, test drive a Formula One car or blast off into outer space. See website for special exhibitions and events. Part of the Victorian Royal museum building is closed for refurbishment and will re-open in 2011.

Times Open all year, daily 10-5. **Facilities** ℗ ☕ ⍦ licensed ♿ toilets for disabled shop ⊗

EDINBURGH

National War Museum Scotland

Edinburgh Castle EH1 2NG
☎ 0131 225 7534 📄 0131 225 3848
e-mail: info@nms.ac.uk
web: www.nms.ac.uk
dir: at Edinburgh Castle, a few minutes walk up the Royal Mile to Castlehill

Explore the Scottish experience of war and military service over the last 400 years. A chance to experience the poignant stories of the Scots who went to war, through their letters and personal treasures. See website for special exhibitions and events.

Times Open all year, daily, Apr-Sep, 9.45-5.45; Oct-Mar, 9.45-4.45. Closed 25-26 Dec.
Fees Standard Fares £12 (ch £6, ch under 5 free, concessions £10). NMS members £10.80. Free entry to museum with admission to Edinburgh Castle. Peak Fares £13 (ch £6.50, concessions £10.50). NMS Members £11.70. **Facilities** ℗ ♿ toilets for disabled shop ⊗

EDINBURGH

Palace of Holyroodhouse

EH8 8DX

☎ 0131 556 5100 📠 020 7930 9625
e-mail: bookinginfo@royalcollection.org.uk
web: www.royalcollection.org.uk
dir: at east end of Royal Mile

The Palace grew from the guest house of the Abbey of Holyrood, said to have been founded by David I after a miraculous apparition. Mary, Queen of Scots had her court here from 1561 to 1567, and 'Bonnie' Prince Charlie held levees at the Palace during his occupation of Edinburgh. Today the Royal Apartments are used by HM The Queen for state ceremonies and official entertaining, and are finely decorated with works of art from the Royal Collection.

Times Open all year, daily, Apr-Oct 9.30-6 (last admission 5); Nov-Mar 9.30-4.30 (last admission 3.30). Closed Good Fri, 25-26 Dec and when The Queen is in residence.* **Fees** £10.50 (ch £6.50, concessions £9.50). Family ticket (2ad+3ch) £28. Provides unlimited admission for 12 months. **Facilities** 🅿 ⓟ 🍽🦽 (partly accessible) (historic apartments accessible by spiral staircase) toilets for disabled shop ⊗

EDINBURGH

The Royal Yacht Britannia

Ocean Terminal, Leith EH6 6JJ

☎ 0131 555 5566 📠 0131 555 8835
e-mail: enquiries@tryb.co.uk
web: www.royalyachtbritannia.co.uk
dir: follow signs to North Edinburgh & Leith. Situated within Ocean Terminal

Visit the Royal Yacht Britannia, now in Edinburgh's historic port of Leith. The experience starts in the Visitor Centre where you can discover Britannia's fascinating story. Then step aboard for a self-led audio tour which takes you around five decks giving you a unique insight into what life was like for the Royal Family, officers and yachtsmen. Highlights include the State Apartments, Admiral's Cabin, Engine Room, Laundry and Sick Bay. Visit the new Royal Deck tearoom.

Times Open all year daily from 10 (Jul & Aug from 9.30). Last admission 4 (Apr-Jul, Sep-Oct), 4.30 (Aug) or 3.30 (Nov-Mar). Closed 25 Dec & 1 Jan. **Fees** £10.50 (ch 5-17 £6.25, concessions £9) Family ticket (2ad+3ch) £29.75. **Facilities** 🅿 ⓟ 🍽🦽 toilets for disabled shop ⊗

BIRKHILL

Birkhill Fireclay Mine

EH51 9AQ

☎ 01506 825855 & 822298

🖹 01506 828766

e-mail: mine@srps.org.uk

web: www.srps.org.uk

dir: A706 from Linlithgow, A904 from Grangemouth, follow brown signs to Steam Railway & Fireclay Mine. Main access is by train from Bo'ness

Tour guides will meet you at Birkhill Station and lead you down into the ancient woodland of the beautiful Avon Gorge, and then into the caverns of the Birkhill Fireclay mine. See how the clay was worked, what it was used for and find the 300-million-year-old fossils in the roof of the mine.

Times Open wknds Apr-Oct, daily in Jul-Aug.
Fees Mine & Train £9 (ch £5, concessions £7.50) Family ticket (2ad+2ch) £23. Mine only £3.10 (ch £2.10, concessions £2.60) Family ticket £8.25.*
Facilities 🅿 ℗ 🛱 (outdoor) toilets for disabled

BO'NESS

Bo'ness & Kinneil Railway

Bo'ness Station, Union St EH51 9AQ

☎ 01506 825855 & 822298

🖹 01506 828766

e-mail: enquiries.railway@srps.org.uk

web: www.srps.org.uk

dir: A904 from all directions, signed

Historic railway buildings, including the station and train shed, have been relocated from sites all over Scotland. The Scottish Railway Exhibition tells the story of the development of railways and their impact on the people of Scotland. Take a seven mile return trip by steam train to the tranquil country station at Birkhill. Thomas the Tank Engine weekends in May, August and September, and Santa Specials in December. Booking is essential for these special events.

Times Open wknds Apr-Oct, daily Jul-Aug.
Fees Return fare £9 (ch 5-15 £5, concessions £7.50). Family ticket £23. (Ticket for return train fare & tour of Birkhill Fireclay Mine).* **Facilities** 🅿 ℗ ⊊🛱 (outdoor) 🧑‍🦽 toilets for disabled shop

FALKIRK

Callendar House **FREE**

Callendar Park FK1 1YR
☎ 01324 503770 📄 01324 503771
e-mail: callendar.house@falkirk.gov.uk
web: www.falkirk.gov.uk/cultural
dir: On south side of town centre, Callendar
House is signposted. Easily accessible from M9

Mary, Queen of Scots, Oliver Cromwell, Bonnie
Prince Charlie, noble earls and wealthy
merchants all feature in the history of Callendar
House. Costumed interpreters describe early
19th-century life in the kitchens and the 900-
year history of the house is illustrated in the
'Story of Callendar House' exhibition. The house
is set in parkland, offering boating and woodland
walks. Regular temporary heritage, natural
history and visual arts exhibitions in Callendar
House's Large Gallery.

Times Open all year, Mon-Sat, 10-5 (Sun Apr-Sep
only 2-5).* **Facilities** 🅿 🅟 ⊑ 🚻 (outdoor) ♿
(partly accessible) (ramped access, lift to all
floors, no wheelchair access to shop/reception)
toilets for disabled shop 🚫

ANSTRUTHER

Scottish Fisheries Museum

St Ayles, Harbour Head KY10 3AB
☎ 01333 310628 📄 01333 310628
e-mail: info@scotfishmuseum.org
web: www.scotfishmuseum.org
dir: A917 through St Monans & Pittenweem to
Anstruther

This award-winning national museum tells the
story of Scottish fishing and its people from the
earliest times to the present. With 10 galleries,
2 large boatyards, and a restored fisherman's
cottage, which contain many fine paintings and
photographs, boat models and 17 actual boats,
clothing and items of daily life to see, a visit to
the museum makes for an exceptional day out.
Contact the museum for details of events.

Times Open all year, Apr-Sep, Mon-Sat 10-5.30,
Sun 11-5; Oct-Mar, Mon-Sat 10-4.30, Sun
12-4.30. Closed 25-26 Dec & 1-2 Jan. (Last
admission 1 hr before closing).* **Fees** £5 (ch
in school groups £1.50, accompanied ch free,
concessions £4).* **Facilities** 🅟 ⊑ ♿ toilets for
disabled shop 🚫

DUNFERMLINE

Andrew Carnegie Birthplace Museum FREE

Moodie St KY12 7PL
☎ 01383 724302 📠 01383 749799
e-mail: info@carnegiebirthplace.com
web: www.carnegiebirthplace.com
dir: 400yds S from Abbey

The museum tells the story of the handloom weaver's son, born here in 1835, who created the biggest steel works in the USA and then became a philanthropist on a huge scale. The present-day work of the philanthropic Carnegie Trust is also explained. 175th anniversary of the birth of Andrew Carnegie on 25th November 2010.

Times Open Apr-Oct, Mon-Sat 11-5, Sun 2-5.
Facilities 🅿 Ⓟ 🍽 ♿ (partly accessible)
(cottage inaccessible, main hall and shop accessible) toilets for disabled shop ⊗

DUNFERMLINE

Dunfermline Abbey

Pittencrieff Park KY12 7PE
☎ 01383 739026
web: www.historic-scotland.gov.uk

The monastery was a powerful Benedictine house, founded by Queen Margaret in the 11th century. A modern brass in the choir marks the grave of King Robert the Bruce. The monastery guest house became a royal palace, and was the birthplace of Charles I.

Times Open all year, Apr-Sep, daily 9.30-5.30; Oct, 9.30-4.30; Nov-Mar, daily, 9.30-4.30, closed Thu (pm), Fri & Sun (am). Closed 25-26 Dec & 1-2 Jan.* Fees £3.70 (ch £1.85, concessions £3). Please phone or check website for further details.* Facilities Ⓟ shop ⊗ 🪧

ST ANDREWS

British Golf Museum

Bruce Embankment KY16 9AB
☎ 01334 460046 & 460053
📄 01334 460064
e-mail: judychance@randa.org
web: www.britishgolfmuseum.co.uk
dir: opposite Royal & Ancient Golf Club

Where better to find out about golf than in St Andrews, the home of golf. Using diverse and exciting interactive displays, this museum explores the history of British golf from its origins to the personalities of today. The 18th Hole is fun for all the family, with dressing up, a mini-putting green and loads to do!

Times Open all year, Apr-Oct, Mon-Sat 9.30-5, Sun 10-5. Nov-Mar, Mon-Sun 10-4. Fees £5.50 (ch £2.90, concessions £4.50). Family ticket £14.* Facilities 🅿 Ⓟ ♿ toilets for disabled shop ⊗

GLASGOW

Burrell Collection **FREE**

Pollok Country Park, 2060 Pollokshaws Rd
G43 1AT
☎ 0141 287 2550 📄 0141 287 2597
e-mail: museums@csglasgow.org
web: www.glasgowmuseums.com
dir: 3.5m S of city centre, signposted from M77 junct 2

Set in Pollok Country Park, this award-winning building makes the priceless works of art on display seem almost part of the woodland setting. Shipping magnate Sir William Burrell's main interests were medieval Europe, Oriental art and European paintings. Colourful paintings and stained glass show the details of medieval life. Furniture, paintings, sculpture, armour and weapons help to complete the picture. Rugs, ceramics and metalwork represent the art of Islam. There is also a strong collection of Chinese and other Oriental ceramics. Paintings on display include works by Bellini, Rembrandt and the French Impressionists.

Times Open all year, Mon-Thu & Sat 10-5, Fri & Sun 11-5. Closed 25-26 & 31 (pm) Dec & 1-2 Jan Facilities 🅿 ☕ 🍴 licensed ♿ toilets for disabled shop ⊗

GLASGOW

Holmwood House

61-63 Netherlee House, Cathcart G44 3YG
☎ 0844 493 2204 ▤ 0844 493 2204
e-mail: information@nts.org.uk
web: www.nts.org.uk
dir: off Clarkston Rd

Completed in 1858, Holmwood is considered to be the finest domestic design by the architect Alexander 'Greek' Thomson. Many rooms are richly ornamented in wood, plaster and marble.

Times Open Apr-Oct, Thu-Mon 12-5.* **Fees** £5.50 (concessions £4.50). Family £15, (1 Parent £10).* **Facilities** ❷ ⌷ ⊼ ⴲ (partly accessible) (access to first floor via lift) shop ⊗ ⵛ

GLASGOW

Hunterian Museum **FREE**

Gilbert Scott Building, The University of Glasgow G12 8QQ
☎ 0141 330 4221 ▤ 0141 330 3617
e-mail: hunter@museum.gla.ac.uk
web: www.hunterian.gla.ac.uk
dir: on University of Glasgow campus in Hillhead District, 2m W of city centre

Named after the 18th-century physician, Dr William Hunter, who bequeathed his large and important collections of coins, medals, fossils, geological specimens and archaeological and ethnographic items to the university. The exhibits are shown in the main building of the university, and temporary exhibitions are held.

Times Open all year, Mon-Sat 9.30-5. Closed certain BHs phone for details.* **Facilities** ⓟ toilets for disabled shop ⊗

GLASGOW

Museum of Transport FREE

1 Bunhouse Rd G3 8DP
☎ 0141 287 2720 📄 0141 287 2692
e-mail: museums@csglasgow.org
web: www.glasgowmuseums.com
dir: 1.5m W of city centre

Visit the Museum of Transport and the first impression is of gleaming metalwork and bright paint. All around you there are cars, caravans, carriages and carts, fire engines, buses, steam locomotives, prams and trams. The museum uses its collections of vehicles and models to tell the story of transport by land and sea, with a unique Glasgow flavour. Visitors can even go window shopping along the recreated Kelvin Street of 1938. Upstairs 250 ship models tell the story of the great days of Clyde shipbuilding. The Museum of Transport has something for everyone.

Times Open all year, Mon-Thu & Sat 10-5, Fri & Sun 11-5 until Apr 2010 when museum closes due to collections moving to a new museum.
Facilities 🅿 Ⓟ ⊑ ♿ toilets for disabled shop ⊗

GLASGOW

The Scottish Football Museum

Hampden Park G42 9BA
☎ 0141 616 6139 📄 0141 616 6101
e-mail: info@scottishfootballmuseum.org.uk
web: www.scottishfootballmuseum.org.uk
dir: 3m S of city centre, follow brown tourist signs

Using 2500 pieces of footballing memorabilia, the Scottish Football Museum covers such themes as football's origins, women's football, fan culture, other games influenced by football, and even some social history. The exhibits include the world's oldest football, trophy and ticket, a reconstructed 1903 changing room and press box, and items of specific import, such as Kenny Dalglish's silver cap, Jimmy McGrory's boots, and the ball from Scotland's 5-1 win over England in 1928. Visit the Scottish Football Hall of Fame, and take the guided Hampden Stadium tour.

Times Open all year, Mon-Sat 10-5, Sun 11-5. Closed match days, special events and Xmas/New Year, please telephone in advance for confirmation **Fees** Museum £6 (ch 16 & concessions £3) Stadium £6 (ch 16 & concessions £3). Combined Ticket £9 (ch 16 & concessions £4.50) under 5's free. **Facilities** 🅿 Ⓟ ⊑ ♿ toilets for disabled shop ⊗

GLASGOW

The Tenement House

145 Buccleuch St, Garnethill G3 6QN
☎ 0844 493 2197 📄 0844 493 2197
e-mail: information@nts.org.uk
web: www.nts.org.uk
dir: N of Charing Cross

This shows an unsung but once-typical side of Glasgow life: it is a first-floor flat, built in 1892, with a parlour, bedroom, kitchen and bathroom, furnished with the original recess beds, kitchen range, sink, and coal bunker, among other articles. The home of Agnes Toward from 1911 to 1965, the flat was bought by an actress who preserved it as a `time capsule'. The contents vividly portray the life of one section of Glasgow society.

Times Open Mar-Oct, daily 1-5.* Fees £5.50 (concessions £4.50). Family £15 (1 Parent £10).*
Facilities ℗ ♿ (partly accessible) (steps to first floor) shop ⊗ ☙

GLASGOW

Trades Hall of Glasgow

85 Glassford St G1 1UH
☎ 0141 552 2418 📄 0141 552 5053
e-mail: info@tradeshallglasgow.co.uk
web: www.tradeshallglasgow.co.uk
dir: in city centre in Merchant City. Accessible from George Square & Argyle St

The Trades Hall is one of Glasgow's most historic buildings and was home to the 14 incorporated crafts who regulated trade and played a vital role in shaping and making Glasgow the city it is today. Visitors can explore the impressive rooms of the building taking in the Grand Hall with its spectacular soaring windows, baroque chandeliers and striking dome, and the Saloon which features an original Adam fireplace and beautiful stained glass windows.

Times Open all year, Mon-Fri, 10-4, subject to availability* Facilities ℗ toilets for disabled ⊗

BETTYHILL

Strathnaver Museum

KW14 7SS

☎ 01641 521418

e-mail: strathnavermus@ukonline.co.uk

dir: By the A386 on outskirts of Bettyhill on the E of the village

The museum has displays on the Clearances, with a fine collection of Strathnaver Clearances furnishings, domestic and farm implements, and local books. There is also a Clan Mackay room. The museum's setting is a former church, a handsome stone building with a magnificent canopied pulpit dated 1774. The churchyard contains a carved stone known as the Farr Stone, which dates back to the 9th century and is a fine example of Pictish art.

Times Open Apr-Oct, Mon-Sat 10-5. Fees £2 (ch 50p, under 5's free, concessions £1.50, student/groups £1). Facilities ℗ Ⓟ ♿ (partly accessible) (ground floor only accessible) shop ⊗

CAWDOR

Cawdor Castle

IV12 5RD

☎ 01667 404401   📄 01667 404674

e-mail: info@cawdorcastle.com

web: www.cawdorcastle.com

dir: on B9090, off A96

Home of the Thanes of Cawdor since the 14th century, this lovely castle has a drawbridge, an ancient tower built round a tree, and a freshwater well inside the house.

Times Open May-10 Oct, daily 10-5.30 (last admission 5). Fees £7.90 (ch 5-15 £4.90, pen £6.90). Family ticket £24. Party 20+ £6.50 each. Gardens, grounds & nature trails only £4.* Facilities ℗ ⬚ ⦿ licensed ♨ (outdoor) ♿ (partly accessible) (ramps to restaurant, shops and garden, ground floor only of castle accessible) toilets for disabled shop ⊗

CULLODEN MOOR

Culloden Battlefield

IV2 5EU

☎ 0844 493 2159   📠 0844 493 2160
e-mail: information@nts.org.uk
web: www.nts.org.uk
dir: B9006, 5m E of Inverness

A cairn recalls this last battle fought on mainland Britain, on 16 April 1746, when the Duke of Cumberland's forces routed 'Bonnie' Prince Charles Edward Stuart's army. The battlefield has been restored to its state on the day of the battle, and in summer there are 'living history' enactments. This is a most atmospheric evocation of tragic events. Telephone for details of guided tours. A Visitors' Centre exploring the impact of the battle opened in 2007.

Times Open all year: Visitor Centre, Restaurant & Shop: 4 Feb-Mar, daily 10-4; Apr-Oct, daily 9-6; Nov-Dec, daily 10-4. (Closed 24-26 Dec). Site: All year, daily.* **Fees** £12 (concessions £7.50). Family £24 (1 Parent £20). (Price includes a PDA for all visitors).* **Facilities** 🅿 🍽 licensed ♿ toilets for disabled shop ⊗ 🏵

FORT GEORGE

Fort George

IV2 7TD

☎ 01667 460232
web: www.historic-scotland.gov.uk
dir: 11m NE of Inverness

Built following the Battle of Culloden as a Highland fortress for the army of George II, this is one of the outstanding artillery fortifications in Europe and still an active army barracks.

Times Open all year, Apr-Sep, daily, 9.30-5.30; Oct-Mar, daily, 9.30-4.30. Closed 25-26 Dec.* **Fees** £6.70 (ch £3.35, concessions £5.20). Please phone or check website for further details.* **Facilities** 🅿 🍽 licensed ⏚ toilets for disabled shop ⊗ 🏵

FORT GEORGE

The Highlanders Regimental Museum

IV2 7TD
☎ 0131 310 8701   🖹 0131 310 8701
dir: off A96 5m from Inverness

Fort George has been a military barracks since it was built in 1748-69, and was the Depot of the Seaforth Highlanders until 1961. The museum of the Queen's Own Highlanders (Seaforth and Camerons) is sited in the former Lieutenant Governor's house, where uniforms, medals and pictures are displayed.

Times Open all year, Apr-Sep daily 9.30-5.15; Oct-Mar Mon-Fri 10-4 (closed 24-25 Dec & BHs).* **Fees** Free. (Admission charged by Historic Scotland for entry to Fort George). **Facilities** ℗ Ⓟ ᓚ (partly accessible) (2nd floor accessible via stairs) toilets for disabled shop ⊗

GLENFINNAN

Glenfinnan Monument

NTS Visitor Centre PH37 4LT
☎ 0844 493 2221   🖹 0844 493 2221
e-mail: information@nts.org.uk
web: www.nts.org.uk
dir: on A830, 18.5m W of Fort William

The monument commemorates the Highlanders who fought for Bonnie Prince Charlie in 1745. It stands in an awe-inspiring setting at the head of Loch Shiel. There is a visitor centre with information (commentary in four languages) on the Prince's campaign.

Times Visitor Centre, Apr-30 Jun, daily 10-5; Jul-Aug, daily 9.30-5.30; Sep-Oct, daily 10-5.* **Fees** £3 (concessions £2). Family £8 (1 Parent £6).* **Facilities** ℗ ⊡ ⊓ ᓚ (partly accessible) shop ☃

HELMSDALE

Timespan

Dunrobin St KW8 6JX

☎ 01431 821327 📄 01431 821058

e-mail: enquiries@timespan.org.uk

web: www.timespan.org.uk

dir: off A9 in centre of village, by Telford Bridge

Located in a historic fishing village, this museum relates to the social and natural history of the area, and the art gallery has changing exhibitions of contemporary art and works by local artists. The garden has over 100 varieties of herbs and plants. There is a gift shop, and a café with beautiful views of the Telford Bridge.

Times Open Etr-end Oct, Mon-Sat 10-5, Sun 12-5.* Fees £4 (ch £2, concessions £3). Family ticket £10.* Facilities ❷ ℗ ⊡ & toilets for disabled shop ⊗

NEWTONMORE

Highland Folk Museum FREE

Aultlarie Croft PH20 1AY

☎ 01540 673551 📄 01540 673693

e-mail: highland.folk@highland.gov.uk

web: www.highlandfolk.com

dir: on A86, follow signs off A9

An early 18th-century farming township with turf houses has been reconstructed at this award-winning museum. A 1930s school houses old world maps, little wooden desks and a teacher rules! Other attractions include a working croft and tailor's workshop. Squirrels thrive in the pinewoods and there is an extensive play area at reception. A vintage bus runs throughout the site.

Times Open daily Etr-Aug, 10.30-5.30; Sep-Oct, 11-4.30. Facilities ❷ ⊡ ⊼ (outdoor) toilets for disabled shop ⊗

STRATHPEFFER

Highland Museum of Childhood

The Old Station IV14 9DH
☎ 01997 421031
e-mail: info@highlandmuseumofchildhood.org.uk
web: www.highlandmuseumofchildhood.org.uk
dir: 5m W of Dingwall on A834

Located in a renovated Victorian railway station of 1885, the museum tells the story of childhood in the Highlands amongst the crofters and townsfolk; a way of life recorded in oral testimony, displays and evocative photographs. An award-winning video, A Century of Highland Childhood is shown. There are also doll and toy collections.

Times Open Apr-Oct, daily 10-5, (Sun 2-5). Other times by arrangement. **Fees** £2.50 (ch £1.50, concessions £2). Family ticket (2ad+4ch) £6. **Facilities** Ⓟ Ⓟ ☕ ⛩ (outdoor) ♿ shop ⊗

THURSO

The Castle & Gardens of Mey

KW14 8XH
☎ 01847 851473 📠 01847 851475
e-mail: enquiries@castleofmey.org.uk
web: www.castleofmey.org.uk
dir: 5m W of John O'Groats on A836

Built in the 1560s, The Castle of Mey was bought by The Queen Mother in 1952. She restored the castle and created the beautiful gardens that can be seen today. For almost half a century The Queen Mother spent many happy summers at Mey. Children will enjoy the animal centre and home baked delicacies can be purchased at the Visitor Centre tea room.

Times Open May-Sep, 10.30-last entry 4. Closed 10 days late Jul-early Aug. **Fees** £9 (ch 5-16 £3.50, under 5 free, concessions & groups £8). Family ticket £22. **Facilities** Ⓟ ☕ ♿ (partly accessible) (visitor centre fully accessible, 1st floor possible, but not 2nd) toilets for disabled shop

WICK

Wick Heritage Museum

18-27 Bank Row KW1 5EY
☎ 01955 605393 📄 01955 605393
e-mail: museum@wickheritage.org
web: www.wickheritage.org
dir: close to the harbour

The heritage centre is near the harbour in a complex of eight houses, yards and outbuildings. The centre illustrates local history from Neolithic times to the herring fishing industry. In addition, there is a complete working 19th-century lighthouse, and the famous Johnston collection of photographs.

Times Open Apr-Oct, Mon-Sat 10-5, last admission 3.45. (Closed Sun).* **Facilities** ℗ 🅰 (outdoor) ♿ (partly accessible) toilets for disabled

NEWTONGRANGE

Scottish Mining Museum

Lady Victoria Colliery EH22 4QN
☎ 0131 663 7519 📄 0131 654 0952
e-mail: visitorservices@scottishminingmuseum.com
web: www.scottishminingmuseum.com
dir: 10m S of Edinburgh on A7, signed from bypass

Based at Scotland's National Coalmining Museum offering an outstanding visit to Britains' finest Victorian colliery. Guided tours with miners, magic helmets, exhibitions, theatres, interactive displays and a visit to the coal face. Home to Scotland's largest steam engine.

Times Open all year, daily Mar-Oct, 10-5. Nov-Feb, daily, 10-4.* **Fees** £6.50 (ch & concessions £4.50). Family ticket £19.95. Party 12+ (£5.50, ch £3.50)* **Facilities** ℗ ℗ 🖵 🍴 licensed 🅰 (outdoor) ♿ toilets for disabled shop ⊗

FORRES

Sueno's Stone FREE

☎ 01667 460232
web: www.historic-scotland.gov.uk
dir: E end of Forres, off A96

The most remarkable sculptured monument in Britain, probably a cenotaph, standing over 20 feet high and dating back to the end of the first millennium AD. Covered by a protective glass enclosure.

Times Open at all reasonable times.* Facilities
🅿 ⊗ 🚩

COATBRIDGE

Summerlee Industrial Museum FREE

Heritage Way, West Canal St ML5 1QD
☎ 01236 638460 📠 01236 638454
e-mail: museums@northlan.gov.uk
web: www.visitlanarkshire.com/summerlee
dir: follow main routes towards town centre, adjacent to Coatbridge central station

A 20-acre museum of social and industrial history centering on the remains of the Summerlee Ironworks which were put into blast in the 1830s. The exhibition hall features displays of social and industrial history including working machinery, hands-on activities and recreated workshop interiors. Outside, Summerlee operates the only working tram in Scotland, a coal mine and reconstructed miners' rows with interiors dating from 1840.

Times Open summer 10-5, winter 10-4. Facilities
🅿 Ⓟ ⊑ 🎋 (outdoor) ♿ (partly accessible) (coal mine tour not accessible, miner's cottages narrow doors and single step) toilets for disabled shop ⊗

MOTHERWELL

Motherwell Heritage Centre FREE

High Rd ML1 3HU
☎ 01698 251000 🖷 01698 268867
e-mail: museums@northlan.gov.uk
web: www.nlcmuseums.bravehost.com
dir: A723 for town centre. Left at top of hill,
after pedestrian crossing and just before railway
bridge

This award-winning audio-visual experience,
'Technopolis', traces the history of the area from
Roman times to the rise of 19th-century industry
and the post-industrial era. There is also a fine
viewing tower, an exhibition gallery and family
history research facilities. A mixed programme of
community events and touring exhibitions occur
throughout the year.

Times Open all year Wed-Sat 10-5 (Thu 10-7),
Sun 12-5. Also open BHs. Local studies library
closed Sun* Facilities ❷ ⓟ ♿ toilets for
disabled shop ⊗

CRIEFF

Innerpeffray Library

PH7 3RF
☎ 01764 652819
e-mail: info@innerpeffraylibrary.co.uk
web: www.innerpeffraylibrary.co.uk
dir: 4.5m SE on B8062

This is Scotland's oldest free lending public
library, founded in 1680. This Georgian library
(1762) with its associated school (1847), chapel
(1508) and castle form an early complete group
of educational and religious buildings. It houses
the original 400 books in English, French,
German, Latin and Italian presented by David
Drummond, Lord Madertie, the Library's founder.
It also has the books on law, history, geography,
maths and works by most of the Enlightenment
authors. There are research facilities available,
special events are planned.

Times Open Wed-Sat 10-12.45 & 2-4.45, Sun
2-4. (Closed Mon-Tue). Nov-Feb by arrangement.*
Fees £5 (ch with parents free)* Facilities ❷ ⌨
⌂ (outdoor) ♿ (partly accessible) ⊗

PERTH

The Black Watch Regimental Museum

Balhousie Castle, Hay St PH1 5HR
☎ 0131 310 8530   📄 01738 643245
e-mail: rhq@theblackwatch.co.uk
web: www.theblackwatch.co.uk
dir: follow signs to Perth & attraction, approach via Dunkeld Rd

The museum of Scotland's oldest highland regiment, which portrays the history of the Black Watch from 1725 to the present day. A memorial room remembers the soldiers of WWI with a lifelike figure in a trench, video footage and many artefacts from the period. Silver, uniforms, weapons and pictures are on display to give visitors an idea of what it was like to be in the regiment.

Times Open all year. May-Sep, Mon-Sat 10-4.30. Closed last Sat in Jun; Oct-Apr, Mon-Fri, 10-3.30. Closed 23 Dec-6 Jan. Other times & Parties 16+ by appointment.* **Facilities** 🅿 🅿 ♿ (partly accessible) (ground floor access only) toilets for disabled shop ⊗

SCONE

Scone Palace

PH2 6BD
☎ 01738 552300   📄 01738 552588
e-mail: visits@scone-palace.co.uk
web: www.scone-palace.co.uk
dir: 2m NE of Perth on A93

Visit Scone Palace, the crowning place of Scottish Kings and the home of the Earls of Mansfield. The Palace dates from 1803 but incorporates 16th century and earlier buildings, and is a unique treasury of furniture, fine art and other objets d'art. As well as beautiful gardens the grounds are home to the Murray Star Maze, the Pinetum, an adventure playground, livestock, Highland cattle and champion trees.

Times Open Apr-Oct, daily 9.30-5.30, Sat last admission 4. **Fees** Palace & Grounds £8.50 (ch £5.30, concessions £7.30). Family ticket £24. Grounds only £4.80 (ch £3.20, concessions £4.20). Group £7.30 (ch £4.80 concessions £6.30)* **Facilities** 🅿 ⊑ ⊚ licensed 🎋 (outdoor) ♿ toilets for disabled shop ⊗

DRYBURGH

Dryburgh Abbey

TD6 0RQ
☎ 01835 822381
web: www.historic-scotland.gov.uk
dir: 5m SE of Melrose on B6404

The abbey was one of the Border monasteries founded by David I, and stands in a lovely setting on the River Tweed. The ruins are equally beautiful, and the church has the graves of Sir Walter Scott and Earl Haig.

Times Open all year, Apr-Sep, daily 9.30-5.30; Oct-Mar, daily 9.30-4.30. Closed 25-26 Dec & 1-2 Jan.* **Fees** £4.70 (ch £2.35, concessions £3.70). Please phone or check website for further details.* **Facilities** ℗ ⊞ shop ⊗ ▮

INNERLEITHEN

Robert Smail's Printing Works

7/9 High St EH44 6HA
☎ 0844 493 2259
e-mail: information@nts.org.uk
web: www.nts.org.uk
dir: 30m S of Edinburgh, A272, 6m from Peebles. (Innerleithen Road)

These buildings contain a Victorian office, a paper store with reconstructed waterwheel, a composing room and a press room. The machinery is in full working order and visitors may view the printer at work and experience typesetting in the composing room.

Times Open 2 Apr-Oct , Thu-Mon 12-5, Sun 1-5.* **Fees** £5.50 (concessions £4.50). Family £15 (1 Parent £10).* **Facilities** ℗ ♿ (partly accessible) (stairs to caseroom) shop ⊗ ☙

MELROSE

Abbotsford

TD6 9BQ

☎ 01896 752043   📠 01896 752916
e-mail: enquiries@scottsabbotsford.co.uk
web: www.scottsabbotsford.co.uk
dir: 2m W off A6091, on B6360

Set on the River Tweed, Sir Walter Scott's romantic mansion remains much the same as it was in his day. Inside there are many mementoes and relics of his remarkable life and also his historical collections, armouries and library, with some 9,000 volumes. Scott built the mansion between 1811 and 1822, and lived here until his death ten years after its completion.

Times Open daily from 3rd Mon in Mar-Oct, Mon-Sat 9.30-5. Mar-May & Oct, Sun 2-5. Jun-Sep, Sun 9.30-5.* **Facilities** 🅿 Ⓟ ⊑ ㅠ (outdoor) ♿ (partly accessible) (ramps at entrance, show rooms, gift shop and tea rooms accessible) toilets for disabled shop ⊗

TRAQUAIR

Traquair House

EH44 6PW

☎ 01896 830323   📠 01896 830639
e-mail: enquiries@traquair.co.uk
web: www.traquair.co.uk
dir: at Innerleithen take B709, house in 1m

Said to be Scotland's oldest inhabited house, dating back to the 12th century, 27 Scottish monarchs have stayed at Traquair House. William the Lion Heart held court here, and the house has associations with Mary, Queen of Scots and the Jacobite risings. The Bear Gates were closed in 1745, not to be reopened until the Stuarts should once again ascend the throne. There is a maze and woodland walks by the River Tweed, craft workshops and a children's adventure playground. Also an 18th-century working brewery with museum shop and tastings. Award-winning 1745 Cottage Restaurant open for lunches and teas.

Times Open daily Apr-May & Sep 12-5, Jun-Aug 10.30-5, Oct 11-4, Nov 11-3 (wknds only).
Fees House & Grounds £7.50 (ch £4, pen £6.80). Family £21. Grounds only £4 (concessions £2.50).
Facilities 🅿 ⊑ 🍽 licensed ㅠ (outdoor) ♿ (partly accessible) (ground floor of house only accessible) toilets for disabled shop

ALLOWAY

Burns National Heritage Park

Murdoch's Lone KA7 4PQ
☎ 01292 443700 📧 01292 441750
e-mail: info@burnsheritagepark.com
web: www.burnsheritagepark.com
dir: 2m S of Ayr

The birthplace of Robert Burns, Scotland's National Poet set in the gardens and countryside of Alloway. An introduction to the life of Robert Burns, with an audio-visual presentation - a multi-screen 3D experience describing the Tale of Tam O'Shanter. This attraction consists of the museum, Burn's Cottage, visitor centre, tranquil landscaped gardens and historical monuments. Please telephone for further details.

Times Open all year, Apr-Sep 10-5.30, Oct-Mar 10-5. Closed 25-26 Dec & 1-2 Jan* **Facilities** ℗ ℗ 💻 🍽 licensed ♿ (partly accessible) (access limited in some parts of property) toilets for disabled shop ⊗

CULZEAN CASTLE

Culzean Castle & Country Park

KA19 8LE
☎ 0844 493 2149 📧 0844 493 2150
e-mail: information@nts.org.uk
web: www.nts.org.uk
dir: 4m W of Maybole, off A77, 12m S of Ayr

This 18th-century castle stands on a cliff in spacious grounds and was designed by Robert Adam for the Earl of Cassillis. It is noted for its oval staircase, circular drawing room and plasterwork. The Eisenhower Room explores the American General's links with Culzean. The 563-acre country park has a wide range of attractions - shoreline, woodland walks, parkland, an adventure playground and gardens.

Times Castle, Visitor centre & other facilities: Apr-1 Nov, daily 10.30-5 (last entry 4). (Visitor centre off season: 2 Nov-29 Mar, Sat-Sun 11-4). Walled garden: all year, daily 9.30-5 (sunset if earlier). Country Park: open all year 9.30-sunset.* **Fees** £13 (concessions £9). Family £32 (1 Parent £25). Country Park only: £8.50 (concessions £5.50). Family £21 (1 Parent £16).* **Facilities** ℗ 💻 🍽 licensed �🪑 (outdoor) ♿ (partly accessible) toilets for disabled shop ⊗ 🐾

TARBOLTON

Bachelors' Club

Sandgate St KA5 5RB
☎ 0844 493 2146 📠 0844 493 2146
e-mail: information@nts.org.uk
web: www.nts.org.uk
dir: In Tarbolton, off A77 S of Kilmarnock & off A76 at Mauchline. 7.5m NE of Ayr

In this 17th-century thatched house, Robert Burns and his friends formed a debating club in 1780. Burns attended dancing lessons and was initiated into freemasonry here in 1781. The house is furnished in the style of the period.

Times Open Burns Night, 25 Jan 1-5, Apr-Sep, Fri-Tue 1-5.* **Fees** £5.50 (concessions £4.50). Family £15 (1 parent £10).* **Facilities** ℗ ♿ (partly accessible) (limited access 12 steps to upper room) ⊗ 🍽

BIGGAR

Moat Park Heritage Centre

Kirkstyle ML12 6DT
☎ 01899 221050
e-mail: suzanne.bmt@googlemail.com
web: www.biggarmuseumtrust.co.uk
dir: On A702

The centre illustrates the history, archaeology and geology of the Upper Clyde and Tweed valleys with interesting displays.

Times Open all year, May-Sep, Mon-Sat 11.30-4.30, Sun 2-4.30; Oct-Apr, open by appointment only.* **Facilities** ❷ ℗ ⊓ (outdoor) ♿ (partly accessible) (upper floor with assistance on request) toilets for disabled shop ⊗

BLANTYRE

David Livingstone Centre

165 Station Rd G72 9BT

☎ 0844 493 2207 🖹 0844 493 2206
e-mail: information@nts.org.uk
web: www.nts.org.uk
dir: M74 junct 5 onto A725, then A724, follow signs for Blantyre, right at lights. Centre is at foot of hill

Share the adventurous life of Scotland's greatest explorer, from his childhood in the Blantyre Mills to his explorations in the heart of Africa, dramatically illustrated in the historic tenement where he was born. Various events are planned throughout the season.

Times Open Apr-24 Dec, Mon-Sat 10-5, Sun 12.30-5.* **Fees** £5.50 (concessions £4.50) Family £15 (1 Parent £10).* **Facilities** 🅿 ℗ ⯑⯑ 🍴 ♿ toilets for disabled shop ⊗ ⛾

EAST KILBRIDE

National Museum of Rural Life Scotland

Wester Kittochside, Philipshill Rd, (off Stewartfield Way) G76 9HR

☎ 0131 225 7534
e-mail: info@nms.ac.uk
web: www.nms.ac.uk/rural
dir: From Glasgow take A749 to East Kilbride. From Edinburgh follow M8 to Glasgow, turn off junct 6 onto A725 to East Kilbride. Kittochside is signed before East Kilbride

Get a healthy dose of fresh air. Take in the sights, sounds and smells as you explore this 170-acre farm. Discover what life was like for country people in the past and how this has shaped Scotland's countryside today. Would you cope with life on a 1950s farm? Try milking 'Clover' by hand, hitch a ride on the farm explorer, meet Mairi the horse and the sheep, cows and hens. See the website for details of a wide range of special events and exhibitions.

Times Open daily 10-5. (Closed 25-26 Dec & 1 Jan). **Fees** £5.50 (ch under 12 free, concessions £4.50) NMS and NTS members free. Charge for some events.* **Facilities** 🅿 ℗ ⯑⯑ 🍴 (outdoor) ♿ (partly accessible) (wheelchair users have access to ground floor of farmhouse only, some steep paths) toilets for disabled shop ⊗

BANNOCKBURN

Bannockburn

Glasgow Rd FK7 0LJ
☎ 0844 493 2139   📠 0844 493 2138
e-mail: information@nts.org.uk
web: www.nts.org.uk
dir: 2m S of Stirling off M80/M9 junct 9, on A872

The Heritage Centre stands close to what is traditionally believed to have been Robert the Bruce's command post before the 1314 Battle of Bannockburn, a famous victory for the Scots and a turning point in Scottish history.

Times Heritage Centre 2 Mar-Oct daily, 10-5. Grounds all year daily, until dusk.* **Fees** £5.50 (concessions £4.50) Family £15 (1 Parent £10).* **Facilities** ❷ ⌑ ♿ (partly accessible) toilets for disabled shop ⊗ ☙

STIRLING

The National Wallace Monument

Hillfoots Rd, Causewayhead FK9 5LF
☎ 01786 472140   📠 01786 461322
e-mail: info@nationalwallacemonument.com
web: www.nationalwallacemonument.com
dir: Monument is signed from city centre & A91

Meet Scotland's national hero, Sir William Wallace, and join his epic struggle for a free Scotland. Step into Westminster Hall and witness his trial. Climb the 220 foot tower and experience one of the finest views in Scotland. Each August there is an 'Encounter with Wallace', a programme of dramatic performances including traditional Scottish music.

Times Open all year daily Apr-Jun & Sep-Oct 10-5, Jul-Aug 10-6, Nov-Mar 10.30-4.* **Fees** £6.50 (ch £4, concessions £4.90). Family ticket £17.* **Facilities** ❷ ⌑ ⚲ (outdoor) shop

STIRLING

Stirling Castle

Upper Castle Hill FK8 1EJ
☎ 01786 450000
web: www.historic-scotland.gov.uk

Sitting on top of a 250ft rock, Stirling Castle has a strategic position on the Firth of Forth. As a result it has been the scene of many events in Scotland's history. James II was born at the castle in 1430. Mary, Queen of Scots spent some years there, and it was James IV's childhood home. Among its finest features are the splendid Renaissance palace built by James V, and the Chapel Royal, rebuilt by James VI.

Times Open all year, Apr-Sep, daily 9.30-6; Oct-Mar, daily 9.30-5. Closed 25-26.* **Fees** £9 (ch £4.50, concessions £7). Please phone or check website for further details.* **Facilities** ℗ 🍽 licensed 🎪 toilets for disabled shop ⊗ 🛆

BRODICK

Isle of Arran Heritage Museum

Rosaburn KA27 8DP
☎ 01770 302636
e-mail: tom.macleod@arranmuseum.co.uk
web: www.arranmuseum.co.uk
dir: right at Brodick Pier, approx 1m

The setting is an 18th-century croft farm, including a cottage restored to its pre-1920 state and a 'smiddy' where a blacksmith worked until the late 1960s. There are also several demonstrations of horse-shoeing, sheep-shearing and weaving and spinning throughout the season - please ring for details. There is a large archaeology and geology section with archive, where help with research is available. Also, a school room set in the 1940's and a new geology display which reflects the importance of Arran in geological terms.

Times Open Apr-Oct, daily 10.30-4.30. **Fees** £3 (ch £1.50, pen £2). Family £7. **Facilities** ℗ ☕ 🎪 (outdoor) toilets for disabled shop ⊗

CALLANISH

Callanish Standing Stones

PA86 9DY

☎ 01851 621422

dir: 12m W of Stornoway off A859

An avenue of 19 monoliths leads north from a circle of 13 stones with rows of more stones fanning out to south, east and west. Probably constructed between 3000 and 1500BC, this is a unique cruciform of megaliths.

Times Site accessible at all times. Visitor Centre open Apr-Sep, Mon-Sat 10-7; Oct-Mar, Mon-Sat 10-4.* Facilities ℗ †⊙⫯ licensed toilets for disabled shop

DOUNBY

Skara Brae

KW16 3LR

☎ 01856 841815

web: www.historic-scotland.gov.uk

dir: 19m W of Kirkwall on B9056

Engulfed in drift sand, this remarkable group of well-preserved Stone Age dwellings is the most outstanding survivor of its kind in Britain. Stone furniture and a fireplace can be seen.

Times Open all year, Apr-Sep, daily 9.30-5.30; Oct-Mar, daily 9.30-4.30. Closed 25-26 Dec & 1-2 Jan.* Fees £6.70 (ch £3.35, concessions £5.20). Winter: Skara Brae only £5.70 (ch £2.85, concessions £4.70) Please phone or check website for details.* Facilities ℗ †⊙⫯ licensed ⏢ toilets for disabled shop ⊗ ▐

Maes Howe Chambered Cairn

KW16 3HA
☎ 01856 761606
web: www.historic-scotland.gov.uk
dir: 9m W of Kirkwall, on A965

The masonry of Britain's finest megalithic tomb is in a remarkably good state of preservation. Dating from neolithic times, it contains Viking carvings and runes.

Times Open all year, Apr-Sep, daily 9.30-5.30; Oct-Mar, daily 9.30-4.30. Closed 25-26 Dec & 1-2 Jan. (Visits must be pre-booked).*
Fees £5.20 (ch £2, concessions £4.20). Please phone or check website for further details.*
Facilities ℗ ⑩ licensed shop ⊗ 🚩

The Orkney Museum FREE

Broad St KW15 1DH
☎ 01856 87355 ext 2523   📄 01856 871560
e-mail: museum@orkney.gov.uk
web: www.orkney.gov.uk
dir: town centre

One of the finest vernacular town houses in Scotland, this 16th-century building now contains a museum of Orkney history, including the islands' fascinating archaeology and social history.

Times Open all year, Oct-Apr, Mon-Sat 10.30-12.30 & 1.30-5; May-Sep, Mon-Sat 10.30-5. **Facilities** ℗ ♿ (partly accessible) (5 galleries at ground level, 8 galleries require use of stair lift) toilets for disabled shop ⊗

KIRKWALL

Scapa Flow Visitor Centre & Museum FREE

Lyness, Hoy KW16 3NU
☎ 01856 791300 📄 01856 871560
e-mail: museum@orkney.gov.uk
web: www.orkney.gov.uk
dir: on A964 to Houton, ferry crossing takes 30 mins, visitors centre 2 mins walk from ferry terminal

Also known as the Lyness Interpretation Centre, this fascinating museum is home to a large collection of military equipment used in the defence of the Orkneys during the First and Second World Wars. There are also guns salvaged from the German ships scuppered in WWII. Visitors arrive at the island after a short boat trip from the Orkney mainland.

Times Open all year: Mon-Fri 9-4.30 (mid May-Sep also Sat-Sun 10.30-3.30). **Facilities** 🅿 🚻 ♿ toilets for disabled shop ⊗

LERWICK

Shetland Museum FREE

Hay's Dock ZE1 0WP
☎ 01595 695057 📄 01595 696729
e-mail: info@shetlandmuseumandarchives.org.uk
web: www.shetlandmuseumandarchives.org.uk

After a grand re-opening in May 2007, the Museum and Archives sits in a unique dockside setting and is home to 3000 artefacts telling the story of Shetland.

Times Open all year, Jan-Apr & Oct-Dec Mon-Sat 10-5, Sun 12-5; May-Sep Mon-Fri 10-5.30, Sat 10-5, Sun 12-5. Check website for Xmas and New Year. **Facilities** 🅿 🅟 🚻 ❈ licensed ♿ toilets for disabled shop ⊗

MOUSA ISLAND

Mousa Broch **FREE**

☎ 01950 431367
web: www.historic-scotland.gov.uk
dir: accessible by boat from Sandwick

This broch is the best-preserved example of an Iron Age drystone tower in Scotland. The tower is nearly complete and rises to a height of 40ft. The outer and inner walls both contain staircases that may be climbed to the parapet. Boat not available all year. Contact 01950 431367 for more information.

Times Open at all reasonable time.* **Facilities** ▉

SUMBURGH

Jarlshof Prehistoric & Norse Settlement

ZE3 9JN
☎ 01950 460112
web: www.historic-scotland.gov.uk
dir: at Sumburgh Head, approx 22m S of Lerwick

One of the most remarkable archaeological sites in Europe. There are remains of Bronze Age, Iron Age and Viking settlements as well as a medieval farm. There is also a 16th-century Laird's House, once the home of the Earls Robert and Patrick Stewart, and the basis of 'Jarlshof' in Sir Walter Scott's novel The Pirate.

Times Open Apr-Sep, daily 9.30-5.30.*
Fees £4.70 (ch £2.35, concessions £3.70). Please phone or check website for further details.*
Facilities 🅿 shop ▉

DUNVEGAN

Dunvegan Castle and Gardens

IV55 8WF

☎ 01470 521206 📠 01470 521205
e-mail: info@dunvegancastle.com
web: www.dunvegancastle.com
dir: follow A87 over Skye Bridge. Turn onto A863
at Sligachan and continue to castle

Dunvegan Castle is the oldest continuously inhabited castle in Scotland and has been the stronghold of the chiefs of MacLeod for nearly 800 years. Originally designed to keep people out, it was first opened to visitors in 1933. Romantic and historic, the castle is set amid stunning scenery and beautiful formal gardens. The castle and estate are steeped in history and clan legend, and you can take a boat trip onto Loch Dunvegan to see the seal colony, or stay in one of the charming estate cottages.

Times Open Apr-15 Oct, daily 10-5.30 (last entry 5), 16 Oct-Mar open by appointment. Fees Castle & Gardens: £7.50 (ch 5-15 yrs £4, pen, students & groups £6). Facilities 🅿 🅿 ⬛ 🍽 licensed 🎪 (outdoor) ♿ (partly accessible) (gardens, restaurant and shop fully accessible, parts of the castle are not accessible) toilets for disabled shop ⊗

BEAUMARIS

Beaumaris Castle

LL58 8AP

☎ 01248 810361
web: www.cadw.wales.gov.uk

Beaumaris was built by Edward I and took from 1295 to 1312 to complete. In later centuries it was plundered for its lead, timber and stone. Despite this it remains one of the most impressive and complete castles built by Edward I. It has a perfectly symmetrical, concentric plan, with a square inner bailey and curtain walls, round corner towers and D-shaped towers in between. There are also two great gatehouses, but these were never finished.

Times Open all year, Apr-Oct, daily 9-5; Nov-Mar, Mon-Sat 9.30-4, Sun 11-4.* Fees £3.60 (ch 5-15, concessions £3.20, disabled visitors and assisting companion free). Family ticket (2ad+all ch/grandch under 16) £10.40. Group rates available. Prices quoted apply until 31 Mar 2010.* Facilities 🅿 shop ⊗ ♿

CAERPHILLY

Caerphilly Castle

CF8 1JL
☎ 029 2088 3143
web: www.cadw.wales.gov.uk
dir: on A469

The concentrically planned castle was begun in 1268 by Gilbert de Clare and completed in 1326. It is the largest in Wales, and has extensive land and water defences. A unique feature is the ruined tower - the victim of subsidence - which manages to out-lean even Pisa! The south dam platform, once a tournament-field, now displays replica medieval siege-engines.

Times Open all year, Apr-Oct, daily 9-5; Nov-Mar, Mon-Sat 9.30-4, Sun 11-4.* **Fees** £3.60 (ch 5-15, concessions £3.20, disabled visitors and assisting companion free). Family ticket (2ad+all ch/grandch under 16) £10.40. Group rates available. Prices quoted apply until 31 Mar 2010.* **Facilities** ℗ shop ⊗ ⊕

CARDIFF

Cardiff Castle

Castle St CF10 3RB
☎ 029 2087 8100   🖨 029 2023 1417
e-mail: cardiffcastle@cardiff.gov.uk
web: www.cardiffcastle.com
dir: from M4, A48 & A470 follow signs to city centre

Cardiff Castle is situated in the heart of the city. Contained within its mighty walls is a history spanning nearly 2000 years, dating from the coming of the Romans to the Norman Conquest and beyond. Discover spectacular interiors on your guided tour, and enjoy magnificent views of the city from the top of the 12th-century Norman keep. The new Interpretation Centre includes a film presentation and a multimedia guide around the Castle grounds. Regular events throughout the year include a teddy bear's picnic, open air theatre, medieval and Roman re-enactments and much more.

Times Open all year, daily (ex 25-26 Dec & 1 Jan) including guided tours, Mar-Oct, 9.30-6 (last tour 5); Nov-Feb, 9.30-5.00 (last tour 4). Royal Regiment of Wales Museum closed Tue.* **Facilities** ℗ ⊒ & (partly accessible) (Castle apartments and Norman Keep not accessible to wheelchair users, cobblestone path at entrance) toilets for disabled shop ⊗

CARDIFF

National Museum Cardiff

Cathays Park CF10 3NP
☎ 029 2039 7951   🖹 029 2057 3321
e-mail: post@museumwales.ac.uk
web: www.museumwales.ac.uk
dir: in Civic Centre. M4 junct 32, A470, 5 mins walk from city centre & 20 mins walk from bus & train station

National Museum Cardiff is home to spectacular collections from Wales and all over the world. The Museum showcases displays of art, archaeology, geology and natural history all under one roof. The new archaeology gallery traces life in Wales from the earliest humans 230,000 years ago. Discover stories behind some of Wales' most famous works of art in the new art galleries. You can also enjoy changing displays drawn from the collection of Impressionist and Post-Impressionist paintings, including work by Monet, Renoir and Cézanne. Or how about a close encounter with The Big Bang, erupting volcanoes, dinosaurs and woolly mammoths on the journey through time and space?

Times Open all year, Tue-Sun 10-5. Closed Mon (ex BHs). Telephone for Xmas opening times.
Fees Free admission but charge may be made for some events. **Facilities** 🅿 Ⓟ ♿ ▯ 🍽 licensed ♿ toilets for disabled shop ⊗

ST FAGANS

St Fagans: National History Museum

CF5 6XB
☎ 029 2057 3500   🖹 029 2057 3490
web: www.museumwales.ac.uk
dir: 4m W of Cardiff on A4232. From M4 exit at junct 33 and follow brown signs

A stroll around the indoor galleries and 100 acres of beautiful grounds will give you a fascinating insight into how people in Wales have lived, worked and spent their leisure hours since Celtic times. You can see people practising the traditional means of earning a living, the animals they kept and at certain times of year, the ways in which they celebrated the seasons.

Times Open all year daily, 10-5. (Closed 24-26 Dec). **Fees** Free. Charge may apply to some events. **Facilities** 🅿 ▯ 🍽 licensed 🎍 (outdoor) ♿ (partly accessible) (wheelchair access possible to most parts) toilets for disabled shop ⊗

DRE-FACH FELINDRE

National Woollen Museum

SA44 5UP

☎ 01559 370929 📄 01559 371592
e-mail: post@museumwales.ac.uk
web: www.museumwales.ac.uk
dir: 16m W of Carmarthen off A484, 4m E of
Newcastle Emlyn

The museum is housed in the former Cambrian
Mills and has a comprehensive display tracing
the evolution of the industry from its beginnings
to the present day. Demonstrations of the fleece
to fabric process are given on 19th-century textile
machinery.

Times Open all year, Apr-Sep, daily 10-5; Oct-
Mar, Tue-Sat 10-5. Phone for details of Xmas
opening times. **Fees** Free admission but charge
may be made for some events. **Facilities** 🅿 🅟
🖵 🎤 (outdoor) ♿ toilets for disabled shop ⊗

KIDWELLY

Kidwelly Industrial Museum

Broadford SA17 4LW

☎ 01554 891078
dir: signed from Kidwelly bypass & town, stack
visible from bypass

Two of the great industries of Wales are
represented in this museum: tinplate and coal
mining. The original buildings and machinery of
the Kidwelly tinplate works, where tinplate was
hand made, are now on display to the public.
There is also an exhibition of coal mining with
pit-head gear and a winding engine, while the
more general history of the area is shown in a
separate exhibition.

Times Open Etr, Jun-Sep, BH wknds, Mon-Fri
10-5, Sat-Sun 12-5. Last admission 4. Other
times by arrangement for parties only.* **Facilities**
🅟 🖵 🎤 (outdoor) ♿ toilets for disabled shop

LAUGHARNE

Dylan Thomas' Boat House

Dylans Walk SA33 4SD
☎ 01994 427420 📄 01994 427420
e-mail: dylanthomas@carmarthenshire.gov.uk
web: www.dylanthomasboathouse.com
dir: 14m SW of Carmarthen

The home of Dylan Thomas and his family during the last four turbulent and creative years of his life. The house and its surrounding estuary, town and countryside feature considerably in the poet's work, including his famous Under Milk Wood. The house contains interpretive display, original furniture, bookshop and tearoom. Please telephone for details of events running throughout the year.

Times Open all year, May-Oct & Etr wknd, daily 10-5.30 (last admission 5); Nov-Apr, daily 10.30-3.30 (last admission 3)* **Facilities** Ⓟ ☕ shop ⊗

ABERYSTWYTH

The National Library of Wales

Penglais SY23 3BU
☎ 01970 632800 📄 01970 632882
e-mail: holi@llgc.org.uk
web: www.llgc.org.uk
dir: Off Penglais Hill, A487 in N area of Aberystwyth

The largest library in Wales. Its collections include books, manuscripts, archival documents, maps and photographs as well as paintings, film, video and sound recordings. The library is recognised as the leading research centre for Welsh and Celtic studies, and is popular with those studying family history. Lectures, screenings and conferences throughout the year. There are constantly changing exhibitions in the galleries and exhibition halls. Free guided tour every Monday morning at 11am. Group guided tours available by prior arrangement.

Times Open on selected BHs. Please check details before travelling* **Fees** Free. Admission to reading rooms available by readers ticket, two proofs of identity required, one including address. Free admission to all exhibitions **Facilities** Ⓟ ☕ ⍩Ⓞⅼ licensed ⌁ (outdoor) ♿ toilets for disabled shop ⊗

CENARTH

The National Coracle Centre

Cenarth Falls SA38 9JL
☎ 01239 710980
e-mail: martinfowler7@aol.com
web: www.coracle-centre.co.uk
dir: on A484 between Carmarthen and Cardigan, centre of Cenarth village, beside bridge and river

Situated by the beautiful Cenarth Falls, this fascinating museum has a unique collection of coracle-like craft from all over the world, including Tibet, India, Iraq, Vietnam, and North America. Cenarth has long been a centre for coracle fishing, and coracle rides are often available in the village during the summer holiday. Look out for the salmon leap by the flour mill.

Times Open Etr-Oct, daily 10.30-5.30. All other times by appointment.* **Facilities** 🅿 Ⓟ ♿ shop

CONWY

Conwy Castle

LL32 8AY
☎ 01492 592358
web: www.cadw.wales.gov.uk
dir: via A55 or B5106

The castle is a magnificent fortress, built 1283-7 by Edward I. There is an exhibition on castle chapels on the ground floor of the Chapel Tower. The castle forms part of the same defensive system as the extensive town walls, which are among the most complete in Europe.

Times Open all year, Apr-Oct, daily 9-5; Nov-Mar, Mon-Sat 9.30-4, Sun 11-4.* **Fees** £4.60 (ch 5-15, concessions £4.10, disabled visitors & assisting companion free). Family ticket £13.30. Joint ticket for both monuments £6.85 (ch 5-15 & concessions £5.85, family £19.55, disabled visitors & assisting companion free). Group rates available. Prices quoted apply until 31 Mar 2010.* **Facilities** 🅿 toilets for disabled shop ⊗ ⊕

LLANDUDNO

Great Orme Bronze Age Copper Mines

Pyliau Rd, Great Orme LL30 2XG
☎ 01492 870447
e-mail: gomines@greatorme.freeserve.co.uk
web: www.greatormemines.info
dir: Follow 'copper mine' signs from Llandudno Promenade

Take a look at some original 4,000 year old Bronze Age artefacts and a selection of Bronze Age mining tools. After watching two short films take a helmet and make your way down to the mines. Walking through tunnels mined nearly 4,000 years ago look into some of the smaller tunnels and get a feel for the conditions our prehistoric ancestors faced in their search for valuable copper ores. Excavation on the surface will continue for decades and one of the team is usually available to answer visitors' questions as they walk around the site and view the prehistoric landscape being uncovered.

Times Open mid Mar-end Oct, daily 10-5.*
Fees £6 (ch £4, under 5's free). Family ticket (2ad+2ch) £16, extra child £3.* **Facilities** ℗
℗ ⊑⊓ (outdoor) ㊎ (partly accessible) (no wheelchair access to underground mine) toilets for disabled shop

TREFRIW

Trefriw Woollen Mills

Main Rd LL27 0NQ
☎ 01492 640462
e-mail: info@t-w-m.co.uk
web: www.t-w-m.co.uk
dir: on B5106 in centre of Trefriw, 5m N of Betws-y-Coed

Established in 1859, the mill is situated beside the fast-flowing Afon Crafnant, which drives two hydro-electric turbines to power the looms. All the machinery of woollen manufacture can be seen here: blending, carding, spinning, dyeing, warping and weaving. In the Weaver's Garden, there are plants traditionally used in the textile industry, mainly for dyeing. Hand-spinning demonstrations. Traditional Welsh bedspreads, 'tapestries' and tweeds woven on site are available to purchase.

Times Mill Museum open Etr-Oct, Mon-Fri 10-1 & 2-5 (ex BHs). Weaving & turbine house: open all year (ex festive season), Mon-Fri 10-1 & 2-5. Handspinning & weaver's garden open Jun-Sep, Tue-Thu. Shop open all year, daily. **Fees** Free admission but no school parties. **Facilities** ℗
⊑㊎ (partly accessible) (access limited to ground floor of Mill, stairs to top 2 floors) shop ⊗

BODELWYDDAN

Bodelwyddan Castle

LL18 5YA

☎ 01745 584060 📄 01745 584563
e-mail: enquiries@bodelwyddan-castle.co.uk
web: www.bodelwyddan-castle.co.uk
dir: just off A55, near St Asaph, follow brown signs

Bodelwyddan Castle houses over 100 portraits from the National Portrait Gallery's 19th-century collection. The portraits hang in beautifully refurbished rooms and are complemented by sculpture and period furnishings. Interactive displays show how portraits were produced and used in the Victorian era. The Castle Gallery hosts a programme of temporary exhibitions and events. The castle is set within 200 acres of parkland, including formal gardens, an aviary, woodlands, a butterfly glade and an adventure playground. Lots of events, contact the castle for details.

Times Opening times not confirmed for 2010. Please telephone for details. **Fees** £6 (ch 5-16 £2.50, ch under 4 free, concessions £5). Family ticket (2ad+2ch) £15 (1ad+2ch) £12.* **Facilities** 🅿 Ⓟ ⏄ ⑩ licensed ⍰ (outdoor) ♿ (partly accessible) toilets for disabled shop ⊗

LLANGOLLEN

Horse Drawn Boats Centre

The Wharf, Wharf Hill LL20 8TA

☎ 01978 860702 & 01691 690322
📄 01978 860702
e-mail: bill@horsedrawnboats.co.uk
web: www.horsedrawnboats.co.uk
dir: A5 onto Llangollen High St, across river bridge to T-junct. Wharf opposite, up the hill

Take a horse drawn boat trip along the beautiful Vale of Llangollen. There is also a narrow boat trip that crosses Pontcysyllte Aqueduct, the largest navigable aqueduct in the world. Full bar on board, commentary throughout. Tea room serving light meals & breakfast.

Times Open Etr-end Oct, daily, 9.30-5; Tea room Nov-Mar, wknds 10-4.30. **Fees** Horse Drawn Boat Trip from £5 (ch £2.50). Family £12.50 Aquaduct Trip £11 (ch £9).* **Facilities** Ⓟ ⏄ ♿ (partly accessible) (no access to motor boat, access to tea room & Horse Drawn Boats) toilets for disabled shop ⊗

CAERNARFON

Caernarfon Castle

LL55 2AY
☎ 01286 677617
web: www.cadw.wales.gov.uk

Edward I began building the castle and extensive
town walls in 1283 after defeating the last
independent ruler of Wales. Completed in 1328,
it has unusual polygonal towers, notably the
10-sided Eagle Tower. There is a theory that
these features were copied from the walls
of Constantinople, to reflect a tradition that
Constantine was born nearby. Edward I's son and
heir was born and presented to the Welsh people
here, setting a precedent that was followed in
1969, when Prince Charles was invested as
Prince of Wales.

Times Open all year, Apr-Oct, daily 9-5; Nov-Mar,
Mon-Sat 9.30-4, Sun 11-4.* **Fees** £4.95 (ch
5-15, pen & students £4.60, disabled visitors
& assisting compainion free). Family ticket (2
ad & all ch/grandch under 16) £14.50. Group
rates available. Prices quoted apply until 31 Mar
2010.* **Facilities** Ⓟ shop ⊗ ✛

CAERNARFON

Segontium Roman Museum **FREE**

Beddgelert Rd LL55 2LN
☎ 01286 675625   📠 01286 678416
e-mail: info@segontium.org.uk
web: www.segontium.org.uk
dir: on A4085 to Beddgelert approx 1m from
Caernarfon

Segontium Roman Museum tells the story of the
conquest and occupation of Wales by the Romans
and displays the finds from the auxiliary fort of
Segontium, one of the most famous in Britain.
You can combine a visit to the museum with
exploration of the site of the Roman Fort, which is
in the care of Cadw: Welsh Historic Monuments.
The exciting discoveries displayed at the museum
vividly portray the daily life of the soldiers
stationed in this most westerly outpost of the
Roman Empire.

Times Open all year, Tue-Sun 12.30-4. Closed
Mon except BH* **Facilities** Ⓟ shop ⊗

HARLECH

Harlech Castle

LL46 2YH
☎ 01766 780552
web: www.cadw.wales.gov.uk
dir: from A496

Harlech Castle was built in 1283-89 by Edward I, with a sheer drop to the sea on one side. Owain Glyndwr starved the castle into submission in 1404 and made it his court and campaigning base. Later, the defence of the castle in the Wars of the Roses inspired the song Men of Harlech. Today the sea has slipped away, and the castle's great walls and round towers stand above the dunes.

Times Open all year, Apr-Oct, daily 9-5; Nov-Mar, Mon-Sat 9.30-4, Sun 11-4.* **Fees** £3.60 (ch 5-15, concessions £3.20, disabled visitors & assisting companion free). Family ticket (2ad+all ch/grandch under 16) £10.40. Group rates available. Prices quoted apply until 31 Mar 2010.* **Facilities** ❷ shop ⊗ ⬦

LLANYSTUMDWY

Lloyd George Museum

LL52 0SH
☎ 01766 522071   📄 01766 522071
e-mail: amgueddfeydd-museums@gwynedd.gov.uk
web: www.gwynedd.gov.uk/museums
dir: on A497 between Pwllheli & Criccieth

Explore the life and times of David Lloyd George in this museum. His boyhood home is recreated as it would have been when he lived there between 1864 and 1880, along with his Uncle Lloyd's shoemaking workshop.

Times Open Etr, daily 10.30-5; Apr-May, Mon-Fri 10.30-5 (open Sat in Jun); Jul-Sep daily 10.30-5; Oct, Mon-Fri, 11-4. Open BHs; Other times by appointment, telephone 01286 679098 for details.* **Facilities** ❷ Ⓟ ⊼ (outdoor) toilets for disabled shop ⊗

PORTHMADOG

Ffestiniog Railway

Harbour Station LL49 9NF
☎ 01766 516000 📠 01766 516006
e-mail: enquiries@festrail.co.uk
web: www.festrail.co.uk
dir: SE end of town beside the harbour, on A487

One of the Great Little Train of Wales, this railway runs for 13.5 through Snowdonia. Originally built to carry slate from the quarries at Blaenau Ffestiniog to the harbour at Porthmadog, the little trains now carry passengers through the beautiful scenery of the national park. A licensed at-your-seat refreshment service is available on all main trains. Day rover tickets allow you to break your journey to make the most of your day. First class observation carriage on all trains.

Times Open daily late Mar-late Oct. Limited Winter service mid wk trains Nov & early Dec. Santa specials in Dec. Open Feb half term.
Fees Full distance return £17.95 (1 ch under 16 free, concessions £16.15). Other fares available.*
Facilities 🅿 🅟 ⬜ 🍴 licensed 🏕 (outdoor) ♿ (partly accessible) (most train services accessible, phone in advance, main station/ platforms & restaurant accessible) toilets for disabled shop ⊗

CAERWENT

Caerwent Roman Town **FREE**

☎ 01443 336000
web: www.cadw.wales.gov.uk
dir: just off A48

A complete circuit of the town wall of 'Venta Silurum', together with excavated areas of houses, shops and a temple.

Times Open - access throughout the year. There is a facilitator on site each Tue. For group bookings Tel: (01633) 430576.* **Facilities** ⊗ ♿

CHEPSTOW

Chepstow Castle

NP16 5EY
☎ 01291 624065
web: www.cadw.wales.gov.uk

Built by William FitzOsbern, Chepstow is the first recorded Norman stone castle. It stands in a strategic spot above the Wye. The castle was strengthened in the following centuries, but was not besieged (as far as is known) until the Civil War, when it was twice lost to the Parliamentarians. The remains of the domestic rooms and the massive gatehouse with its portcullis grooves and ancient gates are still impressive, as are the walls and towers.

Times Open all year, Apr-Oct, daily 9-5; Nov-Mar, Mon-Sat 9.30-4, Sun 11-4.* **Fees** £3.60 (ch 5-15, concessions £3.20, disabled visitors and assisting companion free). Family ticket (2ad+all ch/grandch under 16) £10.40. Group rates available. Prices quoted apply until 31 Mar 2010.* **Facilities** 🅿 shop ⊗ ✛

GROSMONT

Grosmont Castle **FREE**

☎ 01981 240301
web: www.cadw.wales.gov.uk
dir: on B4347

Grosmont is one of the 'trilateral' castles of Hubert de Burgh (see also Skenfrith and White Castle). It stands on a mound with a dry moat, and the considerable remains of its 13th-century great hall can be seen. Three towers once guarded the curtain wall, and the western one is well preserved.

Times Open all year, access available at all reasonable times, which will normally be 10-4 daily.* **Facilities** ⊗ ✛

MONMOUTH

The Nelson Museum & Local History Centre **FREE**

New Market Hall, Priory St NP25 3XA
☎ 01600 710630
e-mail: nelsonmuseum@monmouthshire.gov.uk
dir: in town centre

One of the world's major collections of Admiral Nelson-related items, including original letters, glass, china, silver, medals, books, models, prints and Nelson's fighting sword feature here. The local history displays deal with Monmouth's past as a fortress market town, and include a section on the co-founder of the Rolls Royce company, Charles Stewart Rolls, who was also a pioneer balloonist, aviator and, of course, motorist. A major exhibition on C S Rolls and his family will take place between January and August 2010. 12 July 2010 commemorates the centenary of the death of C S Rolls.

Times Open all year, Mar-Oct, Mon-Sat & BH 11-1 & 2-5, Sun 2-5; Nov-Feb, Mon-Sat 11-1 & 2-4, Sun 2-4. **Facilities** ℗ ♿ (partly accessible) (mezzanine display area accessible only by stairs - 25% of whole museum display area) toilets for disabled shop ⊗

SKENFRITH

Skenfrith Castle **FREE**

☎ 01443 336000
web: www.cadw.wales.gov.uk
dir: on B4521

This 13th-century castle has a round keep set inside an imposing towered curtain wall. Hubert de Burgh built it as one of three 'trilateral' castles to defend the Welsh Marches.

Times Open all year, access available at all reasonable times, which will normally be 10-4 daily. Key keeper arrangement.* **Facilities** ℗ ⊗ ✛ ♨

WHITE CASTLE

White Castle

NP7 8UD

☎ 01600 780380

web: www.cadw.wales.gov.uk

dir: 7m NE of Abergavenny, unclass road N of B4233

The impressive 12th to 13th-century moated stronghold was built by Hubert de Burgh to defend the Welsh Marches. Substantial remains of walls, towers and a gatehouse can be seen. This is the finest of a trio of castles, the others being at Skenfrith and Grosmont.

Times Open Apr-Oct, 10-5 daily. Open 10-4 daily and unstaffed with no admission charge at all other times.* **Fees** £2.60 (ch 5-15, concessions £2.25, disabled visitors & assisting companion free). Family ticket (2ad+all ch/grandch under 16) £7.45. Group rates available. Prices quoted apply until 31 Mar 2010.* **Facilities** 🅿 ⊗ ♿

CRYNANT

Cefn Coed Colliery Museum   **FREE**

SA10 8SN

☎ 01639 750556   📄 01639 750556

e-mail: colliery@btconnect.com

web: www.neath-porttalbot.gov.uk

dir: 1m S of Crynant, on A4109

The museum is on the site of a former working colliery, and tells the story of mining in the Dulais Valley. A steam-winding engine has been kept and is now operated by electricity, and there is also a simulated underground mining gallery, boilerhouse, compressor house, and exhibition area. Outdoor exhibits include a stationary colliery locomotive. Exhibitions relating to the coal mining industry are held on a regular basis. The museum is now home to the Dulais Valley Historical Model Railway Society who, with the help from the Heritage Lottery Fund have created an ever increasing layout depicting the Neath-Brecon railway through the valley.

Times Open Apr-Oct, daily 10.30-5; Nov-Mar, groups welcome by prior arrangement.* **Facilities** 🅿 🚉 (outdoor) ♿ (partly accessible) (access to exhibition areas, but not to underground gallery) toilets for disabled shop

CAERLEON

Caerleon Roman Baths FREE

NP18 1AE

☎ 01663 422518
web: www.cadw.wales.gov.uk
dir: on B4236

Caerleon was an important Roman military base, with accommodation for thousands of men. The foundations of barrack lines and parts of the ramparts can be seen, with remains of the cookhouse, latrines and baths. The amphitheatre nearby is one of the best examples in Britain.

Times Open all year, Apr-Oct, daily 9.30-5; Nov-Mar, Mon-Sat, 9.30-5, Sun 11-4.* **Facilities** Ⓟ shop ⊗ ♿

CAERLEON

National Roman Legion Museum FREE

High St NP18 1AE

☎ 01633 423134 📄 01633 422869
e-mail: roman@museumwales.ac.uk
web: www.museumwales.ac.uk
dir: close to Newport, 20 min from M4, follow signs from Cardiff & Bristol

The museum illustrates the history of Roman Caerleon and the daily life of its garrison. On display are arms, armour and equipment, with a collection of engraved gemstones, a labyrinth mosaic and finds from the legionary base at Usk. Please telephone for details of children's holiday activities.

Times Open all year: Mon-Sat 10-5, Sun 2-5.*
Facilities Ⓟ toilets for disabled shop ⊗

CAREW

Carew Castle & Tidal Mill

SA70 8SL

☎ 01646 651782   📄 01646 651782
e-mail: enquiries@carewcastle.com
web: www.carewcastle.com
dir: on A4075, just off A477 Pembroke to Kilgetty road

This magnificent Norman castle has royal links with Henry Tudor and was the setting for the Great Tournament of 1507. Nearby is the Carew Cross (Cadw), an impressive 13ft Celtic cross dating from the 11th century. Carew Mill is one of only four restored tidal mills in Britain, with records dating back to 1558.

Times Open Castle Jan-Etr, Nov-Dec, daily 11-3 (closed Xmas). Castle & Mill Etr-Oct, daily 10-5.*
Fees £3.90 (concessions £2.75). Family ticket £10.50.* **Facilities** 🅿 Ⓟ 🍴 (outdoor) ♿ (partly accessible) (ground floors, toilets and shop are acccessible) toilets for disabled shop

CRYMYCH

Castell Henllys Iron Age Fort

Pant-Glas, Meline SA41 3UT

☎ 01239 891319   📄 01239 891319
e-mail: celts@castellhenllys.com
web: www.castellhenllys.com
dir: off A487 between Cardigan and Newport

This Iron Age hill fort is set in the beautiful Pembrokeshire Coast National Park. Excavations began in 1981 and three roundhouses have been reconstructed, another roundhouse has been completed and is the largest on the site. Celtic roundhouses have been constructed in the original way using hazel wattle walls, oak rafters and thatched conical roofs. A forge, smithy and looms can be seen, with other attractions such as trails and a herb garden. Please telephone for details of special events.

Times Open all year, Etr-Oct, daily 10-5 (last entry 4.30); Nov-Mar 11-3 (last entry 2.30). Closed 24-31 Dec. **Fees** £3.90 (concessions £2.75). Family £10.50.* **Facilities** 🅿 🍴 (outdoor) ♿ toilets for disabled shop

PEMBROKE

Pembroke Castle

SA71 4LA

☎ 01646 681510 & & 684585

📠 01646 622260

e-mail: info@pembrokecastle.co.uk

web: www.pembrokecastle.co.uk

dir: W end of main street

This magnificent castle commands stunning views over the Milford estuary. Discover its rich medieval history, and that of Henry VII, the first Tudor king, through a variety of exhibitions. There are lively guided tours and events each Sunday in July and August. Before leaving, pop into the Brass Rubbing Centre and make your own special souvenir. To complete the day, wander round the tranquil millpond and medieval town walls, which surround other architectural gems from Tudor and Georgian times. Special Events: 1st week in Sep 'Pembroke Festival'. Please telephone for details.

Times Open all year, daily, Apr-Sep 9.30-6; Mar & Oct 10-5; Nov-Feb, 10-4. Closed 24-26 Dec & 1 Jan.* Facilities Ⓟ ⚏ ☕ ⏚ (outdoor) toilets for disabled shop

BRECON

Regimental Museum of The Royal Welsh

The Barracks, The Watton LD3 7EB

☎ 01874 613310   📠 01874 613275

e-mail: swb@rrw.org.uk

web: www.rrw.org.uk

dir: close to town centre, well signed

The museum of the South Wales Borderers and Monmouthshire Regiment (now the Royal Welsh), which was raised in 1689 and has been awarded 23 Victoria Crosses. Amongst the collections is the Zulu War Room, devoted to the war and in particular to the events at Rorke's Drift, 1879, when 121 men fought 4,500 Zulus.

Times Open all year wkdys 10-5, Apr-Sep Sat & BHs 10-4. Call for special Sun opening times.* Fees £3 (ch up to 16 free).* Facilities Ⓟ ⚹ toilets for disabled shop ⊗

TREHAFOD

Rhondda Heritage Park

Lewis Merthyr Colliery, Coed Cae Rd CF37 7NP
☎ 01443 682036   🖶 01443 687420
e-mail: info@rhonddaheritagepark.com
web: www.rhonddaheritagepark.com
dir: between Pontypridd & Porth, off A470, follow
brown heritage signs from M4 junct 32

Based at the Lewis Merthyr Colliery, the Heritage
Park is a fascinating 'living history' attraction.
You can take the Cage Ride to 'Pit Bottom' and
explore the underground workings of a 1950s
pit, guided by men who were miners themselves.
There are children's activities, an art gallery and
a museum illustrating living conditions in the
Rhondda Valley. Special events throughout the
year, phone for details.

Times Open all year, daily 10-6. Closed Mon
from Oct-Etr. (Last admission 4). Closed 25 Dec-
early Jan.* **Fees** £5.60 (ch £4.30, pen £4.95).
Family(4)ticket from £16.50, (6) £21.* **Facilities**
🅿 Ⓟ 🖵 🍽 licensed 🎪 (indoor & outdoor) ♿
(partly accessible) toilets for disabled shop ⊗

PARKMILL

Gower Heritage Centre

Y Felin Ddwr SA3 2EH
☎ 01792 371206   🖶 01792 371471
e-mail: info@gowerheritagecentre.co.uk
web: www.gowerheritagecentre.co.uk
dir: follow signs for South Gower on A4118 W
from Swansea. W side of Parkmill village

Based around a 12th-century water-powered
cornmill, the site also contains a number of craft
workshops, two play areas, animals, a museum
and a miller's cottage, all set in attractive
countryside in an Area of Outstanding Natural
Beauty.

Times Open all year, daily, Mar-Oct 10-5.30; Nov-
Feb 10-4.30. Closed 25 Dec.* **Facilities** 🅿 Ⓟ
🖵 🍽 licensed 🎪 toilets for disabled shop

SWANSEA

Swansea Museum   FREE

Victoria Rd, Maritime Quarter SA1 1SN
☎ 01792 653763   📄 01792 652585
e-mail: swansea.museum@swansea.gov.uk
web: www.swanseaheritage.net
dir: M4 junct 42, on main road into city centre,
just past Sainsurys on left

This is the oldest museum in Wales, showing
the history of Swansea from the earliest times
until today. The museum has a Tramshed and
floating boats to explore (summer only). There is
a continuous programme of temporary exhibitions
and events all year around. The collections
centre is nearby which is open to the public every
Wednesday.

Times Open all year, Tue-Sun 10-5 (last
admission 4.45). Closed Mon except BH Mon,
25-26 Dec & 1 Jan. **Facilities** 🅿 🅟 🍴 (outdoor)
♿ (partly accessible) (lower floor/gallery
accessible) toilets for disabled shop ⊗

BLAENAVON

Big Pit National
Coal Museum   FREE

NP4 9XP
☎ 01495 790311   📄 01495 792618
e-mail: post@museumwales.ac.uk
web: www.museumwales.ac.uk
dir: M4 junct 25/26, follow signs on A4042 &
A4043 to Pontypool & Blaenavon. Signed off A465

The Real Underground Experience, Big Pit is the
UK's leading mining museum. It is a real colliery
and was the place of work for hundreds of men,
woman and children for over 200 years. A daily
struggle to extract the precious mineral that
stoked furnaces and lit household fires across
the world.

Times Open all year 9.30-5. Please call for
underground guided tour availability* **Facilities**
🅿 🖵 ♿ (partly accessible) toilets for disabled
shop ⊗

BLAENAVON

Blaenavon Ironworks FREE

North St NP4 9RN
☎ 01495 792615
web: www.cadw.wales.gov.uk

The Blaenavon Ironworks were a milestone in the history of the Industrial Revolution. Constructed in 1788-99, they were the first purpose-built, multi-furnace ironworks in Wales. By 1796, Blaenavon was the second largest ironworks in Wales, eventually closing down in 1904.

Times Open all year, Apr-Oct, daily 10-5; Nov-Mar, Fri-Sat 9.30-4, Sun 11-4.* **Facilities** Ⓟ
Ⓧ ♿

PENARTH

Cosmeston Lakes Country Park & Medieval Village

Lavernock Rd CF64 5UY
☎ 029 2070 1678 🖷 029 2070 8686
e-mail: NColes@valeofglamorgan.gov.uk
web: www.valeofglamorgan.gov.uk
dir: on B4267 between Barry and Penarth

Deserted during the plagues and famines of the 14th century, the original village was rediscovered through archaeological excavations. The buildings have been faithfully reconstructed on the excavated remains, creating a living museum of medieval village life. Special events throughout the year include re-enactments and Living History.

Times Open all year, daily 11-5 in Summer, 11-4 in Winter. Closed 25 Dec. Country park open at all times.* **Facilities** Ⓟ 🖵 🍽 licensed 🎪 toilets for disabled shop

CHIRK

Chirk Castle

LL14 5AF

☎ 01691 777701 📄 01691 774706
e-mail: chirkcastle@nationaltrust.org.uk
dir: 8m S of Wrexham, signed off A483, 5m from
Llangollen signed off A5

Chirk Castle is one of a chain of late 13th-century
Marcher castles. Its high walls and drum towers
have hardly changed, but the inside shows the
varied tastes of 700 years of occupation. One of
the least altered parts is Adam's Tower. Many of
the medieval-looking decorations were created
by Pugin in the 19th century. Varied furnishings
include fine tapestries. In the garden there are
beautiful views that take in seven counties.

Times Open 3 Mar-Oct, Wed-Sun 11-5, Garden
& Tower 10-6, Full Castle 11-5. Closed BH Mon,
Tue in Jul & Aug, 1 wk early Oct. **Fees** Full Castle
£9.60 (ch £4.80) Family £24. Garden & Tower
£6.80 (ch £3.40), Family £17. **Facilities** 🅿
🚻 ⛱ (outdoor) ♿ (partly accessible) (access
to east wing, garden, laundries, servants hall)
toilets for disabled shop 🐾

GIANT'S CAUSEWAY

Giant's Causeway Centre

44 Causeway Rd BT57 8SU

☎ 028 2073 1855 📄 028 2073 2537
e-mail: causewaytic@hotmail.com
web: www.northantrim.com
dir: 2m N of Bushmills on B146

This dramatic rock formation is undoubtedly one
of the wonders of the natural world. The Centre
provides an exhibition and audio-visual show,
and Ulsterbus provides a minibus service to the
stones and there are guided walks, and special
facilities for the disabled.

Times Open all year, daily from 10 (closes 7 Jul &
Aug). Closed 1 wk Xmas.* **Facilities** 🅿 🚻 🍴
licensed ⛱ toilets for disabled shop 🚫

LISBURN

Irish Linen Centre & Lisburn Museum FREE

Market Square BT28 1AG
☎ 028 9266 3377 📄 028 9267 2624
e-mail: irishlinencentre@lisburn.gov.uk
web: www.lisburncity.gov.uk
dir: Signed both in and outside town centre. Follow tourist signs from M1

The centre tells the story of the Irish linen industry past and present. The recreation of individual factory scenes brings the past to life and a series of imaginative hands-on activities describe the linen manufacturing processes. The Museum has a range of temporary exhibitions of local interest.

Times Open all year, Mon-Sat, 9.30-5.* Facilities ℗ ⊑ & toilets for disabled shop ⊗

ARMAGH

Armagh County Museum FREE

The Mall East BT61 9BE
☎ 028 3752 3070 📄 028 3752 2631
e-mail: acm.info@nmni.com
web: www.magni.org.uk
dir: in city centre

Housed in a 19th-century schoolhouse, this museum contains an art gallery and library, as well as a collection of local folkcrafts and natural history. Special events are planned thoughout the year.

Times Open all year, Mon-Fri 10-5, Sat 10-1 & 2-5. Facilities ℗ & toilets for disabled shop ⊗

ARMAGH

Navan Centre & Fort

81 Killylea Rd BT60 4LD
☎ 028 3752 9655 📠 028 3752 6431
e-mail: navan@armagh.gov.uk
web: www.navan.com
dir: 2.5m W on A28

Navan was once known as Emain Macha, the ancient seat of kings and earliest capital of Ulster. Today it is an impressive archaeological site with its own museum and visitor centre located in a building that blends into the landscape. The Navan Centre uses audio-visuals and interactive devices to unravel history from myth. Travel into the 'Real World' of archaeology and the 'Other World' to hear the legends of the Ulster Cycle.

Times Open daily Jul-Sep 10-7, Oct-Dec 10-4.*
Fees £5.15 (ch £3.45, concessions £4.20). Family ticket £14.95.* **Facilities** 🅿 ⎕ ⊼ (outdoor) ♿ toilets for disabled shop ⊗

ARMAGH

Saint Patrick's Trian Visitor Complex

40 English St BT61 7BA
☎ 028 3752 1801 📠 028 3751 0180
e-mail: info@saintpatrickstrian.com
web: www.visitarmagh.com
dir: in city centre

An exciting visitor complex in the heart of the city. Incorporating three major exhibitions - The Armagh story: traces Armagh's historic Pagan monuments through to the coming of St Patrick and Celtic Christianity to the modern day city. Patrick's Testament: takes a closer look at Ireland's patron saint through the writings found in ancient manuscript the Book of Armagh. The Land of Lilliput: Jonathan Swift's most famous book, Gulliver's Travels is narrated by a 20-foot giant.

Times Open all year, Mon-Sat 10-5, Sun 2-5. Closed 12 Jul.* **Fees** £5.15 (ch £3.45, concessions £4.20). Family ticket £14.95.*
Facilities 🅿 Ⓟ ⑩ licensed ♿ toilets for disabled shop ⊗

BELFAST

Ulster Museum FREE

Botanic Gardens BT9 5AB
☎ 028 9038 3000　🖹 028 9038 3003
e-mail: uminfo@nmni.com
web: www.nmni.com
dir: 1m S of city centre on Stranmillis road

The Ulster Museum is the perfect place to explore the arts, ancient and modern history, and the nature of Ireland. Art displays change regularly but always include a rich variety of Irish and international paintings, drawings and sculpture, along with ceramics, glass and costume. The history galleries tell the story of the north of Ireland from the Ice Age to the present day. The natural environment is explored in the Habitas galleries.

Times Due to open Oct 2009 after major redevelopment. Please phone or check website for further details.* **Facilities** Ⓟ ⌷ toilets for disabled shop ⊗

HOLYWOOD

Ulster Folk and Transport Museum

Cultra BT18 0EU
☎ 028 9042 8428　🖹 01232 428728
e-mail: uftm.info@magni.org.uk
web: www.uftm.org.uk
dir: 12m outside Belfast on A2, past Holywood on main road to Bangor

Voted Northern Ireland's Best Visitor Attraction and Irish Museum of the Year, this attraction illustrates the way of life and traditions of Northern Ireland. The galleries of the Transport Museum display collections of horse drawn carts, cars, steam locomotives and the history of ship and aircraft building. Please telephone for details of special events running throughout the year.

Times Open all year Mar-Jun, Mon-Fri 10-5, Sat 10-6, Sun 11-6; Jul-Sep, Mon-Sat 10-6, Sun 11-6; Oct-Feb, Mon-Fri 10-4, Sat 10-5, Sun 11-5.* **Facilities** Ⓟ Ⓟ ⌷ ⊼ (outdoor) toilets for disabled shop

LONDONDERRY

City Walls

☎ 028 7126 7284   🖹 028 7137 7992
e-mail: info@derryvisitor.com
web: www.ehsni.gov.uk

The finest and most complete city walls to
be found in Ireland. The walls, 20-25ft high,
are mounted with ancient cannon, and date
back to the 17th century. The walled city is a
conservation area with many fine buildings.
Visitors can walk round the city ramparts - a
circuit of one mile.

Times Open all times.* **Facilities** 🅿 ♿ (partly
accessible) (limited wheelchair access to Walls)

BALLYGAWLEY

U S Grant Ancestral Homestead

Dergenagh Rd BT70 1TW
☎ 028 8555 7133   🖹 028 8555 7133
e-mail: killymaddy.reception@dungannon.gov.uk
web: www.dungannon.gov.uk
dir: off A4, 2m on Dergenagh road, signed

Ancestral homestead of Ulysses S Grant, 18th
President of the United States of America. The
homestead and farmyard have been restored to
the style and appearance of a mid-19th-century
Irish smallholding. There are many amenities
including a children's play area, purpose built
barbecue and picnic tables and butterfly garden.
Bike hire available (£1/hr).

Times Open all year daily 9-5. **Fees** Free
admission. Advisable to book in advance for
audio visual show.* **Facilities** 🅿 🅵 (outdoor)
♿ 🚫

OMAGH

Ulster American Folk Park

2 Mellon Rd, Castletown BT78 5QY
☎ 028 8224 3292 📠 028 8224 2241
e-mail: uafpinfo@nmni.com
web: www.nmni.com
dir: 5m NW Omagh on A5

An award winning outdoor museum of emigration which tells the story of millions of people who emigrated from these shores throughout the 18th and 19th centuries. The Old World and New World layout of the park illustrates the various aspects of emigrant life on both sides of the Atlantic. Traditional thatched buildings, American log houses and a full-scale replica emigrant ship plus the dockside gallery help to bring a bygone era back to life. Costumed demonstrators go about their everyday tasks including spinning, open hearth cookery, printing and textiles. The museum also includes an indoor Emigrants Exhibition and a centre for Migration Studies/library which is accessible to all visitors if they wish to find further information on the history of emigration and the place of their families in it.

Times Open all year Apr-Oct daily 10.30-6, Sun & BH 11-6.30; Nov-Mar Mon-Fri 10.30-5. (Last admission 1hr 30mins before closing).*
Facilities ℗ ℗ ⬚ ⑩ licensed ⋈ (outdoor) ♿ toilets for disabled shop ⊗

BUNRATTY

Bunratty Castle & Folk Park

☎ 061 360788 📠 061 361020
e-mail: reservations@shannonheritage.com
web: www.shannonheritage.com
dir: off the main dual carriageway (N18) between Limerick and Ennis. Signed from the N18

This magnificent castle was built around 1425 and contains mainly 15th and 16th century furnishings and tapestries. 19th-century Irish life is recreated in the Folk Park, including rural farmhouses, a village street and Bunratty House. Medieval Banquets in the castle throughout the year (booking necessary).

Times Open all year, Jan-May & Sep-Dec 9 5.30; Jun-Aug, Mon-Fri 9 5.30 (last admission 4.15) & Sat & Sun 9-6 (last admission 5.15). Last admission to the castle is 4pm. Closed 24-26 Dec. Opening times may be subject to change*
Fees Castle & Folk Park €15.75 (ch €9.45) Family tickets, senior, student tickets also available.*
Facilities ℗ ⬚ ⑩ licensed ⋈ (outdoor) ♿ (partly accessible) (castle is not accessible to wheelchair users) toilets for disabled shop

KILLALOE

Brian Boru Heritage Centre

☎ 061 360788 🖷 061 361020
e-mail: reservations@shannonheritage.com
web: www.shannonheritage.com
dir: off the N7 between Limerick & Nenagh, take the R494 to Killaloe & Ballina

The 11th century High King of Ireland, Brian Boru one of the most influential and colourful figures in Irish history. The heritage centre reveals the story of Brian Boru is through a series of colourful exhibits, graphic illustrations and inter-active audio-visual presentation.

Times Open May-Sep, daily 10-5 (last admission 4.30) Opening times may be subject to change*
Fees €3.35 (ch €1.75) family tickets, senior, student tickets also available.* **Facilities** ℗ shop ⊗

BLARNEY

Blarney Castle & Rock Close

☎ 021 4385252 🖷 021 4381518
e-mail: info@blarneycastle.ie
web: www.blarneycastle.ie
dir: 5m from Cork on main road towards Limerick

The site of the famous Blarney Stone, known the world over for the eloquence it is said to impart to those who kiss it. The stone is in the upper tower of the castle, and, held by your feet, you must lean backwards down the inside of the battlements in order to receive the 'gift of the gab'. There is also a large area of garden open to the public all year round, woodland walks, lake, fern garden, rock close (laid out in the 18th century) and stable yard.

Times Open Blarney Castle & Rock Close. Mon-Fri, May & Sep 10-4, Jun-Aug 9-7. Oct-Apr 9-sundown or 6. Sun, Summer 9.30-5.30, Winter 9.30-sundown. Closed 24-25 Dec.
Fees Blarney Castle & Rock Close €10 (ch 8-14 €3.50, concessions €8). Family ticket (2ad+2ch) €23.50* **Facilities** ❶ ℗ ♿ (partly accessible) shop ⊗

CORK

Cork City Gaol

Convent Av, Sundays Well
☎ 021 4305022   📄 021 4307230
e-mail: corkgaol@indigo.ie
web: www.corkcitygaol.com
dir: 2km NW from Patrick St off Sundays Well Rd

A restored 19th-century prison building.
Furnished cells, lifelike characters and sound
effects combine to allow visitors to experience
day-to-day life for prisoners and gaoler. There
is an audio-visual presentation of the social
history of Cork City. Individual sound tours are
available in a number of languages. A permanent
exhibition, the Radio Museum Experience, is
located in the restored 1920s broadcasting
studio, home to Cork's first radio station, 6CK.
Unfortunately the 1st and 2nd floors are not
accessible to wheelchair users.

Times Open all year Mar-Oct, daily 9.30-5; Nov-
Feb, daily 10-4. Closed 23-28 Dec.* **Facilities** ℗
℗ ⊑🍴 (outdoor) ♿ (partly accessible) (3 cells
on the first floor inaccessible) toilets for disabled
shop ⊗

KINSALE

Desmond Castle

Cork St
☎ 021 4774855
e-mail: desmondcastle@opw.ie
web: www.desmondcastle.ie
dir: R600 from Cork city to Kinsdale. From post
office, 1st left then right, opposite Regional
Museum then left and right again, castle on left

Built by the Earl of Desmond around the
beginning of the 16th century, this tower was
originally a custom house, but has also served as
an ordnance office, prison, workhouse, stable and
meeting place for the Local Defence Force during
World War II. In 1938 it was declared a National
Monument and restored. The Castle now houses
the International Museum of Wine.

Times Open early Apr-late Sep, daily 10-6. (Last
admission 45mins before closing).* **Fees** €3, (ch
& students €1, pen €2) Family €8.* **Facilities**
℗ ⊗

MALAHIDE

Malahide Castle

☎ 01 8462184 📠 01 8462537
e-mail: malahidecastle@dublintourism.ie
web: www.malahidecastle.com
dir: from Dublin city centre follow signs for Malahide, then approaching village, main entrance to castle is signed to right off main road

One of Ireland's oldest castles, this romantic and beautiful structure, set in 250 acres of grounds, has changed very little in 800 years. Tours offer views of Irish period furniture and historical portrait collections. Additional paintings from the National Gallery depict figures from Irish life over the last few centuries.

Times Open Jan-Dec, Mon-Sat 10-5; Apr-Sep, Sun & PHs, 10-6; Oct-Mar, Sun & PHs 11-5* **Facilities** 🅟 Ⓟ ☕ 🍽 licensed ⛩ (outdoor) shop ⊗

DUBLIN

Dublin Castle

Dame St
☎ 01 6777129 📠 01 6797831

With two towers and a partial wall, this is the city's most outstanding legacy of the Middle Ages. Of interest are the Record Tower, state apartments, Church of the Most Holy Trinity and Heraldic Museum. The inauguration of the President of Ireland and related ceremonies are held in St Patrick's Hall, an elegant state apartment.

Times Open all year, Mon-Fri 10-5, Sat-Sun & BH 2-5. Closed 24-26 Dec & Good Fri.* **Facilities** Ⓟ 🍽 licensed toilets for disabled

DUBLIN

Dublinia & The Viking World

St Michael's Hill, Christ Church
☎ 01 6794611 📄 01 6797116
e-mail: info@dublinia.ie
web: www.dublinia.ie
dir: in city centre

The story of medieval Dublin. Housed in the former Synod Hall beside Christ Church Cathedral and developed by the Medieval Trust, Dublinia recreates the period from the arrival of Strongbow and the Anglo-Normans in 1170 to the closure of the monasteries by Henry VIII in 1540. Also included is the exhibition on the Viking World which tells the story of their way of life and turbulent voyages.

Times Open all year daily 10-5 (last admission 4.15) **Fees** €6.25 (ch €3.95, concessions €5). Family ticket (2ad+3ch) €17* **Facilities** ⓟ ⬜ ♿ (partly accessible) (2 floors accessible, but bridge and tower are not) toilets for disabled shop ⊗

DUBLIN

Dublin Writers Museum

18 Parnell Square
☎ 01 8722077 📄 01 8722231
e-mail: writers@dublintourism.ie
web: www.writersmuseum.com
dir: on Parnell Sq, at North end of O'Connell St

The Dublin Writers Museum is housed in a restored 18th-century mansion and is a collection featuring personal items, portraits, books and letters relating to Dublin's most important literary figures, including Swift, Sheridan, Shaw, Wilde, Yeats, Joyce and Beckett. The mansion is a pleasure in itself, with sumptuous plasterwork and decorative stained windows. There is a special room dedicated to children's literature and a full programme of workshops, lectures and receptions.

Times Open all year, Mon-Sat 10-5, Sun & BH 11-5; Jun-Aug, Mon-Fri 10-6.* **Facilities** ⓟ ⬜ ⑪ licensed shop ⊗

DUBLIN

James Joyce Centre

35 North Great George's St
☎ 01 8788547 📄 01 8788488
e-mail: info@jamesjoyce.ie
web: www.jamesjoyce.ie
dir: signed from N end of O'Connell Street and Parnell Square

Situated in a beautifully restored 18th-century Georgian town house, the Centre is dedicated to the promotion of a greater interest in, and understanding of, the life and works of James Joyce. Visitors follow a self-guided tour through the house, that includes the door to No 7 Eccles Street, home of Leopold Bloom, the hero of Ulysses; furniture from Joyce's Paris flat, computer installations, video documentaries and a reconstruction of period rooms. Events are centred every year around 'Bloomsday', the 16th of June, which is when the events of Ulysses take place.

Times Open all year, Tue-Sat 10-5, Sun 12-5. Closed Xmas to New Year. **Fees** Exhibition €5 (concessions €4). Walking Tour €10 (concessions €8). Group 10+ €4.50 (concessions €3.50)
Facilities ℗ toilets for disabled shop ⊗

DUBLIN

National Gallery of Ireland

Merrion Square
☎ 01 6615133 📄 01 6615372
e-mail: info@ngi.ie
web: www.nationalgallery.ie
dir: N11, M50, follow signs to City Centre

The gallery, founded in 1854 by an Act of Parliament, houses the national collections of Irish art and European Old Masters including Rembrandt, Caravaggio, Poussin, and El Greco. There is also a special room dedicated to Jack B Yeats, and a National Portrait Collection.

Times Open all year, Mon-Sat 9.30-5.30 (Thu 9.30-8.30), Sun 12-5. Closed 24-26 Dec & Good Fri.* **Facilities** ℗ 🖵 🍴 licensed ♿ toilets for disabled shop ⊗

DUBLIN

National Library of Ireland **FREE**

Kildare St
☎ 01 6030200   🖃 01 6766690
e-mail: info@nli.ie
web: www.nli.ie

Founded in 1877 and based on collections from
The Royal Dublin Society. The National Library
holds an estimated 8 million items. There are
collections of printed books, manuscripts, prints
and drawings, photos, maps, newspapers,
microfilms and ephemera. Included in the
library's collection is the most significant
exhibition on the life and works of the 20th
century poet WB Yeats. The library's research
facilities are open to all those with genuine
research needs. In addition to research facilities,
services include a regular programme of
exhibitions open to the public and Genealogy
Service.

Times Open all year, Mon-Wed 9.30-9 (Kildare
Street); Thu-Fri 9.30-5. Sat 9.30-1 (reading
rooms); 9.30-4.30 (Yeats exhibition). Opening
times may vary during public hols. **Facilities** ℗
🖵 ♿ toilets for disabled shop ⊗

DUBLIN

Natural History Museum **FREE**

Merrion St
☎ 01 6777444   🖃 01 6777828
e-mail: education.nmi@indigo.ie
dir: in city centre

The Natural History Museum, which is part of
The National Museum of Ireland, is a zoological
museum containing diverse collections of world
wildlife. The Irish Room, on the ground floor, is
devoted largely to Irish mammals, sea creatures
and insects. It includes the extinct giant Irish
deer and the skeleton of a basking shark. The
World Collection, has as its centre piece, the
skeleton of a 60ft whale suspended from the roof.
Other displays include the Giant Panda and a
Pygmy Hippopotamus.

Times Open all year, Tue-Sat 10-5, Sun 2-5.
Closed Mon, 25 Dec & Good Fri* **Facilities** ℗ ⊗

KILLARNEY

Museum of Irish Transport

Scotts Hotel Gardens
☎ 064 34677 ▤ 064 36656
dir: town centre, opposite railway station

A unique collection of Irish veteran, vintage and classic cars, motorcycles, bicycles, carriages and fire engines. Exhibits include the 1907 Silver Stream, reputed to be the rarest car in the world, it was designed and built by an Irishman and he only made one!

Times Open Apr & Oct 11-4; May & Sep 11-5; Jun, Jul & Aug 10-6* **Facilities** Ⓟ

TRALEE

Kerry County Museum

Ashe Memorial Hall, Denny St
☎ 066 7127777 ▤ 066 7127444
e-mail: info@kerrymuseum.com
web: www.kerrymuseum.com
dir: in town centre, follow signs for museum & tourist information office

The museum tells the story of Kerry (and Ireland) from the Stone Age to the present day. Archaeological treasures are displayed in the Museum Gallery, while a stroll through the Medieval Experience reveals the streets of Tralee as they were in 1450, with all the sights, sounds and smells of a bustling community. Discover what people wore, what they ate and where they lived, and find out why the Earls of Desmond, who founded the town, also destroyed it.

Times Open all year, Jan-Mar, Tue-Fri 10-4.30; Apr-May, Tue-Sat 9.30-5.30; Jun-Aug, daily 9.30-5.30; Sep-Dec, Tue-Sat 9.30-5; BH wknds Sun & Mon 10-5.* **Facilities** Ⓟ Ⓟ ⌨ toilets for disabled shop ⊗

FOYNES

Foynes Flying Boat Museum

☎ 069 65416 🖷 069 65416
e-mail: info@flyingboatmuseum.com
web: www.flyingboatmuseum.com
dir: on N69 in Foynes

The museum recalls the era of the flying boats during the 1930s and early 1940s when Foynes was an important airport for air traffic between the United States and Europe. There is a comprehensive range of exhibits, graphic illustrations and a 1940s style cinema featuring a 17-minute film - all original footage from the 30s and 40s. This is where Irish coffee was first invented by chef Joe Sheridan, in 1942. Fly B314 flight simulators and go on board the world's only full scale B314 flying boat model.

Times Open Mar-Oct daily 10-6, Nov 10-4 (last admission 1hr before closing). Fees €9 (ch €5). Family ticket €25. Facilities ❷ ℗ 🖵 ♿ toilets for disabled shop ⊗

LIMERICK

The Hunt Museum

The Custom House, Rutland St
☎ 061 312833 🖷 061 312834
e-mail: info@huntmuseum.com
web: www.huntmuseum.com
dir: a short walk from Arthur's Quay

On show at the Hunt Museum is one of Ireland's finest private collections of art and antiquities. Reflecting Ireland's Celtic past as well as masterworks by da Vinci and Renoir. Set in an 18th-century Custom House beside the River Shannon.

Times Open all year Mon-Sat 10-5, Sun 2-5, except Good Fri, 25 Dec & 1 Jan. Fees €8 (ch €4.25, concessions €6.25). Family ticket €18. Free admission Sun. Facilities ℗ 🖵 †⊙† licensed ♿ toilets for disabled shop ⊗

CASHEL

Brú Ború Heritage Centre

☎ 062 61122   🖷 062 62700
e-mail: bruboru@comhaltas.com
web: www.comhaltas.com
dir: below Rock of Cashel in town

At the foot of the Rock of Cashel, a 4th-century stone fort, this Heritage Centre is dedicated to the study and celebration of native Irish music, song, dance, story telling, theatre and Celtic studies. There's a Folk Theatre where performances are held daily in the summer, and in the evening, banquets evoke the Court of Brian Ború, 11th-century High King of Ireland with music, song and dance. There is also a subterranean, 'Sounds of History', experience.

Times Open all year, Jan-May & Oct-Dec, Mon-Fri 9-5; Jun-Sep, Mon-Sat 9-11.30. **Fees** Admission to centre free. Night show €20. Exhibition, 'Sounds of History' €5 (students €3. Dinner Show/ Option €50 ch €25 **Facilities** 🅿 🅿 ⛁ 🍽 licensed ♿ toilets for disabled shop ⊗

FERRYCARRIG

The Irish National Heritage Park

☎ 053 9120733   🖷 053 9120911
e-mail: info@inhp.com
web: www.inhp.com
dir: 3m from Wexford, on N11

Sixteen historical sites set in a magnificent 35-acre mature forest explaining Ireland's history from the Stone and Bronze Ages, through the Celtic period and concluding with the Vikings and Normans. Among the exhibits are a reconstructed Mesolithic camp, a Viking boatyard with two full-size ships and a Norman motte and bailey. Please visit website for details of events running throughout the year.

Times Open all year, daily, Oct-Mar 9.30-5.30; Apr-Sep 9.30-6.30.* **Facilities** 🅿 ⛁ 🍽 licensed 🪑 (outdoor) ♿ toilets for disabled shop ⊗

WEXFORD

The Irish Agricultural Museum

Johnstown Castle Estate
☎ 053 9184671 & 9171247
e-mail: info@irishagrimuseum.ie
web: www.irishagrimuseum.ie
dir: 4m SW of town, signed off N25

This museum is located in the old farm and stable buildings of the Johnstown Castle Estate. Farming and rural life are the main themes explored, with exhibits covering rural transport, farming and the activities of the farmyard and farmhouse; and includes a large exhibition on the history of the potato and the Great Famine (1845-49). Johnstown Castle Garden is a delightful 50 acres of ornamental grounds surrounding a Victorian castle. Famous architect Daniel Robertson designed both Johnstown Castle Gardens and Powerscourt Gardens. The grounds contain a wide variety of trees and shrubs, as well as two lakes and various follies.

Times Open all year: Museum Apr-Nov, Mon-Fri 9-5, Sat-Sun & BHs 11-5; Dec-Mar, Mon-Fri 9-5 (closed for lunch 12.30-1.30, wknds & BHs). Grounds open daily 9-5. **Fees** Museum €6 (ch & students €4, concessions & group €5). **Facilities** ℗ Ⓟ ▱ ☴ (outdoor) ♿ (partly accessible) (ground floor accessible) toilets for disabled shop ⊗

ENNISKERRY

Powerscourt House & Gardens

Powerscourt Estate
☎ 01 2046000 ▤ 01 2046900
web: www.powerscourt.ie
dir: Entrance 600mtrs out of Enniskerry village

19 hectares of gardens, begun by Richard Wingfield in the 1740s, a blend of formal plantings, sweeping terraces, statuary and ornamental lakes together with rambling walks and walled gardens. The house incorporates an exhibition which traces the history of the estate. The grounds contain Ireland's highest waterfall at 398ft, 6km from the main estate.

Times Open all year: Gardens & House daily 9.30-5.30 (Gardens close at dusk in winter), closed 25-26 Dec. Waterfall open daily, Mar-Apr & Sep-Oct 9.30-5.30; May-Aug 9.30-7; Nov-Feb 10.30-4 (closed 2 weeks before Xmas). Ballroom & Garden rooms open every Sun & Mon 9.30-1.30 (May-Sep) **Fees** House & Gardens €8 (ch under 13 €5 ch under 5 free, concessions €7). Waterfall €5 (ch under 13 €3.50 ch under 2 free, concessions €4.50). **Facilities** ℗ Ⓟ ▱ ⊙ licensed ♿ (partly accessible) (some areas in gardens are flat and suitable for wheelchair users) toilets for disabled shop ⊗